Middle School 3-1
기말고사 완벽대비

KB101209

적중100

영어 기출 문제집

중3

능률 | 김성곤

Best Collection

구성과 특징

교과서의 주요 학습 내용을 중심으로 학습 영역별 특성에 맞춰 단계별로 다양한 학습 기회를 제공하여
단원별 학습능력 평가는 물론 중간 및 기말고사 시험 등에 완벽하게 대비할 수 있도록 내용을 구성

Words & Expressions

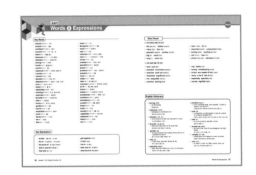

Step1   Key Words 단원별 핵심 단어 설명 및 풀이
Key Expression 단원별 핵심 숙어 및 관용어 설명
Word Power 반대 또는 비슷한 뜻 단어 배우기
English Dictionary 영어로 배우는 영어 단어

Step2   실력평가 단원별 수시평가 대비 주관식, 객관식 문제풀이

Step3   서술형 대비 학업성취도 및 수행능력평가 대비 서술형 문제풀이

Conversation

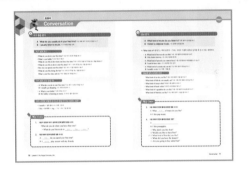

Step1   핵심 의사소통 소통에 필요한 주요 표현 방법 요약
핵심 Check 기본적인 표현 방법 및 활용능력 확인

Step2   대화문 익히기 교과서 대화문 심층 분석 및 확인

Step3   교과서 확인학습 빈칸 채우기를 통한 문장 완성 능력 확인

Step4   기본평가 시험대비 기초 학습 능력 평가

Step5   실력평가 단원별 수시평가 대비 주관식, 객관식 문제풀이

Step6   서술형 대비 학업성취도 및 수행능력평가 대비 서술형 문제풀이

Grammar

Step1   주요 문법 단원별 주요 문법 사항과 예문을 알기 쉽게 설명
핵심 Check 기본 문법사항에 대한 이해 여부 확인

Step2   기본평가 시험대비 기초 학습 능력 평가

Step3   실력평가 단원별 수시평가 대비 주관식, 객관식 문제풀이

Step4   서술형 대비 학업성취도 및 수행능력평가 대비 서술형 문제풀이

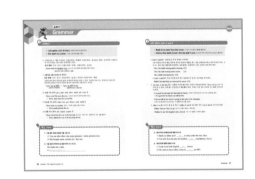

Reading

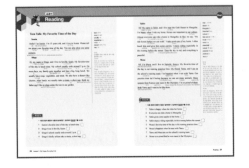

Step1   구문 분석 단원별로 제시된 문장에 대한 구문별 분석과 내용 설명
확인문제 문장에 대한 기본적인 이해와 인지능력 확인

Step2   확인학습A 빈칸 채우기를 통한 문장 완성 능력 확인

Step3   확인학습B 제시된 우리말을 영어로 완성하여 작문 능력 키우기

Step4   실력평가 단원별 수시평가 대비 주관식, 객관식 문제풀이

Step5   서술형 대비 학업성취도 및 수행능력평가 대비 서술형 문제풀이
교과서 구석구석 교과서에 나오는 기타 문장까지 완벽 학습

Composition

|영역별 핵심문제|

단어 및 어휘, 대화문, 문법, 독해 등 각 영역별 기출문제의 출제 유형을 분석하여 실전에 대비하고 연습할 수 있도록 문제를 배열

|단원별 예상문제|

기출문제를 분석한 후 새로운 시험 출제 경향을 더하여 새롭게 출제될 수 있는 문제를 포함하여 시험에 완벽하게 대비할 수 있도록 준비

|서술형 실전 및 창의사고력 문제|

학교 시험에서 점차 늘어나는 서술형 시험에 집중 대비하고 고득점을 취득하는데 만전을 기하기 위한 학습 코너

|단원별 모의고사|

영역별, 단계별 학습을 모두 마친 후 실전 연습을 위한 모의고사

교과서 파헤치기

- 단어Test1~3 영어 단어 우리말 쓰기, 우리말을 영어 단어로 쓰기, 영영풀이에 해당하는 단어와 우리말 쓰기
- 대화문Test1~2 대화문 빈칸 완성 및 전체 대화문 쓰기
- 본문Test1~5 빈칸 완성, 우리말 쓰기, 문장 배열연습, 영어 작문하기 복습 등 단계별 반복 학습을 통해 교과서 지문에 대한 완벽한 습득
- 구석구석지문Test1~2 지문 빈칸 완성 및 전문 영어로 쓰기

Contents

Lesson 3

Always Aware, Always Prepared

🎙 의사소통 기능

- 궁금증 표현하기
  I'm curious about how that happened.

- 경고하기 · 주의 주기
  Make sure you don't take the elevators in a real fire.

🎙 언어 형식

- 과거완료
  One night in February, after I **had gone** to bed, an earthquake hit.

- 여러 가지 접속사
  Since it was my first time experiencing an earthquake, I didn't know how to react.

Words & Expressions

Key Words

- **actually** [ǽktʃuəli] 분 실제로
- **affect** [əfékt] 통 영향을 주다
- **avoid** [əvɔ́id] 통 ~을 피하다
- **amusement park** 놀이 공원
- **aware** [əwɛ́ər] 형 인식하는
- **cause** [kɔːz] 통 초래하다
- **character** [kǽriktər] 명 등장인물
- **chest** [tʃest] 명 가슴
- **collapse** [kəlǽps] 통 붕괴되다, 무너지다
- **common** [kámən] 형 흔한
- **confusion** [kənfjúːʒən] 명 혼란, 혼동
- **crawl** [krɔːl] 통 기어가다
- **curious** [kjúəriəs] 형 호기심이 많은
- **damage** [dǽmidʒ] 명 손상
- **destroy** [distrɔ́i] 통 파괴하다
- **disaster** [dizǽstər] 명 재난
- **drill** [dril] 명 훈련
- **earthquake** [ɔ́ːrθkweik] 명 지진
- **exactly** [igzǽktli] 분 정확하게
- **exit** [égzit] 통 나가다, 퇴장하다
- **flood** [flʌd] 명 홍수
- **heat wave** 폭염
- **heavy rain** 폭우
- **hit** [hit] 통 치다, 때리다, 부딪치다
- **immediately** [imíːdiətli] 분 즉시
- **include** [inklúːd] 통 포함하다
- **mention** [ménʃən] 통 언급하다
- **missing** [mísiŋ] 형 실종된
- **natural disaster** 자연 재해
- **nervously** [nɔ́ːrvəsli] 분 불안하게
- **occur** [əkɔ́ːr] 통 (일·사건 등이) 일어나다, 발생하다
- **panic** [pǽnik] 명 극심한 공포, 공황
- **perform** [pərfɔ́ːrm] 통 공연하다, 수행하다
- **prepared** [pripɛ́ərd] 형 준비된
- **press** [pres] 통 누르다
- **properly** [prápərli] 분 제대로, 적절하게
- **reaction** [riǽkʃən] 명 반응
- **realize** [ríːəlàiz] 통 깨닫다
- **recently** [ríːsntli] 분 최근에
- **scary** [skɛ́əri] 형 무서운
- **serious** [síəriəs] 형 심각한
- **shake** [ʃéikiŋ] 통 흔들리다, 흔들다
- **smash** [smæʃ] 통 세게 부딪치다
- **special effect** 특수 효과
- **suddenly** [sʌ́dnli] 분 갑자기, 급작스럽게
- **survival kit** 생존 장비
- **swing** [swiŋ] 통 흔들리다, 흔들다
- **tap** [tæp] 통 두들기다
- **urgently** [ɔ́ːrdʒəntli] 분 긴급하게
- **violently** [váiələntli] 분 격렬하게, 심하게
- **weight** [weit] 명 무게
- **whole** [houl] 형 전체의
- **wildfire** [wáildfaiər] 명 들불, 산불
- **worse** [wəːrs] 형 더 나쁜

Key Expressions

- **a large number of** 매우 많은
- **as well** 역시, 또한
- **at any time** 어느 때든지
- **a variety of** 다양한
- **based on ~** ~에 바탕을 둔
- **break into pieces** 산산조각이 나다
- **get a discount** 할인을 받다
- **in case of ~** ~의 경우에
- **in the middle of** ~의 한가운데에
- **keep ~ing** 계속해서 ~하다
- **make one's way** 가다, 나아가다
- **make sure** 확실하게 하다
- **pull over** 길 한쪽으로 차를 대다
- **put in** 집어넣다
- **pull out** 끌어내다
- **roll off** 굴러 떨어지다
- **take ~ seriously** 진지하게 받아들이다
- **tip over** 넘어지다, 기울어지다

Word Power

※ 서로 비슷한 뜻을 가진 어휘

- □ **damage** 손상 : **harm** 손해
- □ **include** 포함하다 : **involve** 포함하다
- □ **exactly** 정확하게 : **correctly** 정확하게
- □ **nervously** 불안하게 : **anxiously** 불안하게

- □ **affect** 영향을 주다 : **influence** 영향을 주다
- □ **properly** 적절하게 : **rightly** 적절하게
- □ **recently** 최근에 : **lately** 최근에
- □ **actually** 실제로 : **really** 실제로

※ 서로 반대의 뜻을 가진 어휘

- □ **aware** 아는, 인식하는 ↔ **unaware** 알지 못하는
- □ **destroy** 파괴하다 ↔ **construct** 건설하다
- □ **exit** 나가다 ↔ **enter** 들어가다
- □ **violently** 격렬하게 ↔ **nonviolently** 비폭력적으로

- □ **common** 흔한 ↔ **rare** 드문
- □ **include** 포함하다 ↔ **exclude** 제외하다
- □ **whole** 전체의 ↔ **partial** 부분적인
- □ **avoid** 피하다 ↔ **face** 마주하다

※ 명사 – 동사

- □ **confuse** 혼란을 주다 – **confusion** 혼란
- □ **weigh** 무게가 나가다 – **weight** 무게

- □ **destroy** 파괴하다 – **destruction** 파괴
- □ **perform** 공연하다 – **performance** 공연, 수행

English Dictionary

- □ **cause** 초래하다
  → to make something happen, especially something bad
  어떤 일, 특히 나쁜 일이 일어나게 만들다

- □ **collapse** 붕괴하다
  → to break apart and fall down suddenly
  갑자기 부서지거나 무너지다

- □ **common** 흔한
  → happening often and to many people or in many places
  너무 많은 사람에게 또는 너무 많은 장소에서 자주 일어나는

- □ **crawl** 기어가다
  → to move along on your hands and knees with your body close to the ground
  바닥에 몸을 가까이 하고 손이나 무릎으로 이동하다

- □ **curious** 호기심이 많은
  → wanting to know about something
  어떤 것에 대해 알기를 원하는

- □ **destroy** 파괴하다
  → to damage something so badly that it no longer exists or cannot be used or repaired
  더 이상 존재하거나 사용할 수 없거나 고칠 수 없도록 심하게 손상시키다

- □ **disaster** 재난
  → a sudden event such as a flood, storm, or accident which causes great damage or suffering
  큰 손상이나 고통을 초래하는 홍수, 폭풍 또는 사고와 같은 갑작스러운 사건

- □ **earthquake** 지진
  → a sudden shaking of the Earth's surface that often causes a lot of damage
  종종 많은 손상을 가져오는 지표면의 갑작스러운 흔들림

- □ **exit** 나가다, 퇴장하다
  → to leave a place
  어떤 장소를 떠나다

- □ **flood** 홍수
  → a very large amount of water that covers an area that is usually dry
  대개는 건조한 한 지역을 덮는 아주 많은 양의 물

- □ **include** 포함하다
  → to make someone or something part of a larger group
  어떤 사람 또는 어떤 것을 더 큰 집단의 구성원이 되도록 만들다

- □ **properly** 적절하게
  → correctly, or in a way that is considered right
  정확하게 또는 올바르다고 여겨지는 방식으로

01 다음 짝지어진 단어의 관계가 같도록 빈칸에 알맞은 말을 고르시오.

> damage : harm = _____ : correct

① exact ② aware
③ serious ④ legal
⑤ worse

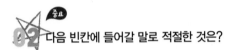

02 다음 빈칸에 들어갈 말로 적절한 것은?

> I was driving home when the shaking started. But I _____ immediately. I'm listening to the radio to find out what's going on.

① pulled in ② pulled out
③ pulled down ④ pulled off
⑤ pulled over

03 다음 중 영영풀이가 어색한 것은?

① flood: a very large amount of water that covers an area that is usually dry
② storm: a sudden shaking of the Earth's surface that often causes a lot of damage
③ disaster: a sudden event such as a flood, storm, or accident which causes great damage or suffering
④ common: happening often and to many people or in many places
⑤ exit: to leave a place

04 다음 중 밑줄 친 부분의 뜻풀이가 바르지 않은 것은?

① We nervously made our way down the stairs. (내려갔다)
② What natural disasters have you experienced? (재난)
③ Make sure you place your hands in the middle of the person's chest. (한 가운데에)
④ Make sure that you exit the building immediately. (들어가다)
⑤ Soon the whole room began to shake violently. (전체의)

05 다음 중 〈보기〉에 있는 단어를 사용하여 자연스러운 문장을 만들 수 없는 것은? (대·소문자 무시)

> ┌─ 보기 ─┐
> rang based crawling destroyed

① We started _____ toward the door.
② _____ on the report, earthquakes are fourth.
③ Many houses and building were _____ by the earthquake.
④ Then suddenly the _____ seemed to stop.
⑤ At that moment, my mom's cell phone _____.

서답형

06 다음 밑줄 친 단어와 의미가 같은 단어를 쓰시오. (주어진 철자로 시작할 것)

> Although I had done many earthquake drills in school, I had never thought I'd experience a real earthquake.

➡ t_____

01 다음 주어진 단어를 이용해 빈칸을 완성하시오.

> Performing CPR _____ can save someone's life. Here are the steps for proper CPR.

➡ _____ (proper)

02 다음 빈칸에 공통으로 들어가기에 적절한 단어를 쓰시오.

> • In case of yellow dust, make sure that you wear a mask when you go _____.
> • I'm listening to the radio right now to find _____ what's going on.

➡ _____

03 다음 문장의 빈칸에 들어가기에 적절한 단어를 주어진 철자로 시작하여 쓰시오.

> 나는 건물이 붕괴될까봐 걱정이 되기 시작했다.
> ➡ I started to worry that the building would c_____.

04 다음 우리말에 맞게 빈칸에 알맞은 말을 쓰시오.

(1) 나는 여전히 정확하게 무엇이 일어나고 있는지 몰랐다.
  ➡ I still didn't know what _____ was happening.
(2) 엄마는 나와 동생을 침대 밖으로 끌어내셨다.
  ➡ My mom _____ me and my brother _____ _____ bed.
(3) 화재가 났을 경우에는 무엇을 해야 할까요?
  ➡ _____ _____ _____ a fire, what should I do?

05 다음 짝지어진 단어의 관계가 같도록 빈칸에 알맞은 말을 쓰시오.

> destroy : construct = _____ : exclude

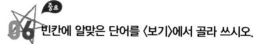

06 빈칸에 알맞은 단어를 〈보기〉에서 골라 쓰시오.

> ┤ 보기 ├
> scared   seriously   prepared
> made our way

(1) We nervously _____ down the stairs and outside.
(2) I still get _____ when I remember that night.
(3) After that night, I began to take earthquake drills _____.

07 다음 영영풀이에 해당하는 단어를 주어진 철자로 쓰시오.

> to damage something so badly that it no longer exists or cannot be used or repaired

➡ d_____

08 밑줄 친 단어의 반대말을 쓰시오. (주어진 철자로 시작할 것)

> A: In case of a fire, what should I do?
> B: Make sure that you cover your mouth with a wet cloth.
> A: Anything else?
> B: Make sure that you <u>exit</u> the building immediately.

➡ e_____

Conversation

교과서

① 궁금증 표현하기

• **I'm curious about how that happened.** 나는 어떻게 그것이 일어났는지 궁금하다.

■ 'curious'는 '호기심이 생기는, 궁금한'이라는 뜻이다. 상대방에게 궁금한 것을 질문으로 표현하는 대신 '나는 ~에 관하여 호기심이 생긴다, ~에 관하여 궁금하다'라는 뜻으로 'I'm curious about ~'의 형태로 궁금증이나 호기심을 표현할 수 있다. '나는 ~이 궁금하다.'라는 뜻의 'I wonder ~.' 또는 'I would like to know ~.'를 쓸 수도 있다.

■ '나는 ~에 대하여 궁금하다'의 의미는 '나는 ~을 알고 싶다'의 의미로 'I want to know ~'의 의미이기도 하다. 좀 더 직접적으로 'Do you know ~?'라는 형태로 물어볼 수도 있다. 보통 '~에 대하여 궁금하다.'는 표현을 들었을 때 그 내용을 알면 자세한 설명을 해주고 그렇지 않을 때는 '같이 알아보자'는 표현 등이 따라 온다.

궁금증 표현하기

• I am curious about ~. 나는 ~이 궁금하다.
• I wonder ~. 나는 ~인지 궁금하다.
• I would like/want to know ~. 나는 ~이 알고 싶다.

궁금증을 나타내는 유사 표현

• Do you know ~? 너는 ~을 알고 있니?
• I'd be very interested to know ~. 나는 ~이 알고 싶다.
• Can you tell me about ~? ~에 대해 말해 줄 수 있니?

핵심 Check

1. 다음 대화의 순서를 바르게 배열하시오.

A: I heard that there have been many wildfires in Korea.

(A) I'm curious about when it happened.

(B) Yes. There was a big one in Yangyang.

(C) It happened in 2005.

① (A) – (C) – (B)   ② (B) – (A) – (C)

③ (B) – (C) – (A)   ④ (C) – (A) – (B)

⑤ (C) – (B) – (A)

② 경고하기 · 주의 주기

- **Make sure you don't take the elevators in a real fire.**
  실제 화재에서는 절대로 엘리베이터를 타지 않도록 해라.

■ 상대방에게 주의 사항을 알려주어서 경고할 때는 'Make sure ~'를 사용한다. 'make sure ~'는 '반드시 ~하도록 하다' '~임을 확인하다'의 의미로 상대에게 '반드시 확인하라.'의 의미로 경고하는 경우에 자주 쓰인다. 'Be sure ~'도 마찬가지 의미가 될 수 있다. 우리말로 해석할 때는 '~을 확실하게 해라' '반드시 ~해라'가 된다.

■ 'Make sure' 또는 'Be sure' 뒤에는 접속사 that이 이끄는 절이 온다. 그래서 'Make sure that 주어+동사 ~', 'Be sure that 주어+동사 ~'의 형태가 되지만 접속사 that은 대부분 생략하고 'Make sure 주어+동사 ~', 'Be sure 주어+동사 ~'의 형태가 된다.

■ 보통 상대방에게 직접적인 경고를 할 때는 '~을 조심해라.'의 의미로 'Watch out for ~', 'Look out for ~'를 쓴다. 'Make sure you don't ~' 'Be sure you don't ~'은 '절대로 ~하지 마라'의 의미이다.

경고하기 · 주의하기 표현

- Make sure (that) ~. : 반드시 ~해라.
- Watch out for ~. : ~을 조심해라.
- Make sure you don't ~. : ~하지 않도록 명심해라.
- You need to keep in mind that ~ : ~라는 사실을 명심해라.
- Be sure (that) ~. : ~을 확실하게 해라.
- Look out for ~. : ~을 잘 살펴라.
- Be careful not to ~. : ~하지 않도록 조심해라.

핵심 Check

2. 다음 대화의 밑줄 친 말 대신 쓸 수 있는 것을 고르시오.

B: Mom, what else do we need to put in the natural disaster survival kit?

W: Well, we need water, some food, and radio.

B: Anything else, Mom?

W: Oh, <u>make</u> sure that you include batteries for the radio.

① be   ② keep   ③ need   ④ watch   ⑤ look

3. 우리말과 일치하도록 주어진 어구를 배열하여 문장을 만드시오.

A: In case of yellow dust, what should I do?

B: _____ (밖에 나갈 때는 반드시 마스크를 착용하도록 해라.)

(that / make / you / you / sure / a mask / when / wear / go out)

Listen & Talk 1 B

G: There seem to be many natural disasters in Korea these days.

B: I agree. There was an earthquake in the south last week. Also a storm is coming this week.

G: I'm curious about ❶which type of natural disaster causes the most damage in Korea.

B: Actually I read a report yesterday about the damage from each type of natural disaster. Number one is storms.

G: I see. I guess earthquakes are second.

B: No, second is heavy rain, and third is heavy snow.

G: What about earthquakes?

B: Based on the report, earthquakes are fourth. But the damage from earthquakes ❷has been increasing recently because they have been happening more often in Korea.

G: I see. It seems like we have to be prepared for a variety of natural disasters in Korea.

G: 요즈음 한국에서 많은 자연 재해가 있는 것 같아.

B: 동의해. 지난주에 남부에서 지진이 있었어. 또한 이번 주에는 태풍이 올 거야.

G: 나는 어떤 종류의 자연 재해가 한국에서 가장 큰 피해를 주는지 궁금해.

B: 사실 나는 어제 각 유형의 자연 재해로 인한 피해에 관한 보고서를 읽었어. 첫 번째가 폭풍이야.

G: 그렇구나. 지진이 두 번째인 것 같아.

B: 아니야. 두 번째는 폭우이고 세 번째는 폭설이야.

G: 지진은?

B: 보고서에 따르면, 지진은 네 번째야. 하지만 최근 한국에서 지진이 더 자주 일어나기 때문에 지진으로 인한 피해가 증가하고 있어.

G: 그렇구나. 한국에서는 다양한 자연 재해에 대비를 해야 할 것 같아.

❶ 'which type of ~'는 간접의문문으로 전치사 about의 목적어이다.
❷ 'has been increasing'은 현재완료진행형으로 과거로부터 시작해서 지금도 계속되는 일을 나타낸다.

Check(√) True or False

(1) Storms cause the most damage in Korea.　　　T ☐　F ☐

(2) The damage from heavy rain is increasing recently.　　　T ☐　F ☐

 Listen & Talk 2 B

W: Performing ❶CPR properly can save someone's life. Here are the steps for proper CPR. First, check that the person needs help. Tap the person and shout, "Are you okay?" If there's no reaction, call 119 for help. Second, ❷listen, look, and feel for breathing. If the person's not breathing, begin CPR. Make sure you place your hands in the middle of the person's chest. Use your body weight to press harder on the chest. After 30 presses, give the person two breaths. ❸Keep doing CPR until help arrives.

W: 제대로 심폐소생술을 수행하는 것은 누군가의 생명을 구할 수 있습니다. 여기 적절한 심폐소생술을 위한 단계가 있습니다. 첫째, 그 사람이 도움을 필요로 하는지 확인하십시오. 그 사람을 두드리며 "괜찮으세요?"라고 큰소리로 외치세요. 반응이 없으면 119에 전화를 걸어 도움을 요청하세요. 둘째, 호흡을 하는지 듣고, 보고, 느끼세요. 그 사람이 숨을 쉬지 않으면 심폐소생술을 시작하세요. 손을 반드시 그 사람의 가슴 가운데에 놓도록 하세요. 가슴을 더 세게 누르기 위해 체중을 이용하세요. 30번 누른 후, 그 사람에게 두 번 바람을 불어 넣으시오. 도움이 올 때까지 심폐소생술을 계속하세요.

❶ CPR = 심폐소생술 (cardiopulmonary resuscitation)
❷ 호흡이 있는지 살피라는 의미로 귀, 눈, 촉감을 모두 동원해서 확인한다는 의미로 'listen, look, feel'을 사용했다.
❸ keep ~ing = ~을 계속하다

Check(√) True or False

(3) When someone needs help, first begin CPR.　　　T ☐　F ☐

(4) You should place your hands in the middle of the person's chest to perform CPR.　　　T ☐　F ☐

Listen & Talk 1 A

B: There was a big flood in Europe. Did you hear about it?

G: No, I didn't. But floods aren't that common in winter, ❶are they? I'm curious about how that happened.

B: ❷Me too. Let's do some online research.

❶ be동사가 있는 문장의 부가의문문이다.
❷ Me too. = I agree.

Listen & Talk 1 C

B: Hey, did you hear about the big fires in California?

G: No, I didn't. How serious are they?

B: They've destroyed ❶a large number of houses and other buildings.

G: Are the fires still going on?

B: Yes, actually the wind has made the fires worse. I hope all the people ❷living there are okay.

G: ❸So do I. I'm curious about how many people had to leave their homes.

B: Actually more than 20,000 people had to leave their homes, and about 400 people are missing in that area.

G: That's terrible. I hope they're somewhere safe.

❶ 'a number of'를 강조하여 'a large number of'라고 했다.
❷ 현재분사 living은 people을 뒤에서 수식한다.
❸ 'So do I.'는 '나도 마찬가지야.'의 의미로 'Me, too.' 또는 'I agree.'에 해당한다.

Listen & Talk 1 D

A: I heard that there have been many wildfires in Korea.

B: Yes. There was a big ❶one in Yangyang.

A: I'm curious about ❷when it happened.

B: It happened in 2005.

❶ one = wildfire
❷ 전치사 about의 목적어로 간접의문이다.

Listen & Talk 2 A

B: Mom, what else do we need to put in the natural disaster survival kit?

W: Well, we need water, some food, and a radio.

B: ❶Anything else, Mom?

W: Oh, ❷make sure that you include batteries for the radio.

❶ Anything else? = Is there anything else?
❷ 접속사 that은 생략 가능하다.

Listen & Talk 2 D

A: ❶In case of a fire, what should I do?

B: Make sure that you cover your mouth with a wet cloth.

A: Anything else?

B: Make sure that you exit the building immediately.

❶ In case of ～ = ～의 경우에

Do It Yourself A

G: Did you hear that earthquakes ❶are occurring more often in Korea than before?

B: Oh, really? I've never felt an earthquake in Korea.

G: They usually occur in the southern part of Korea, but now they are occurring in other places as well.

B: I didn't know that. I'm curious about ❷why earthquakes have occurred so often in Korea recently.

G: ❸Why don't we do some research to find out?

B: Sounds good, but where do we look first?

G: How about asking our science teacher first? I think she can help us.

B: Okay. ❹Let's go and find her.

❶ 현재진행시제를 사용하여 현재에 계속되는 일을 나타내고 있어서 시제 일치를 시키지 않았다.
❷ 전치사 about의 목적어가 되는 간접의문문이다.
❸ Why don't we ～? = ～하는 게 어때?
❹ go and find = go to find

● 다음 우리말과 일치하도록 빈칸에 알맞은 말을 쓰시오.

 해석

Listen & Talk 1 A

B: There _____ a big _____ in Europe. Did you _____ about it?

G: No, I didn't. But _____ aren't that _____ in winter, _____ they? I'm _____ about _____ that happened.

B: Me too. Let's do some online _____.

B: 유럽에 큰 홍수가 있었어. 그것에 대해 들었니?

G: 아니. 하지만 겨울에는 홍수가 그렇게 흔하지 않아, 그렇지 않니? 나는 어떻게 그런 일이 일어났는지 궁금해.

B: 나도 그래. 온라인 검색을 해보자.

Listen & Talk 1 B

G: There _____ to be many _____ _____ in Korea _____ days.

B: I agree. There was an _____ in the _____ last week. Also a _____ is coming this week.

G: I'm _____ about _____ type of _____ _____ causes the _____ _____ in Korea.

B: Actually I read a _____ yesterday about the _____ from _____ _____ of natural disaster. Number one is storms.

G: I see. I _____ earthquakes are _____.

B: No, second is _____ rain, and third is heavy _____.

G: _____ about earthquakes?

B: _____ on the report, _____ are fourth. But the _____ from earthquakes has _____ _____ recently _____ they have _____ happening more often in Korea.

G: I see. It _____ _____ we have to be _____ for a _____ of _____ _____ in Korea.

G: 요즈음 한국에서 많은 자연 재해가 있는 것 같아.

B: 동의해. 지난주에 남부에서 지진이 있었어. 또한 이번 주에는 태풍이 올 거야.

G: 나는 어떤 종류의 자연 재해가 한국에서 가장 큰 피해를 주는지 궁금해.

B: 사실 나는 어제 각 유형의 자연 재해로 인한 피해에 관한 보고서를 읽었어. 첫 번째가 폭풍이야.

G: 그렇구나. 지진이 두 번째인 것 같아.

B: 아니야. 두 번째는 폭우이고 세 번째는 폭설이야.

G: 지진은?

B: 보고서에 따르면, 지진은 네 번째야. 하지만 최근 한국에서 지진이 더 자주 일어나기 때문에 지진으로 인한 피해가 증가하고 있어.

G: 그렇구나. 한국에서는 다양한 자연 재해에 대비를 해야 할 것 같아.

Listen & Talk 1 C

B: Hey, did you _____ _____ the big _____ in California?

G: No, I didn't. How _____ are they?

B: They've _____ a large number of _____ and _____ buildings.

G: _____ the fires still _____ _____?

B: Yes, _____ the wind has made the fires _____. I hope all the people _____ _____ are okay.

G: _____ _____ I. I'm _____ about how many people had to _____ their homes.

B: _____ more than 20,000 people had to _____ their homes, and about 400 people are _____ in that area.

G: That's _____. I hope they're _____ safe.

B: 안녕. 너 캘리포니아에서 일어난 큰 화재에 대해 들었니?

G: 아니. 얼마나 심각하니?

B: 많은 집들과 다른 건물들을 파괴했어.

G: 아직도 화재가 진행되고 있니?

B: 그래. 사실 바람이 화재를 더 악화시켰어. 나는 거기 사는 모든 사람들이 괜찮기를 바라.

G: 나도 그래. 얼마나 많은 사람들이 집을 떠나야 했는지 궁금해.

B: 사실 2만 명 이상이 집을 떠나야 했고, 약 400명이 실종되었어.

G: 끔찍하구나. 나는 그들이 안전한 곳에 있기를 바라.

Listen & Talk 2 A

B: Mom, _____ _____ do we need to _____ _____ the natural disaster _____ _____?

W: Well, we need _____, some food, and a _____.

B: _____ else, Mom?

W: Oh, _____ sure that you _____ batteries for the _____.

Listen & Talk 2 B

W: _____ CPR properly can _____ someone's life. _____ are the _____ for _____ CPR. First, check that the person _____ help. _____ the person and shout, "_____ you okay?" If there's no _____, call 119 for help. Second, _____, look, and _____ for breathing. If the person's not _____, begin CPR. Make _____ you _____ your hands _____ the middle of the person's _____. Use your body _____ to press _____ on the chest. After 30 presses, give the person two _____. Keep doing CPR until _____ arrives.

Listen & Talk 2 D

A: _____ _____ of a fire, _____ should I _____?

B: _____ sure that you _____ your mouth with a _____ cloth.

A: Anything _____?

B: Make sure that you _____ the building _____.

Do It Yourself A

G: Did you _____ that earthquakes are _____ more _____ in Korea than _____?

B: Oh, _____? I've never _____ an earthquake in Korea.

G: They _____ occur in the _____ part of Korea, but now they are occurring in _____ _____ as well.

B: I didn't know that. I'm _____ about _____ earthquakes have _____ so often in Korea recently.

G: Why don't we do some _____ to find out?

B: Sounds good, but where _____ we look first?

G: _____ _____ asking our science teacher first? I think she can _____ us.

B: Okay. _____ go and _____ her.

해석

B: 엄마, 자연 재해 생존 장비에 무엇을 더 넣어야 할까요?

W: 글쎄. 우리는 물, 약간의 식량 그리고 라디오가 필요해.

B: 다른 것은요, 엄마?

W: 오, 라디오 건전지를 반드시 포함하도록 해.

W: 제대로 심폐소생술을 수행하는 것은 누군가의 생명을 구할 수 있습니다. 여기 적절한 심폐소생술을 위한 단계가 있습니다. 첫째, 그 사람이 도움을 필요로 하는지 확인하십시오. 그 사람을 두드리며 "괜찮으세요?"라고 큰소리로 외치세요. 반응이 없으면 119에 전화를 걸어 도움을 요청하세요. 둘째, 호흡을 하는지 듣고, 보고, 느끼세요. 그 사람이 숨을 쉬지 않으면 심폐소생술을 시작하세요. 손을 반드시 그 사람의 가슴 가운데에 놓도록 하세요. 가슴을 더 세게 누르기 위해 체중을 이용하세요. 30번 누른 후, 그 사람에게 두 번 바람을 불어 넣으시오. 도움이 올 때까지 심폐소생술을 계속하세요.

A: 화재가 발생하면 어떻게 해야 하나요?

B: 반드시 젖은 천으로 입을 가리도록 해.

A: 다른 것은 뭐가 있을까요?

B: 즉시 건물 밖으로 나가도록 해야 해.

G: 한국에서 지진이 전보다 자주 일어나고 있다는 말을 들었니?

B: 오, 정말? 나는 한국에서 지진을 느껴본 적이 없어.

G: 보통 지진이 한국의 남부에서 발생하지만, 이제는 다른 지역에서도 발생하고 있어.

B: 그건 몰랐어. 나는 왜 최근에 한국에서 지진이 그렇게 자주 발생하는지 궁금해.

G: 알아내기 위해 조사를 해보는 게 어떨까?

B: 좋은 것 같아. 하지만 먼저 어디에서 찾아야 하지?

G: 먼저 과학 선생님께 여쭤보면 어떨까? 나는 선생님께서 우리를 도울 수 있을 거라고 생각해.

B: 알았어. 가서 선생님을 찾아보자.

[01~02] 다음 대화의 빈칸에 들어갈 말로 알맞은 것을 고르시오.

01

> B: Hey, did you hear about the big fires in California?
>
> G: No, I didn't. How serious are they?
>
> B: They've destroyed a large number of houses and other buildings.
>
> G: _____
>
> B: Yes, actually the wind has made the fires worse. I hope all the people living there are okay.

① Are the fires still going on?

② Have you been there?

③ How did you know about that?

④ How many houses were destroyed?

⑤ Do you know anyone living there?

02

> A: In case of a fire, what should I do?
>
> B: Make sure that you cover your mouth with a wet cloth.
>
> A: Anything else?
>
> B: _____ you exit the building immediately.

① I have wondered   ② Make sure that

③ Run before   ④ I want to ask

⑤ I have heard

03 우리말과 일치하도록 주어진 어구를 배열하여 문장을 만드시오.

> B: Mom, what else do we need to put in the natural disaster survival kit?
>
> W: Well, we need water, some food, and a radio.
>
> B: Anything else, Mom?
>
> W: Oh, 라디오를 위한 건전지를 반드시 포함하도록 해라. (batteries, for, sure, make, that, include, the radio, you)

➡ _____

[01~03] 다음 대화를 읽고 물음에 답하시오.

B: Hey, did you hear about the big fires in California?

G: No, I didn't. How serious are they?

B: They've destroyed a large number of houses and other buildings.

G: Are the fires still going on?

B: Yes, (A)actual the wind has made the fires worse. I hope all the people living there are okay.

G: So do I. (B)I'm curious about how many people had to leave their homes.

B: Actually more than 20,000 people had to leave their homes, and about 400 people are missing in that area.

G: That's terrible. I hope they're somewhere safe.

01 밑줄 친 (A)를 알맞은 형으로 고치시오.

➡ _____

02 밑줄 친 (B)를 다음과 같이 바꾸어 쓸 때 빈칸에 적절한 것은?

➡ I _____ how many people had to leave their homes.

① know　　② find　　③ wonder

④ believe　　⑤ worry

03 위 대화의 내용과 일치하지 <u>않는</u> 것은?

① There were big fires in California.

② The fires were caused by the wind.

③ People who left their homes were more than 20,000.

④ About 400 people are missing in that area.

⑤ Many houses and buildings were destroyed.

[04~07] 다음 대화를 읽고 물음에 답하시오.

G: (A)There seem to be many natural disasters in Korea these days.

B: I agree. There was an earthquake in the south last week. (ⓐ) Also a storm is coming this week.

G: I'm curious about which type of natural disaster causes the most damage in Korea.

B: (ⓑ) Number one is storms.

G: I see. I guess earthquakes are second.

B: No, second is heavy rain, and third is heavy snow. (ⓒ)

G: What about earthquakes?

B: Based on the report, earthquakes are fourth. (ⓓ) But the damage from earthquakes has been increasing recently because they have been happening more often in Korea.

G: I see. (ⓔ) It seems like we have to be (B)prepare for a variety of natural disasters in Korea.

04 ⓐ~ⓔ 중에서 다음 문장이 들어가기에 적절한 곳은?

Actually I read a report yesterday about the damage from each type of natural disaster.

① ⓐ　　② ⓑ　　③ ⓒ　　④ ⓓ　　⑤ ⓔ

05 위 대화의 밑줄 친 (A)와 같은 뜻이 되도록 빈칸에 알맞은 말을 쓰시오.

➡ _____ seems _____ there _____ many natural disasters in Korea these days.

서답형

06 위 대화의 밑줄 친 (B)prepare를 알맞은 형으로 고치시오.

➡ _____

07 위 대화를 읽고, 대답할 수 <u>없는</u> 것은?

① What kinds of natural disasters are occurring in Korea?

② What did the boy read yesterday?

③ Which type of natural disaster causes the most damage in Korea?

④ What disaster occurred in the south last week?

⑤ What disaster causes the least damage?

08 다음 대화의 순서가 바르게 배열된 것을 고르시오.

> A: I heard that there have been many wildfires in Korea.
> (A) Yes. There was a big one in Yangyang.
> (B) It happened in 2005.
> (C) I'm curious about when it happened.

① (A) – (C) – (B)

② (B) – (A) – (C)

③ (B) – (C) – (A)

④ (C) – (A) – (B)

⑤ (C) – (B) – (A)

[09~10] 다음 대화를 읽고 물음에 답하시오.

> G: Did you hear that earthquakes are occurring more often in Korea than before?
> B: Oh, really? _____ ⓐ _____
> G: They usually occur in the southern part of Korea, but _____ ⓑ _____.
> B: I didn't know that. I'm curious about why earthquakes have occurred so often in Korea recently.
> G: _____ ⓒ _____
> B: Sounds good, but where do we look first?
> G: _____ ⓓ _____ I think she can help us.
> B: _____ ⓔ _____

09 위 대화의 빈칸 ⓐ~ⓔ에 들어갈 대화로 가장 <u>어색한</u> 것은?

① ⓐ I've never felt an earthquake in Korea.

② ⓑ now they are occurring in other places as well

③ ⓒ Why don't we do some research to find out?

④ ⓓ How about searching the Internet before asking our science teacher first?

⑤ ⓔ Okay. Let's go and find her.

중요

10 위 대화를 읽고 다음 중 대답할 수 <u>없는</u> 것은?

① Are earthquakes occurring more often in Korea?

② Has the boy felt an earthquake before?

③ Where do earthquakes usually occur in Korea?

④ Why have earthquakes occurred so often in Korea?

⑤ Will they search the Internet at once?

[01~03] 다음 대화를 읽고 물음에 답하시오.

G: There seem to be many natural disasters in Korea these days.

B: I agree. There was an earthquake in the south last week. Also a storm is coming this week.

G: (A)나는 궁금하다 which type of natural disaster causes the most damage in Korea.

B: Actually I read a report yesterday about the damage from each type of natural disaster. Number one is storms.

G: I see. I guess earthquakes are second.

B: No, second is heavy rain, and third is heavy snow.

G: ____(B)____ earthquakes?

B: Based on the report, earthquakes are fourth. But the damage from earthquakes has been increasing recently because they have been happening more often in Korea.

G: I see. (C)한국에서는 다양한 자연 재해에 대하여 준비가 되어야 할 것 같다.(it, like, seems, have to, prepared for, be, we, natural disasters, a variety of, in Korea)

01 밑줄 친 (A)의 우리말에 맞게 영어로 쓰시오. (about 포함)

　➡ _____

02 대화의 내용으로 보아 빈칸 (B)에 들어가기에 적절한 말을 2 단어로 쓰시오.

　➡ _____

03 밑줄 친 (C)의 우리말을 주어진 어구를 배열하여 영작하시오.

　➡ _____
　　_____

[04~06] 다음 글을 읽고 물음에 답하시오.

W: Performing CPR properly can save someone's life. Here are the steps for proper CPR. First, check that the person needs help. Tap the person and shout, "Are you okay?" If there's no ____(A)____ , call 119 for help. Second, listen, look, and feel for breathing. If the person's not breathing, begin CPR. (B)반드시 그 사람의 가슴 가운데에 손을 놓도록 하세요.(sure, place, your hands, you, make, the person's chest, in the middle of). Use your body weight to press harder on the chest. After 30 presses, give the person two breaths. Keep doing CPR until help arrives.

04 빈칸 (A)에 들어가기에 적절한 단어를 쓰시오.

　➡ _____

05 주어진 어구를 배열하여 밑줄 친 (B)의 우리말을 영작하시오.

　➡ _____
　　_____

06 When should we start CPR on the person? Answer in English. (9 words)

　➡ _____
　　_____

Grammar

① 과거완료

> • One night in February, after I **had gone** to bed, an earthquake hit.
> 2월 어느 날 밤, 내가 잠자리에 든 후에 지진이 일어났다.
>
> • It was more beautiful than I **had imagined**. 그건 내가 상상했던 것보다 더 아름답더군요.

■ 과거완료는 과거 이전에 일어난 일이 과거의 어느 시점까지 영향을 미칠 때 쓰며, 'had+과거분사'의 형태로 쓴다. 과거완료도 현재완료처럼 완료, 계속, 경험, 결과의 용법이 있다. 또한 과거의 어느 시점보다 먼저 일어난 일이나 상태를 나타낼 때도 쓰이며 이것을 보통 '대과거'라고 한다.

- I **had** just **finished** my homework when he called me. 〈완료〉 그가 내게 전화했을 때 나는 막 숙제를 마쳤다.
- She **had cleaned** her house for two hours before I visited her. 〈계속〉
  그녀는 내가 그녀를 방문하기 전에 2시간 동안 그녀의 집을 청소했다.
- He **had** never **seen** a live tiger before.. 〈경험〉 그는 전에 살아 있는 호랑이를 한 번도 본 적이 없었다.
- He **had gone** to Seoul when I visited him. 〈결과〉 내가 그를 방문했을 때 그는 서울로 가고 없었다.
- He realized that he **had met** her before. 〈대과거〉 그는 전에 그녀를 만난 적이 있다는 것을 깨달았다. 〈대과거〉

■ 한 문장에 두 가지 과거의 일이 나올 때, 두 동작이 거의 동시에 일어났거나 시간차가 거의 없이 연속적으로 일어났을 경우에는 단순과거로 표현한다. 또, 접속사 after나 before가 쓰여 두 동작의 전후 관계가 명백할 때도 단순과거로 표현할 수 있다.

- I **showed** them how to do it and they **tried**. 나는 그들에게 그것을 어떻게 하는지 보여주었고, 그들은 해 보았다.
  〈시간차가 거의 없는 연속 동작〉
- The village **was** quiet before they **came**. 그들이 오기 전에는 마을이 조용했다. 〈전후 관계가 명백함〉

핵심 Check

1. 다음 괄호 안에서 알맞은 말을 고르시오.

(1) When she came home, her husband (had done / does) the dishes already.

(2) Judy knew that Megan (had finished / finished) her homework the previous day.

(3) The train (has / had) just left when I arrived at the station.

② 여러 가지 접속사

> • **Since** it was my first time experiencing an earthquake, I didn't know how to react. 지진을 경험한 것이 처음이었기 때문에, 나는 어떻게 반응해야 할지 몰랐다.

■ 접속사란 단어와 단어, 구와 구, 절과 절을 연결시켜 주는 말이다.

(1) 이유를 나타내는 since

■ since는 '~이기 때문에'라는 의미로 이유를 나타내는 접속사로 쓰인다. since가 이끄는 부사절이 이유를 나타내고, 주절이 그 결과를 나타내며, 이때의 since는 as나 because로 바꿔 쓸 수 있다.

  • He couldn't go out **since** he was sick. 그는 아파서 나갈 수 없었다.
  = He couldn't go out **as[because]** he was sick.

  cf. since와 같은 의미인 due to나 because of 등은 뒤에 (대)명사나 동명사가 온다.

  • He quit the job **because of** his health. 그는 건강상의 이유로 직장을 그만 두었다.

■ since는 이외에도 전치사나 접속사로 '~한 이래로'의 뜻으로 쓰인다.

  • He has worked **since** he left school. 그는 학교를 나온 이래 일하고 있다.

(2) 양보절을 이끄는 although

■ although는 '비록 ~일지라도'라는 의미로 양보절을 이끌며 이끄는 절의 내용과 주절의 내용은 서로 상반되고 even though나 though로 바꿔 쓸 수 있다.

  • **Although** he is rich, he is not happy. 그는 부자지만 행복하지는 않다.

  cf. although와 비슷한 의미인 despite는 전치사이므로 뒤에 (대)명사나 동명사가 나온다.

  • He is very strong **despite** his age. 그는 노령임에도 불구하고 매우 정정하다.

  cf. even if는 '만일 ~라고 할지라도(가정)' 정도의 뜻이다.

■ **기타 접속사**

  (1) 시간 관계를 나타내는 접속사: after, before, as soon as, when, while, until 등
  (2) 조건을 나타내는 접속사: if, unless, in case (that), in the event (that) 등
  (3) 목적을 나타내는 접속사: so that, in order that 등

핵심 Check

2. 다음 빈칸에 들어갈 말을 〈보기〉에서 골라 쓰시오.

┌─ 보기 ─┐
> although   after   since

(1) _____ I'm broke, I don't need your help.
(2) We don't worry _____ we are armed with effective tools.
(3) Several years _____ they'd split up, they met again by chance in Paris.

01 다음 빈칸에 들어갈 말로 알맞은 것은?

> I recognized her at once as I _____ her before.

① see   ② saw   ③ seen
④ have seen   ⑤ had seen

02 다음 괄호 안에서 알맞은 말을 고르시오.

(1) When I called, he (already started / had already started).
(2) I admitted to her that I (lied / had lied) to her.
(3) (Although / When) the sun was shining, it wasn't very warm.
(4) I was here a bit early (after / since) my watch gained time.

03 다음 두 문장을 한 문장으로 바꾸어 쓸 때 알맞게 표현한 것을 고르시오.

> • Mike is not honest.
> • I don't believe him.

① Although Mike is not honest, I don't believe him.
② Mike is not honest although I don't believe him.
③ Since Mike is not honest, I don't believe him.
④ Mike is not honest since I don't believe him.
⑤ Mike is not honest after I don't believe him.

04 다음 우리말에 맞게 주어진 어휘를 바르게 배열하시오.

(1) 작년까지 Linda는 Paris를 방문한 적이 전혀 없었다. (until로 시작할 것)
(year, Linda, Paris, had, last, until, visited, never)

➡ _____

(2) 그는 부자였지만, 사람들은 그가 가난한 줄 알았다. (접속사로 시작할 것)
(he, he, people, was, was, thought, poor, rich, although)

➡ _____

(3) 나는 간밤에 너무 무서워서 잠을 잘 수 없었다. ('주절+종속절'의 구조로 쓸 것)
(I, I, night, couldn't, afraid, sleep, was, last, so, since)

➡ _____

01 다음 중 어법상 어색한 것은?

① Our little friends had finished the shoes when we got up.

② They talked about the accident that happened there a few hours before.

③ When I arrived at the bus stop, the bus had already left.

④ He had never been abroad before he became thirty.

⑤ The plane had already taken off when I reached the airport.

02 다음 중 어법상 바르지 않은 것은?

① Although we have to say goodbye for now, we can meet next year.

② Though it rained heavily, we played outside.

③ Even though she had an umbrella, she got wet in the rain.

④ It started to rain though we decided to leave.

⑤ Though I bought it only yesterday, I'll give it to you.

03 다음 빈칸에 알맞은 말이 바르게 짝지어진 것은?

> • _____ he was born in England, he is a Korean boy.
> • It was more beautiful than I _____.

① Even though – had imagined

② Since – had imagined

③ Even though – imagined

④ Since – imagined

⑤ Because – have imagined

서답형

04 다음 괄호 안에서 알맞은 말을 고르시오.

(1) When he came home, his son had (finish / finished) homework.

(2) I realized that I (had made / made) a big mistake.

(3) I (had prepared / prepared) to be a musician since I was a kid.

(4) (Although / Because) he was tall, he couldn't touch the ceiling.

(5) (Since / Although) I didn't have lunch today, I had a big dinner.

(6) (Despite / Though) I love snow, I hope it will stop snowing.

05 주어진 문장의 틀린 부분을 찾아, 올바르게 고친 것을 고르시오.

> When I reached home, my brother go to bed and only Mom was awake.

① When I reached home, my brother went to bed and only Mom was awake.

② When I reached home, my brother has gone to bed and only Mom was awake.

③ When I reached home, my brother had gone to bed and only Mom was awake.

④ When I have reached home, my brother went to bed and only Mom was awake.

⑤ When I had reached home, my brother had gone to bed and only Mom was awake.

06 다음 문장의 밑줄 친 부분 중 어법상 어색한 것은?

> ⓐAlthough she ⓑhas been ill ⓒfor a long time, it still ⓓcame as a shock when she eventually ⓔdied.

① ⓐ   ② ⓑ   ③ ⓒ   ④ ⓓ   ⑤ ⓔ

07 빈칸 (A)와 (B)에 알맞은 것으로 바르게 짝지어진 것은?

> Eric was late for the meeting ___(A)___ he ___(B)___ the bus.

	(A)	(B)
①	since	has missed
②	though	missed
③	because	has missed
④	though	had missed
⑤	because	had missed

서답형

08 〈보기〉에서 알맞은 접속사를 골라 다음 빈칸을 채우시오.

> ┌ 보기 ┐
> when   though   after   since   unless

(1) You'll miss the bus _____ you walk more quickly.

(2) He achieved success _____ he made lots of efforts.

(3) She hasn't phoned, _____ she said she would.

(4) I still get scared _____ I remember that night.

(5) Yesterday he stayed home from work _____ he got a really bad flu.

09 다음 문장의 빈칸에 알맞은 말은?

> _____ their house was not so nice, they looked happy.

① After   ② Unless
③ If   ④ Though
⑤ Since

10 다음 우리말을 바르게 영작한 것을 고르시오.

> 그 진주는 진짜같이 보여도 가짜예요.

① The pearls are fake, so they look real.
② The pearls are fake, though they look real.
③ The pearls are fake, unless they look real.
④ The pearls are fake since they look real.
⑤ The pearls are fake as they look real.

11 다음 문장의 빈칸에 들어갈 알맞은 말은?

> Isabelle _____ in Rome for 15 years when I met her.

① lives   ② lived
③ living   ④ has lived
⑤ had lived

서답형

12 다음 두 문장을 한 문장으로 바꿔 쓰고자 한다. 빈칸에 들어갈 알맞은 말을 쓰시오.

> • Brian started to learn Korean in the year of 2015.
> • Brian gave a speech in Korean at the meeting last weekend.
> = Brian gave a speech in Korean at the meeting last weekend as he _____ it since 2015.

13 다음 밑줄 친 과거완료의 용법이 〈보기〉와 같은 것은?

┌─ 보기 ─┐
Janet <u>had been</u> ill in bed for three days when I visited her.
└───────┘

① When she got to the station, the train <u>had</u> just <u>left</u> for London.
② Herold <u>had</u> never <u>seen</u> such a big animal till then.
③ Christine <u>had lived</u> in Boston since she got married.
④ I thought that he <u>had lost</u> his bag on the train to New York.
⑤ She asked her to feel the eggs that <u>had become</u> hard.

서답형

14 다음 문장에서 문맥상 어색한 접속사를 바르게 고쳐 다시 쓰시오.

(1) I missed the first bus because I got up early in the morning.

　➡ _____

　_____

(2) Although I am a student, I will get a discount.

　➡ _____

　_____

(3) David was doing the dishes since Monica called him.

　➡ _____

　_____

(4) All of them look tired before they worked hard.

　➡ _____

　_____

(5) I'll take the job if the pay is much too low.

　➡ _____

　_____

[15~16] 다음 우리말에 맞게 영작한 것을 고르시오.

15 비록 그것이 사실일지라도, 그는 그것을 믿지 않았다.

① Since it was true, he didn't believe it.
② Since he didn't believe it, it was true.
③ Though it was true, he didn't believe it.
④ It was true, though he didn't believe it.
⑤ As though it was true, he didn't believe it.

16 그때 이전에 바다에서 고래를 본 적이 있었니?

① Do you ever see a whale in the sea before then?
② Did you ever see a whale in the sea before then?
③ Have you ever seen a whale in the sea before then?
④ Have you ever been seeing a whale in the sea before then?
⑤ Had you ever seen a whale in the sea before then?

17 다음 중 어법상 어색한 것을 고르시오. (2개)

① Since it's very hot outside, I will play soccer.
② Our teacher will edit our video after we finish recording it.
③ I had never been in such a situation, so my face got really red.
④ I remembered that I met him at the party.
⑤ When I arrived at school, class had already begun.

01 시간 흐름에 따른 사건 전개에 맞게 빈칸을 채워 문장을 완성하시오.

> (1) Mom bought a smart phone for me last week.
> → I lost the phone yesterday.
> → I don't have the phone now.
> (2) Kyle bought a flower vase last month.
> → He broke the vase by mistake today.
> → His mom knew the fact later.

(1) Yesterday I lost the smart phone that _____ last week.

(2) Today Kyle's mom knew that Kyle broke the vase by mistake that _____ last month.

02 다음을 when을 이용하여 한 문장으로 연결할 때 빈칸을 알맞게 채우시오. (시제에 유의할 것.)

(1) I wanted to go to Seoul. I arrived at the station. The train already left for Seoul.
➡ When I arrived at the station to go to Seoul, the train _____ for Seoul.

(2) I promised to meet Tom at the bookstore. I went there quite late. He was there but went back to work. So, I couldn't meet him.
➡ When I went to the bookstore to meet Tom, _____ to work.

03 다음 우리말에 맞게 주어진 어구를 바르게 배열하시오.

(1) 비록 집은 파괴되었지만 아무도 다치지 않았습니다. (one, the house, even, no, was, was, hurt, destroyed, though) (접속사로 시작할 것)
➡ _____
_____

(2) 설사 그것이 너의 것이 아니라도 낭비하지 마라. (things, they, yours, even, don't, not, are, waste, if) ('주절+종속절'의 구문으로 작성할 것)
➡ _____

(3) 그는 완전히 새로운 인종을 발견했다는 것을 깨달았다. (he, he, human species, a, discovered, realized, had, whole, new, that)
➡ _____
_____

(4) 나는 그가 왜 그런 어리석은 짓을 했는지 의아했다. (I, he, done, wondered, had, a, thing, stupid, such, why)
➡ _____
_____

04 다음 문장에서 내용에 맞게 잘못된 어휘를 알맞게 고치시오.

(1) Because animals do not speak like humans, some of them actually have a "language."
_____ ➡ _____

(2) As though they are so poor, they seem happy together.
_____ ➡ _____

(3) Despite he often talks big, I love him so much.
_____ ➡ _____

05 그림을 보고, 주어진 어휘를 이용하여 빈칸을 알맞게 채우시오.

(1) I noticed that my sister _____ my glasses. (break)

(2) Molly cleaned her living room this afternoon. At night, Mom arrived home. When Mom came home from work, Molly _____ her house. (already, clean)

06 알맞은 접속사를 이용하여 주어진 두 문장을 하나의 문장으로 쓰시오. ((1), (3)은 '주절+종속절'의 구문, (2)는 접속사로 시작할 것)

(1) • Horses sleep just like us.
　　• They do so in a different way.

➡ _____

　_____

(2) • The Earth is rotating.
　　• Two tides occur each day.

➡ _____

(3) • We had lunch.
　　• We had ice cream as dessert.

➡ _____

　_____

07 다음 문장에서 어법상 <u>어색한</u> 것을 바르게 고쳐 다시 쓰시오.

(1) Bella has already done the dishes when he came back home.

➡ _____

　_____

(2) Dave never visited Paris until then.

➡ _____

　_____

(3) She told me why she left him.

➡ _____

　_____

(4) The boy disappeared during walking home from school.

➡ _____

　_____

(5) He made his choice, although regretted it later.

➡ _____

　_____

(6) Anne was fond of Tim, despite he often annoyed her.

➡ _____

　_____

08 다음 두 문장을 알맞은 접속사를 이용하여 한 문장으로 연결하되, 두 사건의 시간차가 드러나도록 쓰시오. ('주절+종속절'의 구문으로 작성할 것)

• Kay didn't recognize any of them.
• She heard of their names.

➡ _____

　_____

Reading

Waking Up to an Earthquake

One night in February, after I had gone to bed, an earthquake hit. I
지진이 일어난 것보다 잠자리에 든 것이 먼저 일어난 일이기 때문에 과거완료로 씀.

woke up suddenly because my bed was shaking. I thought my brother

was shaking my bed as a joke. But then I heard the mirror on my desk
　　　　　　　　　　　　장난으로　　　　　　　　　　지각동사

fall to the floor and break into pieces. I knew it wasn't my brother then,
지각동사(heard)+목적어+목적격보어(원형부정사)

but I still didn't know what exactly was happening.
부정의 조동사 앞에 위치　　　　　know의 목적어(간접의문문)

Soon the whole room began to shake violently, and my confusion
= Before long　　　　　　　　　　　= shaking

turned to panic. My mom shouted that it was an earthquake and ran
　　　　　　　　　　　　　　　명사절을 이끄는 접속사

into my room. Since it was my first time experiencing an earthquake, I
　　　　　　= Because[As]　　　be one's first time+-ing: ~하는 게 처음이다

didn't know how to react. I just kept saying, "What should I do?"
　　　　　　= how I should react　　keep ~ing: 계속해서 ~하다

My mom pulled me and my brother out of bed. We ran to the kitchen
　　　　　　　　　　　　　　　　　　　~의 밖으로

and crawled under the table.

suddenly 갑자기, 급작스럽게

shake 흔들다, 흔들리다

break into pieces 산산조각이 나다

exactly 정확하게

happen (사건이) 일어나다

violently 격렬하게, 심하게

confusion 혼란, 혼동

panic 극심한 공포, 공황

react 반응하다, 반응을 보이다

crawl 기어가다

확인문제

● 다음 문장이 본문의 내용과 일치하면 T, 일치하지 <u>않으면</u> F를 쓰시오.

1 The writer woke up suddenly because her bed was shaking. ☐

2 The writer's brother was shaking her bed as a joke. ☐

3 The mirror on the writer's desk fell to the floor and broke into pieces. ☐

4 The writer's brother shouted that it was an earthquake. ☐

5 The writer didn't experience an earthquake before. ☐

6 The writer pulled her brother out of bed. ☐

I could see the light swinging violently and books falling to the floor.
지각동사(see)+목적어+현재분사   목적어+현재분사

Our family picture dropped from the wall and the glass covering it
앞에 있는 명사 the glass를 수식

broke. A cup tipped over and rolled off the kitchen table. Every second,
= Every moment

I could hear something else in the apartment break. I started to worry
다른 어떤 것   = worrying

that the building would collapse.

Then the shaking seemed to stop. We started crawling toward the
= it seemed that the shaking stopped

door. At that moment, my mom's cell phone rang. It was my dad, who
전화를 한 사람   = and he

was coming home from work.

He shouted, "It stopped! Get out of the building! Take the stairs!
= The shaking

Don't take the elevator! Hurry!" "Where are you? Are you okay?" my

mom asked urgently. My dad answered, "Don't worry. I'm okay. I was

driving home when the shaking started. But I pulled over immediately.
to home(×)   = at once

I'm listening to the radio right now to find out what's going on."
to부정사의 부사적 용법(목적)   = happening

swing 흔들다, 흔들리다

drop 떨어지다, 쓰러지다

cover 가리다, 덮다

tip over 넘어뜨리다, 넘어지다

roll 굴러가다

collapse 붕괴되다, 무너지다

seem to V …인 것 같다

urgently 긴급하게, 급히

pull over 길 한쪽으로 차를 대다

immediately 즉시, 당장

📎 **확인문제**

● 다음 문장이 본문의 내용과 일치하면 T, 일치하지 <u>않으면</u> F를 쓰시오.

1 The writer could see the light swinging violently and books falling to the floor. ☐

2 The writer's family picture dropped from the table and the glass covering it broke. ☐

3 The writer started to worry that the building would collapse. ☐

4 When the shaking seemed to be violent, the writer's family started crawling toward the door. ☐

5 The writer's dad was driving home when the shaking started. ☐

6 The writer's mom was listening to the radio to find out what was going on. ☐

We nervously <u>made our way down</u> the stairs and outside. I looked
make one's way: 나아가다, 가다

around. Parts of buildings <u>had fallen and had smashed</u> several cars. We
밖으로 나가기 전에 건물의 일부분이 떨어져 나갔고 몇몇 차들은 박살이 난 것이므로 과거완료로 씀.

went to an open space <u>to avoid</u> more falling pieces. How could all this
to부정사의 부사적 용법(목적)

have happened <u>in a few minutes</u>?
몇 분 만에

Although I <u>had done</u> many earthquake drills in school, I <u>had</u> never
과거(지진이 일어났던 상황)보다 더 이전에 지진 훈련을 했었기 때문에 과거완료로 씀.   과거(지진이 일어났던 상황)보다 더 이전에 지진을 겪으리라고는 생각해 본 적 없었기 때문에 과거완료로 씀.

<u>thought</u> I'd experience a real earthquake. I still get scared when I

remember that night. I can't forget <u>the panic I felt</u> when the furniture
the panic과 I 사이에 목적격 관계대명사 that[which]이 생략   furnitures(×):
항상 단수로 쓰는 집합명사

was shaking and things were falling to the floor. After that night, I

<u>began to take</u> earthquake drills seriously. I realized <u>that</u> I should be
= taking   목적어를 이끄는 접속사(생략 가능함.)

prepared for the next earthquake, <u>which</u> can occur <u>at any time</u>.
that(×)   언제든

nervously 신경질적으로, 초조하게
smash 박살내다, 때려 부수다
avoid …을 피하다
drill 훈련
seriously 심각하게, 진지하게
occur (일·사건 등이) 일어나다, 발생하다

📎 확인문제

● 다음 문장이 본문의 내용과 일치하면 T, 일치하지 <u>않으면</u> F를 쓰시오.

1 The writer's family nervously made their way down the stairs and outside. ☐

2 All the buildings had fallen and had smashed several cars. ☐

3 The writer's family went to an open space to avoid more falling pieces. ☐

4 The writer had never done an earthquake drill in school. ☐

5 The writer had never thought she would experience a real earthquake. ☐

6 The writer realized that she should be prepared for the next earthquake, though it

seldom occurs. ☐

• 우리말을 참고하여 빈칸에 알맞은 말을 쓰시오.

1 _____ _____ to an Earthquake

2 One night in February, after I _____ _____ _____ _____, an earthquake hit.

3 I woke up suddenly because my bed _____ _____.

4 I thought my brother was shaking my bed _____ _____ _____.

5 But then I heard the mirror on my desk _____ _____ _____ _____ and _____ _____ _____.

6 I knew it wasn't my brother then, but I still didn't know _____ _____ _____ _____.

7 Soon the whole room began to shake violently, and my confusion _____ _____ _____.

8 My mom shouted that it was an earthquake and _____ _____ my room.

9 Since it was _____ _____ _____ _____ an earthquake, I didn't know how to react.

10 I just _____ _____, "What should I do?"

11 My mom pulled me and my brother _____ _____ _____.

12 We ran to the kitchen and _____ _____ the table.

13 I could see the light _____ violently and books _____ to the floor.

---

1 지진에 눈을 뜨는 것

2 2월 어느 날 밤, 내가 잠자리에 든 후에 지진이 일어났다.

3 침대가 흔들렸기 때문에 나는 갑자기 잠에서 깼다.

4 나는 남동생이 장난으로 침대를 흔들고 있다고 생각했다.

5 하지만 그때 나는 내 책상 위에 있던 거울이 바닥으로 떨어져 산산조각이 나는 소리를 들었다.

6 그때 나는 남동생이 그런 것이 아니라는 것을 알았지만, 정확히 무슨 일이 일어나고 있었는지를 여전히 알지 못했다.

7 머지않아 방 전체가 심하게 흔들리기 시작했고 혼란스러움은 공포로 변했다.

8 엄마가 지진이라고 소리를 지르며 내 방으로 뛰어 들어왔다.

9 지진을 경험한 것이 처음이었기 때문에, 나는 어떻게 반응해야 할지 몰랐다.

10 나는 그저 "어떻게 해야 하지?"라는 말을 반복했다.

11 엄마는 나와 남동생을 침대 밖으로 잡아끌었다.

12 우리는 주방으로 달려가서 식탁 아래로 기어들어 갔다.

13 나는 전등이 심하게 흔들리는 것과 책이 바닥으로 떨어지는 것을 볼 수 있었다.

14 Our family picture dropped from the wall and the glass _____
_____ _____.

15 A cup _____ _____ and _____ _____ the kitchen table.

16 _____ _____, I could hear something else in the apartment
break.

17 I started _____ _____ that the building would _____.

18 Then the shaking _____ _____ _____.

19 We started _____ _____ the door.

20 _____ _____ _____ _____, my mom's cell phone rang.

21 It was my dad, who was _____ _____ _____ _____.

22 He shouted, "_____ _____!

23 Get _____ _____ the building!

24 _____ the stairs!

25 _____ _____ the elevator!

26 _____!"

27 "_____ are you?

28 Are you okay?" my mom asked _____.

29 My dad answered, "_____ _____.

30 I'm _____.

---

14 우리 가족 사진이 벽에서 떨어졌고 사진을 덮고 있던 유리가 깨졌다.

15 컵이 넘어지고 식탁에서 굴러 떨어졌다.

16 매 순간, 나는 아파트에 있는 다른 어떤 것들이 부서지는 소리를 들을 수 있었다.

17 나는 건물이 무너지지는 않을까 하는 걱정이 들기 시작했다.

18 그때 흔들림이 멈추는 것 같았다.

19 우리는 문으로 기어가기 시작했다.

20 그 순간, 엄마의 휴대 전화가 울렸다.

21 전화를 한 사람은 바로 아빠였는데, 직장에서 퇴근하던 중이었다.

22 아빠는 소리쳤다. "지진이 멈췄어요!

23 건물 밖으로 나와요!

24 계단을 이용해요!

25 엘리베이터를 타면 안 돼요!

26 서둘러요!"

27 "어디예요?

28 괜찮아요?"라고 엄마가 다급하게 물었다.

29 아빠가 대답했다. "걱정 말아요.

30 나는 괜찮아요.

---

31 I _____ _____ _____ when the shaking started.

32 But I _____ _____ immediately.

33 I'm listening to the radio _____ _____ to find out what's _____ _____."

34 We nervously _____ _____ _____ down the stairs and outside.

35 I looked _____.

36 Parts of buildings _____ _____ and _____ _____ several cars.

37 We went to an open space _____ _____ more falling pieces.

38 How _____ all this _____ _____ in a few minutes?

39 Although I had done many _____ _____ in school, I had never thought I'd experience _____ _____ _____.

40 I still _____ _____ when I remember that night.

41 I can't forget _____ _____ _____ _____ when the furniture was shaking and things were falling to the floor.

42 After that night, I began to _____ earthquake _____ _____.

43 I realized that I should _____ _____ _____ the next earthquake, which can occur _____ _____ _____.

31 진동이 시작할 때 운전해서 집으로 가던 중이었어요.

32 하지만 즉시 차를 길 한쪽에 댔어요.

33 무슨 일이 일어나는지 알기 위해 지금 라디오를 듣고 있어요."

34 우리는 초조한 마음으로 계단을 내려가서 밖으로 나갔다.

35 나는 주변을 둘러보았다.

36 건물의 일부분이 떨어져 나갔고 몇몇 차들은 박살이 났다.

37 우리는 추가적인 낙하물을 피하기 위해 공터로 갔다.

38 어떻게 이런 일이 몇 분 만에 일어날 수 있단 말인가?

39 비록 학교에서 많은 지진 대피 훈련을 해 왔지만, 내가 실제 지진을 겪으리라고는 전혀 생각해 보지 않았었다.

40 그날 밤을 기억하면 나는 여전히 두려워진다.

41 가구가 흔들리고 물건들이 바닥으로 떨어졌을 때 내가 느꼈던 공포심을 나는 잊을 수가 없다.

42 그날 밤 이후, 나는 지진 대피 훈련에 진지하게 임하기 시작했다.

43 나는 언제든 발생할 수 있는 다음 지진을 대비해야 한다는 것을 깨달았다.

● 우리말을 참고하여 본문을 영작하시오.

1 지진에 눈을 뜨는 것

➡ _____

2 2월 어느 날 밤, 내가 잠자리에 든 후에 지진이 일어났다.

➡ _____

3 침대가 흔들렸기 때문에 나는 갑자기 잠에서 깼다.

➡ _____

4 나는 남동생이 장난으로 침대를 흔들고 있다고 생각했다.

➡ _____

5 하지만 그때 나는 내 책상 위에 있던 거울이 바닥으로 떨어져 산산조각이 나는 소리를 들었다.

➡ _____

6 그때 나는 남동생이 그런 것이 아니라는 것을 알았지만, 정확히 무슨 일이 일어나고 있었는지를 여전히 알지 못했다.

➡ _____

7 머지않아 방 전체가 심하게 흔들리기 시작했고 혼란스러움은 공포로 변했다.

➡ _____

8 엄마가 지진이라고 소리를 지르며 내 방으로 뛰어 들어왔다.

➡ _____

9 지진을 경험한 것이 처음이었기 때문에, 나는 어떻게 반응해야 할지 몰랐다.

➡ _____

10 나는 그저 "어떻게 해야 하지?"라는 말을 반복했다.

➡ _____

11 엄마는 나와 남동생을 침대 밖으로 잡아끌었다.

➡ _____

12 우리는 주방으로 달려가서 식탁 아래로 기어들어 갔다.

➡ _____

13 나는 전등이 심하게 흔들리는 것과 책이 바닥으로 떨어지는 것을 볼 수 있었다.

➡ _____

14 우리 가족 사진이 벽에서 떨어졌고 사진을 덮고 있던 유리가 깨졌다.

➡ _____

15 컵이 넘어지고 식탁에서 굴러 떨어졌다.

➡ _____

16 매 순간, 나는 아파트에 있는 다른 어떤 것들이 부서지는 소리를 들을 수 있었다.

➡ _____

17 나는 건물이 무너지지는 않을까 하는 걱정이 들기 시작했다.

➡ _____

18 그때 흔들림이 멈추는 것 같았다.

➡ _____

19 우리는 문으로 기어가기 시작했다.

➡ _____

20 그 순간, 엄마의 휴대 전화가 울렸다.

➡ _____

21 전화를 한 사람은 바로 아빠였는데, 직장에서 퇴근하던 중이었다.

➡ _____

22 아빠는 소리쳤다, "지진이 멈췄어요!

➡ _____

23 건물 밖으로 나와요!

➡ _____

24 계단을 이용해요!

➡ _____

25 엘리베이터를 타면 안 돼요!

➡ _____

26 서둘러요!"

➡ _____

27 "어디예요?

➡ _____

28 괜찮아요?"라고 엄마가 다급하게 물었다.

➡ _____

29 아빠가 대답했다, "걱정 말아요.

➡ _____

30 나는 괜찮아요.

➡ _____

31 진동이 시작할 때 운전해서 집으로 가던 중이었어요.

➡ _____

32 하지만 즉시 차를 길 한쪽에 댔어요.

➡ _____

33 무슨 일이 일어나는지 알기 위해 지금 라디오를 듣고 있어요."

➡ _____

34 우리는 초조한 마음으로 계단을 내려가서 밖으로 나갔다.

➡ _____

35 나는 주변을 둘러보았다.

➡ _____

36 건물의 일부분이 떨어져 나갔고 몇몇 차들은 박살이 났다.

➡ _____

37 우리는 추가적인 낙하물을 피하기 위해 공터로 갔다.

➡ _____

38 어떻게 이런 일이 몇 분 만에 일어날 수 있단 말인가?

➡ _____

39 비록 학교에서 많은 지진 대피 훈련을 해 왔지만, 내가 실제 지진을 겪으리라고는 전혀 생각해 보지 않았었다.

➡ _____

_____

40 그날 밤을 기억하면 나는 여전히 두려워진다.

➡ _____

41 가구가 흔들리고 물건들이 바닥으로 떨어졌을 때 내가 느꼈던 공포심을 나는 잊을 수가 없다.

➡ _____

42 그날 밤 이후, 나는 지진 대피 훈련에 진지하게 임하기 시작했다.

➡ _____

43 나는 언제든 발생할 수 있는 다음 지진을 대비해야 한다는 것을 깨달았다.

➡ _____

[01~04] 다음 글을 읽고 물음에 답하시오.

One night in February, after I (A)had gone to bed, an earthquake hit. (①) I woke up suddenly because my bed was shaking. (②) But then I heard the mirror on my desk fall to the floor and break ___ⓐ___ pieces. (③) I knew it wasn't my brother then, but I still didn't know what exactly was happening. (④) Soon the whole room began to shake violently, and my confusion turned ___ⓑ___ panic. (⑤) My mom shouted that it was an earthquake and ran into my room. Since it was my first time experiencing an earthquake, I didn't know how to react. I just kept saying, "What should I do?"

01 위 글의 빈칸 ⓐ, ⓑ에 들어갈 말이 바르게 짝지어진 것은?

      ⓐ   ⓑ   ⓐ   ⓑ
① by － into   ② into － by
③ for － by   ④ for － into
⑤ into － to

02 위 글의 흐름으로 보아, 주어진 문장이 들어가기에 가장 적절한 곳은?

> I thought my brother was shaking my bed as a joke.

①   ②   ③   ④   ⑤

03 위 글의 밑줄 친 (A)had gone과 과거완료의 용법이 같은 것을 고르시오.

① I did not tell him at first, for I had never seen him before.
② I had just finished my homework when she came.

③ I couldn't buy it as I had lost my purse.
④ He had been to France twice before he was twenty years old.
⑤ When I visited her, she had been ill for a week.

04 중요 According to the passage, which is NOT true?

① One night in February, the writer had gone to bed before an earthquake hit.
② The writer's brother was shaking the writer's bed as a joke.
③ Before long the whole room began to shake violently.
④ The writer had never experienced an earthquake before.
⑤ The writer didn't know how to react to the earthquake.

[05~07] 다음 글을 읽고 물음에 답하시오.

My mom pulled me and my brother out of bed. We ran to the kitchen and crawled under the table. ⓐI could see the light to swing violently and books to fall to the floor. Our family picture dropped from the wall and the glass covering ⓑit broke. A cup tipped over and rolled off the kitchen table. Every second, I could hear something else in the apartment break. I started to worry that the building would collapse.

서답형

05 위 글의 밑줄 친 ⓐ에서 어법상 틀린 부분을 찾아 고치시오. (두 군데)

_____ ➡ _____

_____ ➡ _____

06 위 글의 밑줄 친 ⓑit이 가리키는 것을 본문에서 찾아 쓰시오.

➡ _____

07 다음 중 위 글의 지진 때문에 일어난 일이 <u>아닌</u> 것을 고르시오.

① 전등이 심하게 흔들렸다.
② 책이 바닥으로 떨어졌다.
③ 가족 사진이 벽에서 떨어졌다.
④ 컵이 넘어지고 식탁에서 굴러 떨어졌다.
⑤ 아파트 건물이 무너졌다.

[08~10] 다음 글을 읽고 물음에 답하시오.

　Then the shaking seemed to stop. We started crawling toward the door. At that moment, my mom's cell phone rang. It was my dad, who was coming home from work.
　He shouted, "It stopped! Get out of the building! Take the stairs! Don't take the elevator! Hurry!" "Where are you? Are you okay?" my mom asked urgently. My dad answered, "Don't worry. I'm okay. I was driving home when the shaking started. But I pulled over immediately. I'm listening to the radio right now ⓐto find out what's going on."

08 아래 〈보기〉에서 위 글의 밑줄 친 ⓐto find와 to부정사의 용법이 같은 것의 개수를 고르시오.

┤ 보기 ├
① He tried to stop smoking.
② There's nothing to stop you from doing it.
③ The policeman ran to stop the flight.
④ I wanted the baby to stop crying.
⑤ You must be crazy to stop the car in the middle of the street.

① 1개　② 2개　③ 3개　④ 4개　⑤ 5개

09 위 글의 분위기로 가장 알맞은 것을 고르시오.

① exciting　② urgent　③ touching
④ fantastic　⑤ boring

서답형

10 주어진 영영풀이에 해당하는 단어를 본문에서 찾아 쓰시오.

moved to the side of the road and stopped

➡ _____

[11~14] 다음 글을 읽고 물음에 답하시오.

　We nervously made our way down the stairs and outside. I looked around. ⓐParts of buildings fell and smashed several cars. We went to an open space to avoid more falling pieces. ⓑHow could all this have happened in a few minutes?
　Although I had done many earthquake drills in school, I had never thought I'd experience a real earthquake. I still get scared when I remember that night. ⓒ가구가 흔들리고 물건들이 바닥으로 떨어졌을 때 내가 느꼈던 공포심을 나는 잊을 수가 없다. After that night, I began to take earthquake drills seriously. I realized that I should be prepared for the next earthquake, which can occur at any time.　<I: a girl>

서답형

11 위 글의 밑줄 친 ⓐ에서 어법상 <u>틀린</u> 부분을 찾아 고치시오. (두 군데)

_____ ➡ _____
_____ ➡ _____

12 위 글의 밑줄 친 ⓑ에서 알 수 있는 글쓴이의 심경으로 가장 알맞은 것을 고르시오.

① excited　　　② ashamed
③ disappointed　④ puzzled
⑤ depressed

13 위 글의 밑줄 친 ⓒ의 우리말에 맞게 주어진 어휘를 알맞게 배열하시오.

> were falling / when / I / the furniture / can't forget / to the floor / felt / things / and / I / was shaking / the panic / .

➡ _____

_____

14 위 글에 어울리는 속담으로 가장 알맞은 것을 고르시오.

① A friend in need is a friend indeed.
② Prevention is better than cure.
③ Every cloud has a silver lining.
④ Look before you leap.
⑤ Make hay while the sun shines.

15 주어진 글 다음에 이어질 글의 순서로 가장 적절한 것은?

> One night in February, after I had gone to bed, an earthquake hit. I woke up suddenly because my bed was shaking.
>
> (A) I knew it wasn't my brother then, but I still didn't know what exactly was happening. Soon the whole room began to shake violently, and my confusion turned to panic.
>
> (B) I thought my brother was shaking my bed as a joke. But then I heard the mirror on my desk fall to the floor and break into pieces.
>
> (C) My mom shouted that it was an earthquake and ran into my room. Since it was my first time experiencing an earthquake, I didn't know how to react. I just kept saying, "What should I do?"

① (A) – (C) – (B)   ② (B) – (A) – (C)
③ (B) – (C) – (A)   ④ (C) – (A) – (B)
⑤ (C) – (B) – (A)

[16~17] 다음 글을 읽고 물음에 답하시오.

> Then the shaking seemed to stop. We started crawling toward the door. At that moment, my mom's cell phone rang. It was my dad, who was coming home from work.
>
> He shouted, "It stopped! Get out of the building! Take the stairs! Don't take the elevator! Hurry!" "Where are ①you? Are ②you okay?" ③my mom asked urgently. My dad answered, "Don't worry. I'm okay. ④I was driving home when the shaking started. But I pulled over immediately. ⑤I'm listening to the radio right now to find out what's going on."

16 밑줄 친 ①~⑤ 중에서 가리키는 대상이 나머지 넷과 다른 것은?

①   ②   ③   ④   ⑤

17 According to the passage, which is NOT true?

① When the shaking seemed to stop, the writer started crawling toward the door.
② The writer's dad was coming home from work.
③ The writer's dad told the writer's mom to take the elevator.
④ The writer's mom didn't know where the writer's dad was.
⑤ The writer's dad was listening to the radio to find out what was going on.

[18~20] 다음 글을 읽고 물음에 답하시오.

My mom pulled me and my brother out of bed. We ran to the kitchen and crawled under the table. I could see the light swinging violently and books falling to the floor. Our family picture dropped from the wall and the glass ⓐcovering it broke. A cup tipped over and rolled off the kitchen table. Every second, I could hear something else in the apartment break. I started to worry that the building would collapse. <I: a girl>

18 위 글의 밑줄 친 ⓐ를 관계대명사를 사용하여 두 단어로 고치시오.

➡ _____

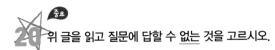

19 주어진 영영풀이에 해당하는 단어를 본문에서 찾아 쓰시오.

to fall down very suddenly

➡ _____

20 위 글을 읽고 질문에 답할 수 없는 것을 고르시오.

① What did the writer's mom do?
② Where did the writer take refuge with her mom and her brother?
③ What could the writer see during the earthquake?
④ How long did the earthquake last?
⑤ Why did the writer start to worry that the building would collapse?

[21~23] 다음 글을 읽고 물음에 답하시오.

One night in February, after I ___ⓐ___ to bed, an earthquake hit. I woke up suddenly because my bed was shaking. I thought my brother was shaking my bed as a joke. But then I heard the mirror on my desk fall to the floor and break into pieces. I knew it wasn't my brother then, but I still didn't know what exactly was happening.

Soon the whole room began to shake violently, and my confusion turned to panic. My mom shouted that it was an earthquake and ran into my room. ⓑ지진을 경험한 것이 처음이었기 때문에, I didn't know how to react. I just kept saying, "What should I do?"

21 위 글의 빈칸 ⓐ에 들어갈 알맞은 말을 모두 고르시오.

① have gone   ② would go
③ had gone   ④ go
⑤ went

22 위 글의 밑줄 친 ⓑ의 우리말에 맞게 주어진 어휘를 이용하여 9단어로 영작하시오.

since, experiencing

➡ _____

_____

23 위 글의 제목으로 알맞은 것을 고르시오.

① Have You Experienced an Earthquake?
② My Brother Likes to Play Jokes on Me
③ Waking Up to an Earthquake
④ Wow! My Room Began Shaking Violently!
⑤ My Mom Ran into My Room in Panic!

[24~26] 다음 글을 읽고 물음에 답하시오.

One night in February, after I had gone to bed, an earthquake hit. I woke up suddenly because my bed was shaking. I thought my brother was shaking my bed as a joke. ⓐBut then I heard the mirror on my desk to fall to the floor and to break into pieces. I knew it wasn't my brother then, but I still didn't know what exactly was happening.

Soon the whole room began to shake violently, and my confusion turned to panic. My mom shouted that it was an earthquake and ran into my room. ⓑSince it was my first time experiencing an earthquake, I didn't know how to react. I just kept saying, "What should I do?" <I: a girl>

서답형

24 위 글의 밑줄 친 ⓐ에서 어법상 틀린 부분을 찾아 고치시오. (두 군데)

_____ ➡ _____

_____ ➡ _____

25 아래 〈보기〉에서 위 글의 밑줄 친 ⓑSince와 같은 의미로 쓰인 것의 개수를 고르시오.

┌─ 보기 ─┐

① She has moved house six times since she came here.

② Let's do our best since we can expect no help from others.

③ He has written to me once since he left here.

④ Since we're not very busy just now, I can get away from the office.

⑤ Since we live in the computer era, you should get used to personal computers.

① 1개 ② 2개 ③ 3개 ④ 4개 ⑤ 5개

26 Why didn't the writer know how to react to the earthquake? Answer in English. (9 words)

➡ _____

[27~29] 다음 글을 읽고 물음에 답하시오.

Although I had done many earthquake drills in school, I ⓐhad never thought I'd experience a real earthquake. I still get (A)[scaring / scared] when I remember that night. I can't forget the panic I felt when the furniture was shaking and things were falling to the floor. After that night, I began to take earthquake drills (B)[serious / seriously]. I realized that I should be prepared for the next earthquake, (C)[that / which] can occur at any time. <I: a girl>

중요

27 위 글의 밑줄 친 ⓑhad never thought와 현재완료의 용법이 같은 것을 모두 고르시오.

① I have eaten Pad thai twice.

② They have lived in Seoul since 1998.

③ How many times have you been to Europe?

④ He has not finished his homework yet.

⑤ Have you ever seen such a wonderful scene before?

서답형

28 위 글의 괄호 (A)~(C)에서 문맥이나 어법상 알맞은 낱말을 골라 쓰시오.

➡ (A) _____ (B) _____ (C) _____

서답형

29 다음 빈칸에 알맞은 단어를 넣어 글쓴이가 이번 지진으로 깨달은 점을 완성하시오.

┌─────────┐

The writer realized that she should be _____ _____ the next earthquake, which can occur at any time.

└─────────┘

[01~03] 다음 글을 읽고 물음에 답하시오.

One night in February, after I had gone to bed, an earthquake hit. I woke up suddenly because my bed was shaking. I thought my brother was shaking my bed as a joke. But then I heard the mirror on my desk fall to the floor and break into pieces. ⓐI knew it wasn't my brother then, but I still didn't know what exactly was happened.

Soon the whole room began to shake violently, and my confusion turned to panic. My mom shouted that it was an earthquake and ran into my room. Since it was my first time experiencing an earthquake, I didn't know ⓑhow to react. I just kept saying, "What should I do?"   <I: a girl>

01 Why did the writer wake up suddenly one night in February? Answer in English. (5 words)

➡ _____

02 위 글의 밑줄 친 ⓐ에서 어법상 틀린 부분을 찾아 고치시오.

_____ ➡ _____

03 위 글의 밑줄 친 ⓑhow to react를 다음과 같이 바꿔 쓸 때 빈칸에 들어갈 알맞은 말을 두 단어로 쓰시오.

➡ how _____ _____ react

[04~06] 다음 글을 읽고 물음에 답하시오.

My mom (A)[pulled / pushed] me and my brother out of bed. We ran to the kitchen and crawled under the table. ⓐ나는 전등이 심하게 흔들리는 것과 책이 바닥으로 떨어지는 것을 볼 수 있었다. Our family picture dropped from the

wall and the glass (B)[covering / covered] it broke. A cup tipped over and rolled off the kitchen table. Every second, I could hear something else in the apartment (C)[break / to break]. I started to worry that the building would collapse.   <I: a girl>

04 위 글의 괄호 (A)~(C)에서 문맥이나 어법상 알맞은 낱말을 골라 쓰시오.

➡ (A) _____ (B) _____ (C) _____

05 위 글의 밑줄 친 ⓐ의 우리말에 맞게 주어진 어휘를 알맞게 배열하시오.

violently / the light / and / I / books / to the floor / see / swinging / falling / could / .

➡ _____
_____

06 다음 빈칸 (A)와 (B)에 알맞은 단어를 넣어 글쓴이의 가족이 지진이 났을 때 취한 행동을 완성하시오.

The writer ran to (A)_____ _____ and (B)_____ under the table with her mom and her brother.

[07~10] 다음 글을 읽고 물음에 답하시오.

ⓐThen the shaking seemed to stop. We started crawling toward the door. At that moment, my mom's cell phone rang. It was my dad, who was coming home from work.

He shouted, "ⓑIt stopped! Get out of the building! Take the stairs! Don't take the elevator! Hurry!" "Where are you? Are you okay?" my mom asked urgently. My dad answered, "Don't worry. I'm okay. I was driving home when the shaking started. But I pulled over ⓒimmediately. I'm listening to the radio right now to find out what's going on."

07 위 글의 밑줄 친 ⓐ를 다음과 같이 바꿔 쓸 때 빈칸에 들어갈 알맞은 단어를 쓰시오.

➡ Then _____ seemed that the shaking stopped.

08 위 글의 밑줄 친 ⓑit이 가리키는 것을 본문에서 찾아 쓰시오.

➡ _____

09 위 글의 밑줄 친 ⓒimmediately와 바꿔 쓸 수 있는 말을 쓰시오. (두 단어)

➡ _____ 또는 _____

10 다음 빈칸 (A)와 (B)에 알맞은 단어를 넣어 글쓴이의 아빠에 대한 소개를 완성하시오.

The writer's dad was (A)_____ _____ when the shaking started, but he pulled over immediately. He was (B)_____ _____ _____ _____ right then to find out what was going on.

[11~14] 다음 글을 읽고 물음에 답하시오.

We nervously made our way down the stairs and outside. I looked around. Parts of buildings had fallen and had smashed several cars. We went to an open space to avoid more falling pieces. (A)어떻게 이런 일이 몇 분 만에 일어날 수 있단 말인가?

Although I _____ⓐ_____ many earthquake drills in school, I had never thought I'd experience a real earthquake. I still get scared when I remember that night. I can't forget the panic I felt when the furniture was shaking and things were falling to the floor. After that night, I began to take earthquake drills seriously. (B)I realized that I should be prepared for the next earthquake, which can be occurred at any time. <I: a girl>

11 위 글의 빈칸 ⓐ에 do를 알맞은 형태로 쓰시오.

➡ _____

12 위 글의 밑줄 친 (A)의 우리말에 맞게 주어진 어휘를 이용하여 10 단어로 영작하시오.

how, could, all, have, in

➡ _____

13 위 글의 밑줄 친 (B)에서 어법상 틀린 부분을 찾아 고치시오.

_____ ➡ _____

14 How does the writer feel when she remembers that night? Fill in the blanks (A) and (B) with suitable words.

She still (A)_____ _____, and she can't forget (B)_____ _____ she felt when the furniture was shaking and things were falling to the floor.

교과서

구석구석

해석

After You Read B

R: How did you feel when the earthquake occurred?

접속사 when은 "~할 때"의 의미로 시간의 부사절이다.

W: I began to panic because the whole room was shaking violently.

R: How scary! What did you do next?

How+형용사+(주어+동사)!의 형태로 감탄문이다.

W: We all crawled under the table after my mom got us out of bed.

get A out of B A를 B에서 끌어내다

R: What was happening at the moment?

W: Lots of things were falling to the floor. I heard many things in the

= Many

apartment break.

지각동사 heard의 목적격보어

R: What did you realize after that night?

W: I realized that I should be prepared for the next earthquake. It can occur

at any time!

어느 때고

구문해설 • occur 발생하다 • violently 격렬하게 • scary 무서운 • crawl 기어가다
• realize 깨닫다

R: 지진이 일어났을 때 어떻게 느끼셨습니까?

W: 방 전체가 심하게 흔들렸기 때문에 공포에 사로잡히기 시작했어요.

R: 얼마나 무서웠을까! 그 다음에 무엇을 했나요?

W: 어머니가 우리를 침대에서 끌어내린 후, 우리는 모두 식탁 아래로 기어갔어요.

R: 그 순간에 무슨 일이 일어나고 있었나요?

W: 많은 것들이 바닥으로 떨어지고 있었어요. 나는 아파트 안에 있는 많은 것들이 깨지는 소리를 들었어요.

R: 그날 밤 이후에 무엇을 깨달았나요?

W: 나는 내가 다음 지진에 대비해야 한다는 것을 깨달았어요. 지진은 언제든지 일어날 수 있어요!

Think & Write Step 3

San Andreas

I would like to tell you about the movie *San Andreas*. This movie is set in Los

want to의 공손한 표현   배경으로 하고 있다

Angeles and San Francisco in 2014. The main character, a search-and-rescue

└ 동격 ┘

pilot, must search for his missing family during an earthquake. The special

missed(×)

effects used in the disaster scenes are very good. The movie is a little sad

which[that] are used   a few(×)

at times, but the story is very interesting. I give *San Andreas* four stars. Go

= sometimes

and watch it!

구문해설 • would like to: ~하고 싶다 • main character: 주인공
• search-and-rescue pilot: 수색구조 조종사 • missing: 행방불명된
• at times: 가끔(=sometimes)

San Andreas

저는 영화 San Andreas에 대해 말하고 싶습니다. 이 영화의 배경은 2014년 Los Angeles와 San Francisco입니다. 수색구조 조종사인 주인공은 지진이 일어난 동안 행방불명된 그의 가족을 찾아야 합니다. 재난 장면에 사용된 특수효과는 매우 좋습니다. 이 영화는 가끔 약간 슬프지만, 이야기는 매우 재미있습니다. 저는 San Andreas에게 별 4개를 줍니다. 가서 보세요!

Words & Expressions

01 다음 두 문장에 공통으로 알맞은 것을 고르시오.

> • I read a report yesterday _____ the damage from each type of natural disaster.
> • I'm curious _____ how that happened.

① at   ② about   ③ in
④ of   ⑤ for

02 다음 문장의 빈칸에 알맞은 단어를 고르시오.

> Soon the whole room began to shake _____, and my confusion turned to panic.

① violently   ② properly   ③ recently
④ actually   ⑤ exactly

03 다음 대화의 빈칸에 들어갈 말로 적절한 것을 고르시오.

> B: There was a big flood in Europe. Did you hear about it?
> G: No, I didn't. But floods aren't that _____ in winter, are they? I'm curious about how that happened.
> B: Me too. Let's do some online research.

① aware   ② missing   ③ exact
④ proper   ⑤ common

04 다음 영영풀이에 해당하는 단어를 주어진 철자로 시작하여 쓰시오.

> to break apart and fall down suddenly

➡ c_____

Conversation

[05~07] 다음 대화를 읽고 물음에 답하시오.

> B: Hey, did you hear about the big fires in California?
> G: _____ (A)
> B: They've destroyed a large number of houses and other buildings.
> G: Are the fires still going on?
> B: Yes, actually the wind has made the fires worse. I hope all the people living there are okay.
> G: So do I. (B)나는 얼마나 많은 사람들이 집을 떠나야 했는지 궁금하다. (curious, had to, how many, leave, I'm, people, about, their homes)
> B: Actually more than 20,000 people had to leave their homes, and about 400 people are missing in that area.
> G: That's terrible. I hope they're somewhere safe.

05 위 대화의 빈칸 (A)에 적절한 것은?

① Really? How did it start?
② Yes. It's not so serious.
③ Well, they stopped at the moment.
④ No, I didn't. How serious are they?
⑤ Of course. I don't know much.

06 밑줄 친 (B)의 우리말에 맞게 주어진 단어를 바르게 배열하시오.

➡ _____
_____

07 위 대화의 내용과 일치하지 <u>않는</u> 것은?

① The fires destroyed a large house.
② The fires are still going on.
③ The fires got worse due to the wind.
④ A lot of people had to leave their homes.
⑤ People missing in that area are about 400.

[08~09] 다음 대화를 읽고 물음에 답하시오.

G: Did you hear that earthquakes are ___(A)___ more often in Korea than before?
B: Oh, really? I've never felt an earthquake in Korea.
G: They usually occur in the southern part of Korea, but now they are ___(B)___ in other places as well.
B: I didn't know that. I'm curious about why earthquakes have occurred so often in Korea recently.
G: Why don't we do some research to find out?
B: Sounds good, but where do we look first?
G: How about asking our science teacher first? I think she can help us.
B: Okay. Let's go and find her.

08 빈칸 (A)와 (B)에 공통으로 들어가기에 적절한 것은?

① watching   ② increasing
③ occurring   ④ researching
⑤ finding

09 According to the dialogue, what does the boy want to know?

① the time when earthquakes occurred
② the places where earthquakes have occurred
③ the reason why earthquakes have occurred so often in Korea recently
④ the way they do some research
⑤ the person who can help them

[10~11] 다음 대화를 읽고 물음에 답하시오.

G: There seem to be many natural disasters in Korea these days.
B: I agree. ⓐThere was an earthquake in the south last week. ⓑAlso a storm is coming this week.
G: ⓒI'm curious about which type of natural disaster causes the most damage in Korea.
B: ⓓActually I read a report yesterday about the damage from each type of natural disaster. Number one is storms.
G: I see. I guess earthquakes are second.
B: ⓔNo, second is earthquakes, and third is heavy snow.

10 위 대화의 ⓐ~ⓔ 중 흐름상 <u>어색한</u> 문장은?

① ⓐ   ② ⓑ   ③ ⓒ   ④ ⓓ   ⑤ ⓔ

11 위 대화의 내용과 일치하지 <u>않는</u> 것은?

① The girl and the boy think natural disasters are occurring more often in Korea.
② The boy read a report about natural disasters.
③ The girl thinks storms cause the second most damage.
④ The boy says heavy snow causes the third most damage.
⑤ The girl wants to know which type of natural disaster causes the most damage.

[12~13] 다음 대화를 읽고 물음에 답하시오.

B: Mom, what else do we need to put in the ___(A)___ survival kit?
W: Well, we need water, some food, and radio.
B: ___(B)___, Mom?
W: Oh, make sure that you include batteries for the radio.

12 빈칸 (A)에 들어가기에 적절한 두 단어를 쓰시오.

➡ _____

13 빈칸 (B)에 적절한 말을 두 단어로 쓰시오.

➡ _____

Grammar

14 다음 두 문장이 뜻이 비슷하도록 빈칸에 들어갈 알맞은 것은?

> Sinclare was young but he was regarded as their leader by them.
> = _____, he was regarded as their leader by them.

① Although Sinclare was young
② Since Sinclare was young
③ While Sinclare was young
④ As Sinclare was young
⑤ Unless Sinclare was young

15 다음 문장 중에서 어법상 어색한 것을 고르시오.

① After you say goodbye today, don't ever come back here.
② When I got home, my daughter had finished her homework.
③ When he had arrived at home, they already ate dinner.
④ Mom had gone to work when I woke up.
⑤ Claudia lost the camera that her boy friend had bought for her.

16 다음 그림을 참고하여 빈칸에 알맞은 말을 쓰시오.

_____ my dad went to work by car this morning, he came back home on foot.

17 다음 문장의 빈칸에 들어갈 수 <u>없는</u> 것은?

> When Monica went back home, he _____.

① had finished cleaning the house
② had walked the dog
③ had already dinner alone
④ had just gone to bed
⑤ had watered the plants

18 다음 두 문장을 since 또는 although를 이용해 한 문장으로 만드시오. (접속사로 시작할 것)

(1) • It's very hot outside.
　 • I will walk my dog.
　 ➡ _____

(2) • They had to paint quickly to capture the effect of light.
　 • They did not sketch their paintings in advance.
　 ➡ _____
　 　 _____

(3) • Most people recognize it as a jewel.
　 • The diamond most directly affects our daily lives as a tool.
　 ➡ _____
　 　 _____

19 다음 ⓐ~ⓕ 중 어법상 옳은 것을 모두 고르시오.

> ⓐ I had never eaten *pho* until I have visited Vietnam.
>
> ⓑ I was wearing the dress that my mom had made for me.
>
> ⓒ When I had got home, the TV was turned on.
>
> ⓓ I knew Francesca well since I had seen her before.
>
> ⓔ While playing basketball, Mike broke his leg.
>
> ⓕ Since they are rich, they don't seem happy at all.

➡ _____

Reading

[20~22] 다음 글을 읽고 물음에 답하시오.

> One night in February, after I had gone to bed, an earthquake hit. I woke up suddenly because my bed was shaking. I thought my brother was shaking my bed as a joke. But then I heard the mirror on my desk fall to the floor and (A)산산조각이 나다. I knew it wasn't my brother then, but I still didn't know what exactly was happening.
>
> Soon the whole room began to shake violently, and my confusion turned to panic. My mom shouted that it was an earthquake and ran into my room. ___ⓐ___ it was my first time experiencing an earthquake, I didn't know how to react. I just kept saying, "What should I do?"

20 위 글의 빈칸 ⓐ에 들어갈 알맞은 접속사를 고르시오.

① Though   ② While   ③ Even if
④ Whereas   ⑤ Since

21 위 글의 밑줄 친 (A)의 우리말에 맞게 3 단어로 영작하시오.

➡ _____

22 위 글에서 알 수 있는 글쓴이의 심경 변화로 가장 알맞은 것을 고르시오.

① bored   →   scared
② nervous   →   satisfied
③ puzzled   →   frightened
④ pleased   →   upset
⑤ confused   →   bored

[23~24] 다음 글을 읽고 물음에 답하시오.

> Then the shaking seemed (A)[to stop / stopping]. We started crawling toward the door. At that moment, my mom's cell phone rang. It was my dad, (B)[that / who] was coming home from work.
>
> He shouted, "It stopped! Get out of the building! Take the stairs! Don't take the elevator! Hurry!" "Where are you? Are you okay?" my mom asked urgently. My dad answered, "Don't worry. I'm okay. I was driving (C)[home / to home] when the shaking started. But I pulled over immediately. I'm listening to the radio right now to find out what's ⓐgoing on."

23 위 글의 괄호 (A)~(C)에서 어법상 알맞은 낱말을 골라 쓰시오.

➡ (A) _____ (B) _____ (C) _____

24 위 글의 밑줄 친 ⓐgoing on과 바꿔 쓸 수 있는 한 단어를 h로 시작하여 쓰시오.

➡ _____

[25~26] 다음 글을 읽고 물음에 답하시오.

> We nervously made our way down the stairs and outside. I looked around. Parts of buildings had fallen and had smashed several cars. We went to an open space ⓐto avoid more falling pieces. How could all this have happened in a few minutes?
>
> Although I had done many earthquake drills in school, I had never thought I'd experience a real earthquake. I still get scared when I remember that night. I can't forget the panic I felt when the furniture was shaking and things were falling to the floor. After that night, I began to take earthquake drills seriously. I realized that I should be prepared for the next earthquake, which can occur at any time.
>
> <I: a girl>

25 위 글의 밑줄 친 ⓐto avoid와 to부정사의 용법이 다른 것을 모두 고르시오.

① It is good to get up early in the morning.
② Do you have anything delicious to eat?
③ She went to the store to buy some pens.
④ His job is to take pictures.
⑤ He can't be rich to ask me for some money.

26 위 글을 읽고 알 수 없는 것을 고르시오.

① What did the writer see when she made her way down the stairs and outside?
② Where did the writer's family go after they got out of the building?
③ How many earthquake drills had the writer done in school?
④ Had the writer thought she'd experience a real earthquake?
⑤ What did the writer realize after this earthquake?

[27~29] 다음 글을 읽고 물음에 답하시오.

> *San Andreas*
>
> I would like ①telling you about ⓐthe movie *San Andreas*. This movie ②is set in Los Angeles and San Francisco in 2014. The main character, a search-and-rescue pilot, must search for his ③missing family during an earthquake. The special effects ④used in the disaster scenes are very good. The movie is a little sad ⑤at times, but the story is very interesting. I give *San Andreas* four stars. Go and watch it!

27 위 글의 밑줄 친 ①~⑤ 중 어법상 틀린 것을 찾아 고치시오.

_____ 번 ➡ _____

28 위 글의 종류로 알맞은 것을 고르시오.

① article   ② essay   ③ review
④ book report   ⑤ biography

29 위 글을 읽고 ⓐthe movie에 대해 알 수 없는 것을 고르시오.

① 제목   ② 배경
③ 주인공의 직업   ④ 주인공의 나이
⑤ 간략한 줄거리

01 짝지어진 단어의 관계가 같도록 빈칸에 들어갈 알맞은 말을 고르시오.

출제율 90%

> destroy : damage = _____ : lately

① recently ② properly ③ urgently
④ nervously ⑤ exactly

02 다음 빈칸에 들어갈 말로 적절한 것은?

출제율 95%

> One night in February, after I had gone to bed, _____ hit. I woke up suddenly because my bed was shaking.

① a yellow dust ② an earthquake
③ a heavy rain ④ a heat wave
⑤ a wildfire

03 다음 문장에 공통으로 들어가기에 적절한 것은?

출제율 90%

> • A cup tipped over and rolled _____ the kitchen table. Every second, I could hear something else in the apartment break.
> • Never put _____ until tomorrow what you can do.

① around ② under ③ over
④ off ⑤ below

04 주어진 우리말에 맞게 빈칸을 채우시오. (철자가 주어진 경우 그 철자로 시작할 것)

출제율 95%

(1) 우리 가족 사진이 벽에서 떨어지고 그것을 덮고 있던 유리가 깨졌다.
➡ Our family picture dropped from the wall and the glass c_____ it broke.

(2) 우리는 초조한 마음으로 계단을 내려가서 밖으로 나갔다.
➡ We nervously _____ _____ _____ down the stairs and outside.

[05~07] 다음 대화를 읽고 물음에 답하시오.

> G: There seem to be many natural disasters in Korea these days. (ⓐ)
> B: I agree. There was an earthquake in the south last week. Also a storm is coming this week. (ⓑ)
> G: I'm curious about _____(A)_____ causes the most damage in Korea. (ⓒ)
> B: Actually I read a report yesterday about the damage from each type of natural disaster. Number one is storms.
> G: I see. (ⓓ)
> B: No, second is heavy rain, and third is heavy snow.
> G: What about earthquakes? (ⓔ)
> B: Based on the report, earthquakes are fourth. But the damage from earthquakes has been increasing recently because they have been happening more often in Korea.
> G: I see. It seems like we have to be prepared for a variety of natural disasters in Korea.

05 ⓐ~ⓔ 중에서 다음 문장이 들어가기에 적절한 곳은?

출제율 95%

> I guess earthquakes are second.

① ⓐ ② ⓑ ③ ⓒ ④ ⓓ ⑤ ⓔ

06 위 대화의 빈칸 (A)에 들어가기에 적절한 것은?

출제율 90%

① what kind of earthquakes
② which type of natural disaster
③ which season of the year
④ whose report on the disaster
⑤ how many natural disasters

출제율 100%

07 위 대화의 내용으로 보아 대답할 수 **없는** 것은?

① What natural disaster was there last week?

② Which type of natural disaster causes the most damage in Korea?

③ How has the damage from earthquakes been recently?

④ How much damage have storms caused?

⑤ Why has the damage from earthquakes been increasing?

[08~09] 다음 대화를 읽고 물음에 답하시오.

R: How did you feel when the earthquake occurred?

W: ⓐI began to panic because the whole room was shaking violently.

R: ⓑHow scary! What did you do next?

W: ⓒWe all crawled over the table after my mom got us out of bed.

R: What was happening at the moment?

W: ⓓLots of things were falling to the floor. I heard many things in the apartment break.

R: ⓔWhat did you realize after that night?

W: I realized that I should be prepared for the next earthquake. It can occur at any time!

출제율 100%

08 밑줄 친 ⓐ~ⓔ 중에서 대화의 흐름으로 보아 어색한 문장을 고르시오.

① ⓐ　　② ⓑ　　③ ⓒ　　④ ⓓ　　⑤ ⓔ

출제율 95%

09 다음 중 위 대화에서 기자가 질문하지 **않은** 것은?

① What was the feeling of the woman when the earthquake occurred?

② How scary was the earthquake?

③ What did the woman do after the panic?

④ What was happening when the woman crawled?

⑤ What did the woman realize after that night?

출제율 95%

10 다음 중 어법상 적절한 문장은?

① After she finished her homework, she had gone to bed.

② I had known the story because I have read the book.

③ I couldn't get in the room because I had forget my key.

④ Jin told me how hard he had prepared for the match.

⑤ He carried out all the responsibilities I gave to him.

출제율 90%

11 빈칸에 알맞은 접속사를 〈보기〉에서 골라 써 넣으시오.

┌─── 보기 ├──
│ though　when　before　if　since │
└──────────────────┘

(1) _____ it was snowing heavily, I stayed home all day.

(2) _____ it is against the law, poor villagers chop down the trees and sell them to make a living.

(3) I can't forget the panic I felt _____ the furniture was shaking and things were falling to the floor.

12 다음 〈보기〉에 주어진 단어를 이용하여 문맥에 맞게 문장을 완성하시오.

> 보기
>
> happen   take   practice

(1) The teacher notified his students of their results from the test they _____ a few days earlier.

(2) He ran as he _____ and finally won the race.

(3) A reporter asked the man what _____.

13 다음 빈칸에 들어갈 말을 순서대로 묶은 것은?

> • They achieved more than they _____ at first.
> • _____ he was new to his firm, people didn't know him.

① had expected – Though
② had expected – Since
③ expected – Since
④ expected – Though
⑤ expected – When

[14~16] 다음 글을 읽고 물음에 답하시오.

One night in February, after I had gone to bed, an earthquake hit. I woke up suddenly because my bed was shaking. I thought my brother was shaking my bed as a joke. But then I heard the mirror on my desk fall to the floor and break into pieces. I knew it wasn't my brother then, but ⓐ정확히 무슨 일이 일어나고 있었는지를 여전히 알지 못했다.

ⓑSoon the whole room began to shake violently, and my confusion turned to comfort. My mom shouted that it was an earthquake and ran into my room. Since it was my first time experiencing an earthquake, I didn't know how to react. I just kept saying, "What should I do?"

14 위 글의 밑줄 친 ⓐ의 우리말에 맞게 주어진 어휘를 알맞게 배열하시오.

> what / still / know / I / was happening / didn't / exactly

➡ _____

15 위 글의 밑줄 친 ⓑ에서 흐름상 어색한 부분을 찾아 고치시오.

_____ ➡ _____

16 Which question CANNOT be answered after reading the passage?

① When did the earthquake occur?
② Was the writer still awake when an earthquake hit?
③ What was the writer's brother doing when the earthquake hit?
④ Did the writer experience an earthquake before?
⑤ Did the writer know how to react to an earthquake?

[17~19] 다음 글을 읽고 물음에 답하시오.

(①) We nervously made our way down the stairs and outside. (②) Parts of buildings had fallen and had smashed several cars. (③) We went to an open space to avoid more falling pieces. (④) How could all this have happened ____ⓐ____ a few minutes? (⑤) Although I had done many earthquake drills in school, I had never thought I'd experience a real earthquake. I still get scared when I remember that night. I can't forget the panic I felt when the furniture was shaking and things were falling to the floor. After that night, I began to take earthquake drills seriously. I realized that I should be prepared ____ⓑ____ the next earthquake, which can occur at any time.

📝 출제율 90%

17 위 글의 빈칸 ⓐ와 ⓑ에 들어갈 전치사가 바르게 짝지어진 것은?

① at – for   ② at – to
③ in – for   ④ for – to
⑤ in – on

📝 출제율 100%

18 위 글의 흐름으로 보아, 주어진 문장이 들어가기에 가장 적절한 곳은?

> I looked around.

📝 출제율 95%
①   ②   ③   ④   ⑤

19 위 글의 주제로 알맞은 것을 고르시오.

① We should know how to avoid more falling pieces.
② We should go to an open space when an earthquake occurs.
③ What could happen in a few minutes?
④ An ounce of prevention is worth a pound of cure.
⑤ We should remember the panic of an earthquake.

[20~21] 다음 글을 읽고 물음에 답하시오.

Haeundae

  I would like to tell you about the movie *Haeundae*. This movie is set in Busan, South Korea in 2009. It is a movie about a tsunami that hits the city of Busan. A tsunami researcher warns people, but everyone believes that Korea is safe. Eventually, people realize ⓐthe deadly wave is coming in only ten minutes. It is one of the few South Korean natural disaster movies. It offers some great shots of Haeundae Beach. The best shot in the film is the moment the wave reaches Diamond Bridge near Gwangalli Beach. The movie is full of good special effects! I give *Haeundae* three stars. Go and watch it!

📝 출제율 100%

20 위 글의 밑줄 친 ⓐthe deadly wave가 가리키는 것을 본문에서 찾아 쓰시오.

➡ _____

📝 출제율 95%

21 According to the passage, which is NOT true?

① *Haeundae* is set in Busan, South Korea in 2009.
② *Haeundae* is a movie about a tsunami that hits the city of Busan.
③ *Haeundae* is one of the few South Korean natural disaster movies.
④ The best shot in the film is the moment the wave reaches Diamond Bridge near Haeundae Beach.
⑤ *Haeundae* is full of good special effects.

[01~02] 다음 대화를 읽고 물음에 답하시오.

> B: There was a big flood in Europe. Did you hear about it?
> G: No, I didn't. But floods aren't that common in winter, are they? I'm _____(A)_____ how that happened.
> B: (B)Me too. Let's do some online research.

01 빈칸 (A)에 들어가기에 적절한 말을 두 단어로 쓰시오.

➡ _____

02 밑줄 친 (B)와 바꿔 쓸 수 있는 말을 쓰시오. (3단어)

➡ _____

03 빈칸에 알맞은 단어를 <보기>에서 골라 쓰시오.

┌─ 보기 ─┐
get cover damage hands
└──────┘

(1) I'm curious about which type of natural disaster causes the most _____ in Korea.

(2) I still _____ scared when I remember that night.

(3) Make sure you place your _____ in the middle of the person's chest.

(4) Make sure that you _____ your mouth with a wet cloth.

04 다음 문장에서 틀린 것을 고쳐 다시 쓰시오.

(1) David has lost his glasses, so he couldn't read anything.

➡ _____
_____

(2) After he moves to a new city, he joined the company baseball team.

➡ _____
_____

(3) In summer, food is easily spoiled because it is kept well.

➡ _____

(4) Our feet remain firmly on the earth since our planet is spinning on its axis.

➡ _____
_____

*spin: 돌다, 뱅뱅 돌다 *axis: 축

05 주어진 단어를 활용하여 빈칸을 완성하시오.

(1) I was shocked to hear that he _____ his job. (quit)

(2) Linda began to tell him that she _____ to a salesman. (marry)

(3) Though _____ it, you must do it. (like)

06 다음 우리말을 주어진 어휘를 이용하여 영작하시오.

(1) 한 남자가 자신의 가게에 강도가 들었다고 경찰에 신고했다. (a man, his store, the police, notify, rob, that)

➡ _____
_____

(2) 비록 손은 없지만, 그녀가 할 수 없는 일은 없습니다. (there, nothing, hands, have, do, cannot, even, 13 단어)

➡ _____
_____

[07~09] 다음 대화를 읽고 물음에 답하시오.

One night in February, after I had gone to bed, an earthquake hit. I (A)[fell asleep / woke up] suddenly (B)[because / because of] my bed was shaking. I thought my brother was shaking my bed as a joke. But then I heard the mirror on my desk fall to the floor and break into pieces. I knew it wasn't my brother then, but I still didn't know what exactly was happening.

Soon the whole room began to shake violently, and my confusion turned to panic. My mom shouted that it was an earthquake and ran into my room. ⓐSince it was my first time experiencing an earthquake, I didn't know (C)[how / what] to react. I just kept saying, "What should I do?"   <I: a girl>

07 위 글의 괄호 (A)~(C)에서 문맥이나 어법상 알맞은 낱말을 골라 쓰시오.

➡ (A) _____ (B) _____ (C) _____

08 위 글의 밑줄 친 ⓐ를 다음과 같이 바꿔 쓸 때 빈칸에 알맞은 단어를 쓰시오.

➡ Since it was the first time that I _____ an earthquake

= Since _____ _____ an earthquake for the first time

09 위 글의 내용과 일치하도록 다음 빈칸 (A)와 (B)에 알맞은 단어를 쓰시오.

When the writer heard the mirror on her desk fall to the floor and break into pieces, she could know that her bed had shaken because of some other reason, not because of (A)_____ _____, but she wasn't sure what was (B)_____.

[10~12] 다음 글을 읽고 물음에 답하시오.

Then the shaking seemed to stop. We started crawling toward the door. At that moment, my mom's cell phone rang. It was my dad, who was coming home from work.

He shouted, "It stopped! Get out of the building! Take the stairs! ⓐ엘리베이터를 타면 안 돼요! Hurry!" "Where are you? Are you okay?" my mom asked urgently. My dad answered, "Don't worry. I'm okay. I was driving home when the shaking started. But I pulled over immediately. I'm listening to the radio right now ⓑto find out what's going on."   <I: a girl>

10 위 글의 밑줄 친 ⓐ의 우리말에 맞게 4 단어로 영작하시오.

➡ _____

11 위 글의 밑줄 친 ⓑ를 다음과 같이 바꿔 쓸 때 빈칸에 들어갈 알맞은 말을 쓰시오.

➡ _____ _____ _____ find out what's going on

= _____ _____ _____ find out what's going on

= _____ _____ _____ I _____ find out what's going on

= _____ _____ I _____ find out what's going on

12 What did the writer do when the shaking seemed to stop? Answer in English. (6 words)

➡ _____

01 다음 〈보기〉의 표현과 접속사 though를 이용하여 예시와 같이 문장을 완성하시오.

> ┤ 보기 ├
>
> | be twins | eat fast food | like English |
> |---|---|---|
> | play soccer | study hard | rain heavily |
>
> →Tony and Tom are twins though they look different.

(1) I _____.
(2) He _____.
(3) She _____.
(4) They _____.

02 다음 내용을 바탕으로 영화 비평문을 쓰시오.

> *Title: Haeundae*
>
> Time and Place: Busan, South Korea in 2009
>
> Story: It is a movie about a tsunami that hits the city of Busan. A tsunami researcher warns people, but everyone believes that Korea is safe. Eventually, people realize the deadly wave is coming in only ten minutes.
>
> Reviews: It is one of the few South Korean natural disaster movies. It offers some great shots of Haeundae Beach. The best shot in the film is the moment the wave reaches Diamond Bridge near Gwangalli Beach. The movie is full of good special effects!
>
> Rate the movie! ★★★☆☆

> *Haeundae*
>
> I would like to tell you about the movie *Haeundae*. This movie (A)_____ in Busan, South Korea in 2009. It is a movie about (B)_____ that hits the city of Busan. A tsunami researcher warns people, but everyone believes that Korea is safe. Eventually, people realize the deadly wave is coming (C)_____. It is one of the few South Korean (D)_____. It offers some great shots of Haeundae Beach. The best shot in the film is the moment the wave reaches Diamond Bridge near Gwangalli Beach. The movie is full of good (E)_____! I give *Haeundae* three stars. Go and watch it!

단원별 모의고사

01 다음 짝지어진 단어의 관계가 같도록 빈칸에 알맞은 것을 고르시오.

> whole : partial = _____ : rare

① aware
② prepared
③ common
④ serious
⑤ worse

02 다음 중 각 단어의 영영풀이로 <u>어색하게</u> 짝지어진 것은?

① curious: wanting to know about something
② flood: a very large amount of snow that covers an area that is usually dry
③ common: happening often and to many people or in many places
④ cause: to make something happen, especially something bad
⑤ wildfire: a fire that moves quickly and cannot be controlled

03 다음 중 〈보기〉의 단어를 사용하여 자연스러운 문장을 만들 수 <u>없는</u> 것은?

> ┌── 보기 ──┐
> made   collapse   react   joke

① I thought my brother was shaking my bed as a _____.
② Soon the whole room began to shake _____.
③ Since it was my first time experiencing an earthquake, I didn't know how to _____.
④ I started to worry that the building would _____.
⑤ We nervously _____ our way down the stairs and outside.

04 다음 문장에 공통으로 들어가기에 적절한 말을 쓰시오.

> • I pulled _____ immediately.
> • He said that _____ 20,000 people had to leave their homes.
> • A cup tipped _____ and rolled off the kitchen table.

➡ _____

[05~06] 다음 대화를 읽고 물음에 답하시오.

> A: In case of a heat wave, what should I do?
> B: Make sure that you drink more water than usual.
> A: _____(A)_____
> B: Make sure that you __(B)__ a cool building immediately.

05 빈칸 (A)에 들어가기에 적절한 말을 고르시오.

① What is it?
② Anything else?
③ Really?
④ How about you?
⑤ Is it necessary?

06 위 대화의 내용으로 보아, 빈칸 (B)에 들어가기에 적절한 것은?

① leave
② exit
③ cause
④ destroy
⑤ move into

[07~09] 다음 대화를 읽고 물음에 답하시오.

> B: Hey, did you hear about the big fires in California?
> G: No, I didn't. ⓐHow serious are they?
> B: They've destroyed a large number of houses and other buildings.
> G: ⓑAre the fires over now?
> B: ⓒYes, actually the wind has made the fires worse. I hope all the people living there are okay.
> G: (A)나도 마찬가지야. ⓓI'm curious about how many people had to leave their homes.
> B: Actually more than 20,000 people had to leave their homes, and about 400 people are missing in that area.
> G: ⓔThat's terrible. I hope they're somewhere safe.

07 밑줄 친 (A)에 해당하는 말을 so를 포함하여 3단어의 영어로 쓰시오.

➡ _____

08 위 대화의 ⓐ~ⓔ 중 문맥상 어색한 것은?

① ⓐ   ② ⓑ   ③ ⓒ   ④ ⓓ   ⑤ ⓔ

09 위 대화의 내용과 일치하지 않는 것은?

① The boy and the girl are talking about the big fires in California.
② The fires destroyed many houses and buildings.
③ Due to the wind, the fire got worse.
④ More than 20,000 people had to leave their homes.
⑤ About 400 people were found in that area.

10 Which is grammatically WRONG?

① Although Mina knew the right answer, she didn't let us know.
② Family members gather even though they may live far apart.
③ I had to go and greet him since I didn't want to.
④ When in Rome, do as the Romans do.
⑤ Some dogs have a long tail, while others have a short one.

11 다음 빈칸에 들어갈 말을 순서대로 묶은 것은?

> • I found out that I _____ my purse at the restaurant.
> • Don't eat too much fast food _____ you love them.

① left – when   ② have left – since
③ have left – though ④ had left – since
⑤ had left – though

12 다음 문장에서 어법상 어색한 것을 바르게 고쳐 다시 쓰시오.

(1) Despite it rained a lot, we enjoyed our holiday.
➡ _____
_____

(2) As though it was cold, I felt very happy today.
➡ _____

(3) Though Laura is very kind, she is loved by all of them.
➡ _____
_____

(4) He learned that he has been chosen to play Harry Potter.
➡ _____
_____

(5) The play already started when we arrived.

➡ _____

13 다음 중 어법상 옳은 문장을 <u>모두</u> 고르시오.

① Winter can have negative effects on many people since it is cold.
② Soon I realized that I left my report at home.
③ Because I had done many earthquake drills in school, I had never thought I'd experience a real earthquake.
④ After I finish the exam, I will go to an amusement park.
⑤ I woke up suddenly though my bed was shaking.

14 위 글의 빈칸 ⓐ에 say를 알맞은 형태로 쓰시오.

➡ _____

15 위 글의 밑줄 친 (A)as와 같은 의미로 쓰인 것을 고르시오.

① They did <u>as</u> I had asked.
② The news came <u>as</u> a shock.
③ He sat watching her <u>as</u> she got ready.
④ <u>As</u> one grows older, one becomes more silent.
⑤ You're <u>as</u> tall as your father.

[14~15] 다음 글을 읽고 물음에 답하시오.

One night in February, after I had gone to bed, an earthquake hit. I woke up suddenly because my bed was shaking. I thought my brother was shaking my bed (A)<u>as</u> a joke. But then I heard the mirror on my desk fall to the floor and break into pieces. I knew it wasn't my brother then, but I still didn't know what exactly was happening.

Soon the whole room began to shake violently, and my confusion turned to panic. My mom shouted that it was an earthquake and ran into my room. Since it was my first time experiencing an earthquake, I didn't know how to react. I just kept ___ⓐ___, "What should I do?"

[16~17] 다음 글을 읽고 물음에 답하시오.

My mom pulled me and my brother out of bed. We ran to the kitchen and crawled under the table. I could see the light ①<u>swinging</u> violently and books ②<u>falling</u> to the floor. Our family picture dropped from the wall and the glass covering it broke. A cup ⓐ<u>tipped</u> over and rolled off the kitchen table. Every ③<u>second</u>, I could hear something else in the apartment ④<u>break</u>. I started ⑤<u>to worry</u> that the building would collapse.

16 위 글의 밑줄 친 ①~⑤와 바꿔 쓸 수 있는 말로 옳지 <u>않은</u> 것을 고르시오.

① swing   ② fall   ③ moment
④ broken   ⑤ worrying

17 위 글의 밑줄 친 ⓐtip과 같은 의미로 쓰인 것을 고르시오.

① It is in the northern tip of the island.

② I need a useful tip on how to save money.

③ It isn't allowed to leave a tip over $5.

④ He gave the waiter a generous tip.

⑤ The machine may tip over and break the dishes.

[18~19] 다음 글을 읽고 물음에 답하시오.

Then the shaking seemed to stop. We started crawling toward the door. At that moment, my mom's cell phone rang. It was my dad, ⓐwho was coming home from work.

He shouted, "It stopped! Get out of the building! Take the stairs! Don't take the elevator! Hurry!" "Where are you? Are you okay?" my mom asked urgently. My dad answered, "Don't worry. I'm okay. I was driving home when the shaking started. But I pulled over immediately. I'm listening to the radio right now to find out what's going on."

18 위 글의 밑줄 친 ⓐwho를 다음과 같이 바꿔 쓸 때 빈칸에 들어갈 알맞은 말을 두 단어로 쓰시오.

➡ _____

19 위 글의 내용과 일치하도록 다음 빈칸 (A)와 (B)에 알맞은 단어를 쓰시오.

The writer's dad called her mom and told her to get out of the building and take (A)_____ _____ instead of (B)_____ _____.

[20~21] 다음 글을 읽고 물음에 답하시오.

We nervously made our way down the stairs and outside. I looked around. Parts of buildings had fallen and had smashed several cars. We went to an open space to avoid more falling pieces. How could all this have happened in a few minutes?

_____ⓐ_____ I had done many earthquake drills in school, I had never thought I'd experience a real earthquake. I still get scared when I remember that night. I can't forget the panic I felt when the furniture was shaking and things were falling to the floor. After that night, I began to take earthquake drills seriously. I realized that I should be prepared for the next earthquake, which can occur at any time.

<I: a girl>

20 위 글의 빈칸 ⓐ에 들어갈 알맞은 접속사를 고르시오.

① Although   ② Because   ③ As

④ If   ⑤ Since

21 According to the passage, which is NOT true?

① The writer's family nervously made their way down the stairs and outside.

② Parts of buildings had fallen and had smashed several cars.

③ The writer had done many earthquake drills in school.

④ The writer still gets scared when she remembers that night.

⑤ The writer had taken earthquake drills seriously before he experienced a real earthquake.

My Roles in Society

🎙 의사소통 기능

- 고민이나 불만족의 원인에 대해 묻기
  What's the matter?

- 확실성 정도 표현하기
  I have no doubt that you will take some wonderful pictures.

🎙 언어 형식

- 접속사 if/whether
  I suddenly started to wonder **if[whether]** these are the only qualities that make a good leader.

- 조동사의 수동태
  I don't think a person like me **can be called** a leader.

Words & Expressions

Key Words

- □ **ability** [əbíləti] 명 능력
- □ **achieve** [ətʃíːv] 동 성취하다, 이루다
- □ **analyst** [ǽnəlist] 명 분석가
- □ **analyze** [ǽnəlàiz] 동 분석하다
- □ **approach** [əpróutʃ] 동 접근하다
- □ **check** [tʃek] 동 점검하다
- □ **clear** [kliər] 형 명확한, 뚜렷한
- □ **confident** [kánfədənt] 형 자신감 있는
- □ **contact** [kántækt] 명 접촉
- □ **create** [kriéit] 동 창조하다
- □ **decide** [disáid] 동 결정하다
- □ **decorate** [dékərèit] 동 장식하다
- □ **deliver** [dilívər] 동 배달하다
- □ **determine** [ditə́ːrmin] 동 결정하다, 결심하다
- □ **director** [diréktər] 명 감독
- □ **discover** [diskʌ́vər] 동 발견하다, 찾다
- □ **divide** [diváid] 동 나누다, 분리하다
- □ **edit** [édit] 동 편집하다
- □ **effective** [iféktiv] 형 효과적인
- □ **election** [ilékʃən] 명 선거
- □ **ensure** [inʃúər] 동 반드시 ~하게 하다, 보장하다
- □ **environment** [inváiərənmənt] 명 환경
- □ **friendly** [fréndli] 형 친절한
- □ **goal** [goul] 명 목적, 목표
- □ **hands-off** [hǽndzɔːf] 형 불간섭주의의, 자유방임의
- □ **instead** [instéd] 부 대신에
- □ **leadership** [líːdərʃip] 명 지도력, 리더십

- □ **logical** [ládʒikəl] 형 논리적인, 타당한, 사리에 맞는
- □ **material** [mətíəriəl] 명 자료, 소재, 재료
- □ **misunderstanding** [mìsʌndərstǽndiŋ] 명 오해
- □ **motivate** [móutəvèit] 동 동기를 부여하다
- □ **outgoing** [áutgouiŋ] 형 외향적인, 사교적인
- □ **positive** [pázətiv] 형 긍정적인
- □ **prepare** [pripέər] 동 준비하다
- □ **presentation** [prèzəntéiʃən] 명 발표
- □ **properly** [prápərli] 부 적절히, 제대로
- □ **quality** [kwáləti] 명 질, 우수함, 자질
- □ **realize** [ríːəlàiz] 동 깨닫다
- □ **reasoning** [ríːzniŋ] 명 추리, 추론
- □ **relieved** [rilíːvd] 형 안심이 되는
- □ **representative** [rèprizéntətiv] 명 대표(자)
- □ **research** [risə́ːrtʃ] 명 조사, 연구
- □ **responsibility** [rispànsəbíləti] 명 책임, 의무
- □ **return** [ritə́ːrn] 동 돌아오다, 반납하다
- □ **role** [roul] 명 역할
- □ **run** [rʌn] 동 달리다, (선거에) 입후보하다
- □ **seem** [siːm] 동 ~인 것 같다
- □ **step** [step] 명 단계
- □ **strict** [strikt] 형 엄격한
- □ **supporter** [səpɔ́ːrtər] 명 지지자
- □ **switch** [switʃ] 동 바꾸다, 전환하다
- □ **translate** [trænsléit] 동 해석하다
- □ **valued** [vǽljuːd] 형 귀중한, 존중 받는
- □ **vision** [víʒən] 명 통찰력, 비전, 시력

Key Expressions

- □ **be good at** ~을 잘하다
- □ **be in charge of** ~을 담당하다, 책임지다
- □ **be responsible for** ~에 책임이 있다
- □ **be stuck in** ~에 갇히다
- □ **belong to** ~에 속하다
- □ **call for** ~을 필요로 하다, 요구하다
- □ **come up** 발생하다, 생기다
- □ **come up with** ~을 생각해 내다, 내놓다
- □ **deal with** 다루다, 처리하다
- □ **field trip** 견학, 체험 학습
- □ **get along** 잘 지내다, 사이좋게 지내다
- □ **hang out** 어울려 밖에서 시간을 보내다

- □ **lead by example** 솔선수범하다, 모범을 보이다
- □ **let down** 기대를 저버리다, ~을 실망시키다
- □ **meet the needs** 필요를 채워주다
- □ **no way** 절대로 아니다
- □ **on time** 정각에
- □ **run for** 출마하다
- □ **take care of** ~을 처리하다, ~을 돌보다
- □ **take sides** 편들다
- □ **turn out** (일·진행·결과가 특정 방식으로) 되다
- □ **work on** 공들여 일하다
- □ **work out** 해결하다
- □ **would love to** ~하고 싶다

Word Power

※ 서로 비슷한 뜻을 가진 어휘

☐ **ability** 능력 : **capability** 능력

☐ **actually** 실제로 : **really** 실제로

☐ **choose** 선택하다 : **select** 선택하다

☐ **environment** 환경 : **surrounding** 환경

☐ **achieve** 성취하다 : **accomplish** 성취하다

☐ **approach** 접근하다 : **access** 접근하다

☐ **decide** 결정하다 : **determine** 결정하다

☐ **goal** 목적, 목표 : **target** 목표

※ 서로 반대의 뜻을 가진 어휘

☐ **effective** 효과적인 ↔ **ineffective** 효과 없는

☐ **positive** 긍정적인 ↔ **negative** 부정적인

☐ **logical** 논리적인, 타당한 ↔ **illogical** 비논리적인

☐ **relieved** 안심이 되는 ↔ **worried** 걱정이 되는

※ 명사 – 형용사

☐ **confidence** 확신 – **confident** 자신 있는

☐ **decision** 결심 – **decisive** 결정적인

☐ **effect** 효과 – **effective** 효과적인

☐ **creation** 창조하다 – **creative** 창조적인

☐ **doubt** 의심 – **doubtful** 의심스러운

☐ **environment** 환경 – **environmental** 환경의

※ 동사 – 명사

☐ **achieve** 성취하다 – **achievement** 성취

☐ **choose** 선택하다 – **choice** 선택

☐ **decorate** 장식하다 – **decoration** 장식

☐ **discover** 발견하다 – **discovery** 발견

☐ **prepare** 준비하다 – **preparation** 준비

☐ **analyze** 분석하다 – **analysis** 분석

☐ **decide** 결정하다 – **decision** 결심

☐ **determine** 결정하다 – **determination** 결정

☐ **motivate** 동기를 부여하다 – **motivation** 동기

☐ **translate** 해석하다 – **translation** 해석

English Dictionary

☐ **analyze** 분석하다
→ to deeply study every piece of something to understand it 이해하기 위해 무언가의 모든 부분을 깊이 연구하다

☐ **approach** 접근하다
→ to come close to someone or something
누군가나 무언가에 가까이 가다

☐ **confident** 자신감 있는
→ sure that one has the ability to do things well
일을 잘하는 능력을 갖고 있음을 확신하는

☐ **effective** 효과적인
→ successful, and working in the way that was intended 성공적인 그리고 의도된 대로 작동하는

☐ **hands-off** 불간섭주의의, 자유방임의
→ letting people do what they want, without telling them what to do
무엇을 하도록 말하지 않고 원하는 대로 하도록 허용하는

☐ **leadership** 지도력, 리더십
→ ability to lead 이끄는 능력

☐ **logical** 논리적인, 타당한
→ making sense; being reasonable 타당한; 합리적인

☐ **motivate** 동기를 부여하다
→ to provide with a reason to do something
무엇인가를 할 이유를 제공하다

☐ **representative** 대표(자)
→ somebody who has been chosen to speak, or make decisions on behalf of a group
그룹을 대신해 말하거나 결정하도록 선택된 사람

☐ **run** (선거에) 입후보하다
→ to compete as a candidate in an election
선거에서 입후보자로 나서다

☐ **task** 일, 과업, 과제
→ a piece of work that must be done 처리되어야 하는 일

01 다음 영영풀이가 가리키는 것을 고르시오.

> someone who has been chosen to speak, or make decisions for someone else

① representative　　② supporter
③ editor　　　　　④ director
⑤ analyst

02 다음 중 밑줄 친 부분의 뜻풀이가 바르지 않은 것은?

① When are you planning to <u>return</u> the books? (되돌아가다)
② There is no <u>doubt</u> about that fact. (의심)
③ Fortunately, she completed her <u>task</u> before deadline. (일, 과업)
④ Mom wants to <u>divide</u> the pizza into eight slices. (나누다)
⑤ Jaemin seems to enjoy <u>editing</u> the school magazine. (편집하다)

03 다음 주어진 문장의 밑줄 친 vision과 같은 의미로 쓰인 것은?

> My grandfather is a man with a great <u>vision</u>.

① Cats have good night <u>vision</u>.
② Have you ever had a <u>vision</u> of great wealth?
③ The scene was beyond my <u>vision</u>.
④ I have normal <u>vision</u>, so I don't need glasses.
⑤ My grandfather has poor <u>vision</u>, so it is dangerous for him to go outside at night.

서답형

04 다음 우리말에 맞게 빈칸에 알맞은 말을 쓰시오. (철자가 주어진 경우 그 철자로 시작할 것.)

(1) 나는 이번 주 금요일에 영어 대회를 준비해야 한다.
　➡ I need to _____ the English contest this Friday.

(2) 나는 마지막 시험이 끝난 후 안도감을 느꼈다.
　➡ I felt r_____ after finishing the final exam.

(3) James는 영어 기사를 한국어로 번역한다.
　➡ James _____ the English article into Korean.

(4) 우리는 환경을 보호하기 위해 쓰레기를 줄여야 한다.
　➡ We should r_____ the trash to protect the environment.

05 다음 문장의 (A)와 (B)에 공통으로 들어갈 말이 바르게 짝지어진 것은?

> • If you ___(A)___ sides, I'll be disappointed with you.
> • My brothers ___(A)___ care of patients at the hospital.
> • I don't know how to ___(B)___ out his situation.
> • You can't imagine how I ___(B)___ on this project.

　　(A)　　　(B)
① take　　　come
② take　　　work
③ lead　　　work
④ lead　　　come
⑤ come　　　deal

01 다음 짝지어진 단어의 관계가 같도록 빈칸에 알맞은 말을 쓰시오.

confident : confidence = creative : _____

02 다음 우리말에 맞게 빈칸에 알맞은 말을 쓰시오. (중요)

(1) 당신이 만약 우리의 제품을 사용한다면 절대 실망하지 않을 것이다.
➡ You will never be _____ _____ if you use our product.

(2) 파티가 시작되었을 때, 나는 교통체증에 갇혀 있었다.
➡ When the party began, I _____ _____ _____ a traffic jam.

(3) 기회는 매일 생기지 않는다, 그래서 당신은 기회를 잡아야 한다.
➡ The chances don't _____ _____ every day, so you have to take them.

03 다음 문장의 빈칸에 들어갈 말을 〈보기〉에서 골라 쓰시오.

┌─ 보기 ─────────────────┐
  analyze   logical   ensure
  valued   reasoning
└─────────────────────────┘

(1) This method will _____ her success.
(2) I'm a _____ person at my workplace.
(3) It was the most _____ thing to do in that situation.
(4) We can understand his _____ about the case.
(5) Could you _____ the test results in details?

04 다음 우리말과 일치하도록 주어진 단어를 모두 배열하여 영작하시오.

(1) 반 대표에 입후보하는 게 어때?
(don't / class / run / representative / why / you / for)
➡ _____
_____

(2) 만약 네가 입후보한다면 당선될 거라고 믿어 의심치 않아.
(no / that / I / if / you / elected / be / you / have / doubt / will / run)
➡ _____
_____

(3) 나는 발표 자료를 만드는 일을 담당한다.
(materials / making / I'm / of / the / charge / in / presentation)
➡ _____
_____

(4) 많은 사람들이 최고의 지도자들은 솔선수범한다고 믿는다.
(that / people / lead / the / leaders / example / believe / best / many / by)
➡ _____
_____

05 다음 우리말을 주어진 단어를 이용하여 영작하시오. (고난이도)

(1) 형제들이 서로 잘 지낸다. (get, with)
➡ _____

(2) 왕은 솔선수범하기를 원한다. (would, example)
➡ _____

(3) 수질 오염을 끝내기 위한 새로운 아이디어를 생각해 보자. (up, end, pollution)
➡ _____
_____

Conversation

① 고민이나 불만족의 원인에 대해 묻기

• **What's the matter?** 무슨 일 있니?

■ 상대방이 뭔가에 불만족하거나 실망하고 있어 보이거나 걱정스러운 표정일 때, 그 원인을 묻는 말로 'What's the matter (with you)?(무슨 일 있니?)'가 있다. 이와 비슷한 표현으로 'What's wrong?(뭐가 잘못됐니?)', 혹은 'What's the problem?(무슨 문제가 있니?)' 등이 있다.

■ 상대방이 안 좋아 보여서 무슨 문제가 있는지 물어볼 때는 'Is something wrong?(뭐가 잘못되었니?)' 또는 'What's wrong (with you)?(뭐가 잘못됐나요?)'와 같은 표현을 쓸 수도 있다. 고민이나 불만족의 원인을 물을 때는 'Why are you sad?(왜 속상한가요?)', 'Why are you disappointed?(왜 실망스러운 가요?)', 'What are you worried/concerned/anxious about?(무엇에 대해 걱정/고민/근심하나요?)' 등 의 표현을 쓴다.

■ 고민이나 불만족의 원인을 물어볼 때는 'Is something worrying you?(무슨 걱정거리가 있나요?)' 또는 'Is there something bothering you?(뭔가 걸리는 일이 있나요?)', 'Is there anything wrong?(뭐 잘못 된 일 있니?)', 'What happened?(무슨 일 있니?)'와 같은 표현을 사용하기도 한다.

고민이나 불만족의 원인을 묻는 표현

• What's wrong? 뭐가 잘못됐나요?   • Why are you sad? 왜 속상한가요?

• Why are you disappointed? 왜 실망스러운가요?

• What are you worried/concerned/anxious about? 무엇에 대해 걱정/고민/근심하나요?

• Is something worrying you? 무슨 걱정거리가 있나요?

• Is there something bothering you? 뭔가 걸리는 일이 있나요?

• Is there anything wrong? 뭐 잘못된 일 있니?   • What happened? 무슨 일 있니?

핵심 Check

1. 다음 대화의 빈칸에 들어가기에 적절하지 <u>않은</u> 것은?

G: Mom, we've got a problem.

W: _____

G: We're going to have dinner with Grandma this Saturday, right? But I just realized that Sujin's birthday party is on Saturday evening. She's my best friend. What should I do?

W: That sounds like a difficult decision. Let's talk about it with your dad.

① What's wrong?   ② What's the matter?
③ Why are you worried?   ④ Is there anything wrong?
⑤ What's so interesting?

② 확실성의 정도 표현하기

- **I have no doubt that you will take some wonderful pictures.**
  나는 네가 멋진 사진들을 찍을 것을 확신해.

■ 앞으로 일어날 일에 대하여 상대방에게 확신을 주는 말로, 원하는 것이나 좋은 일이 일어날 것이 확실함을 나타낼 때 'I have no doubt that ~.'이라는 표현을 사용한다. 이 표현은 '~할 거라고 믿는다, ~할 거라고 확신한다.'라는 의미이다.

■ 확실성 정도를 나타내는 표현에는 sure(확실한), certain(확신하는), positive(긍정적인) 등을 사용하여 'I'm sure/certain/positive about[that] ~.(~에 대해 확신하다.)'라고 할 수 있다. '확실하다'라는 의미로 'I'm 100 percent sure.(나는 100% 장담해.)' 또는 'It is obvious/clear that ~.(~가 분명하다.)'를 쓰기도 한다. 'bet'은 '내기를 걸다, 틀림없다'의 뜻으로 'I bet that ~.'이라고 하면 '틀림없이 ~이다.'라는 뜻이 된다. 상대방의 말에 '당연하지.'라고 할 때는 'You bet.'이라고 한다.

■ 상대에게 확신을 물어볼 때는 'Are you sure about ~?(~에 대해 확신하나요?)' 또는 'How sure are you that ~?(~에 대해 얼마나 확신하나요?)'이라고 한다.

확실성의 정도 표현하기

- I have no doubt that ~. ~할 거라고 믿는다.
- I'm sure/certain/positive about[that] ~. ~에 대해 확신하다.
- I bet that ~. 틀림없이 ~이다.
- How sure are you that ~? ~에 대해 얼마나 확신하나요?
- I'm 100 percent sure. 나는 100% 장담해.
- Are you sure about ~? ~에 대해 확신하나요?
- It is obvious/clear that ~. ~은 확실하다.

핵심 Check

2. 다음 우리말과 일치하도록 주어진 표현을 포함하여 빈칸에 알맞은 말을 쓰시오.

A: What do you want to do for our class?

B: I want to make a student contact information list.

A: That sounds good. _____ (doubt, helpful)
(나는 그것이 매우 도움이 될 것이라고 믿어.)

3. 다음 대화의 순서를 바르게 배열하시오.

(A) That's great. You are really good at taking photos. I have no doubt that you will take some wonderful pictures.

(B) Sports Day is coming. How do you want to help out?

(C) I want to take photos for Sports Day.

➡ _____

Listen & Talk 1 A

G: Mom, we've got a problem.

W: ❶What's the matter?

G: We're going to have dinner with Grandma this Saturday, right? But I just realized ❷that Sujin's birthday party is on Saturday evening. She's my best friend. What should I do?

W: That sounds like a difficult ❸decision. Let's talk about it with your dad.

G: Okay, Mom. I'd love to see Grandma, but I don't want to miss my best friend's birthday party.

소녀: 엄마, 우리에게 문제가 생겼어요.
여성: 무슨 일이니?
소녀: 이번 주 토요일에 할머니와 저녁 식사를 하기로 했잖아요, 그렇죠? 그런데 수진이의 생일 파티가 토요일 저녁이라는 것을 방금 깨달았어요. 수진이는 저와 가장 친한 친구예요. 저 어떡하죠?
여성: 결정하기 힘든 문제인 것 같구나. 네 아빠와 함께 이야기해 보자.
소녀: 네, 엄마. 할머니를 정말 뵙고 싶지만, 가장 친한 친구의 생일 파티에 빠지고 싶지는 않아요.

❶ 고민이나 불만족의 원인에 대해 묻는 표현으로 'What's wrong?', 'What's the problem?' 등으로 바꾸어 쓸 수 있다.
❷ 목적어 역할을 하는 명사절을 이끄는 접속사 that이다. ❸ decision: 결정

Check(√) True or False

(1) The girl is going to see her grandma this Saturday. T ☐ F ☐

(2) The girl does not want to attend Sujin's birthday party. T ☐ F ☐

Listen & Talk 1 B

M: Junsu, are you okay? What's the matter?

B: Hello, Mr. Smith. I have a problem.

M: What happened?

B: You know Jaewoo, Yunho, and I are best friends, right? They ❶had a fight, and now ❷I'm stuck in the middle. I don't know what to do.

M: That sounds hard. Do you know why ❸they had a fight?

B: Yes, but it doesn't sound like a big deal to me. I guess they had some kind of ❹misunderstanding.

M: Why don't you all meet together and talk about it? I think they'll listen to you.

B: That's a good idea. They're both good friends of mine. I can't ❺take sides.

M: I understand. I hope everything works out.

남자: 준수야, 괜찮니? 무슨 일이야?
소년: 안녕하세요, Smith 선생님. 저에게 문제가 생겼어요.
남자: 무슨 일인데?
소년: 재우와 윤호, 그리고 제가 서로 가장 친한 사이라는 거 아시죠, 그렇죠? 그 둘이 싸웠고, 저는 이제 중간에 끼어버린 상태예요. 어떻게 해야 할지 모르겠어요.
남자: 힘들겠구나. 그 둘이 왜 싸웠는지는 아니?
소년: 네, 하지만 제가 보기에는 그다지 대단한 일도 아닌 것 같아요. 아무래도 그 둘 사이에 어떤 오해가 생긴 것 같아요.
남자: 너희 모두 다 같이 만나서 그것에 대해 이야기해 보는 게 어떠니? 그 둘이 네 말은 들을 것 같구나.
소년: 그거 좋은 생각이네요. 두 명 모두 저에게는 좋은 친구들이에요. 저는 누구의 편도 들 수 없어요.
남자: 이해한단다. 모두 잘 해결되기를 바란다.

❶ have a fight with: ~와 싸우다 ❷ be stuck in: ~에 갇히다 ❸ they는 재우와 윤호를 가리킨다.
❹ misunderstanding: 오해 ❺ take sides: 편들다

Check(√) True or False

(3) Junsu had a fight with Jaewoo and Yunho. T ☐ F ☐

(4) Junsu thinks there was some misunderstanding between Jaewoo and Yunho. T ☐ F ☐

Listen & Talk 1 C

B: Hey, Mandy. What's the matter?

G: I don't know what to do, Nick. My brother asked me to help him with his homework this Wednesday, but I told him I can't. I have so many things to do ❶that day.

B: What do you have to do this Wednesday?

G: I need to go to the library to ❷return some books. Then I have to meet you to work on our presentation. After that, I have to prepare for an exam at night.

B: Oh, you ❸do have a lot to do.

G: Yes. But my brother seemed ❹let down, so I feel bad.

B: Well, then ❺how about meeting on Thursday instead for our presentation? Then you can do everything and also help your brother on Wednesday.

G: That would help me out so much! Thanks for understanding, Nick!

❶ that day는 수요일을 가리킨다.　　❷ return: 반납하다
❸ do는 have를 강조한다.　　❹ let down: 실망하다
❺ 'How about ∼?: ∼하는 게 어때?'를 의미하며 'Why don't we ∼?'로 바꾸어 쓸 수 있다.

Listen & Talk 2 A

G: Sports Day is coming. How do you want to help out?

B: I want to take photos for Sports Day.

G: That's great. You ❶are really good at taking photos. ❷I have no doubt that you will take some wonderful pictures.

❶ be good at ∼: ∼을 잘하다
❷ I have no doubt that ∼.: ∼할 거라고 확신한다.

Listen & Talk 2 B

B: In the Send Our Stories project, we are going to make a picture book for children in other countries. We've ❶divided everyone into three groups. Each group will ❷be responsible for a different task. Group A will ❸translate a Korean story into English. Group B will make drawings for the book and ❹edit it. After copies of the book are printed, Group C will ❺be in charge of sending them to the children. It won't be easy, but I have no doubt that the children who receive these books will really enjoy them.

❶ divide: 나누다　　❷ be responsible for ∼: ∼에 책임을 갖다
❸ translate: 번역하다　　❹ edit: 편집하다
❺ be in charge of: ∼을 담당하다, 책임지다

Listen & Talk 2 C

B: I'm so excited about our museum ❶field trip.

G1: Me too. Let's check our ❷tasks. Yen, what are you in charge of?

G2: I'm in charge of taking pictures.

G1: Okay. Sejin, are you going to do some research on the museum?

B: Yes, I am. Are you going to write our field trip report, Emma?

G1: That's right. I think we're ready.

G2: Good. I have no doubt that our project will ❸turn out well.

❶ field trip: 견학, 체험 학습　　❷ task: 일, 업무
❸ turn out: (일 · 진행 · 결과가 특정 방식으로) 되다

Do It Yourself A

Sujin: What's the matter? You ❶look worried.

Minsu: You know I'm going to be giving a presentation on our team's research. But I feel very nervous when I talk ❷in front of many people.

Sujin: Oh, I didn't know that you got nervous. Actually, I also have a problem.

Minsu: What's wrong?

Sujin: I'm in charge of making the presentation materials, but I'm not good at ❸it.

Minsu: You're not? I thought you were good at ❸it.

Sujin: No, I'm not. Hey, then what about switching roles? I've given presentations many times before, so I ❹don't get nervous at all.

Minsu: Really? That would be great. I think I am good at making presentation materials, and I like making ❺them!

Sujin: That's good. Let's talk to the other team members.

Minsu: Cool. I feel so relieved now.

❶ look+형용사: ∼하게 보이다　　❷ in front of: ∼ 앞에
❸ it은 making the presentation materials를 가리킨다.
❹ not ∼ at all: 전혀 ∼ 아니다
❺ them은 presentation materials를 가리킨다.

● 다음 우리말과 일치하도록 빈칸에 알맞은 말을 쓰시오.

Listen & Talk 1 A

G: Mom, we've got a _____.

W: What's the _____?

G: We're going to have dinner with Grandma this Saturday, right? But I just realized that Sujin's birthday party is _____ _____ _____. She's my best friend. _____ _____ _____ _____?

W: That sounds like a difficult _____. Let's talk about it with your dad.

G: Okay, Mom. I'd love to see Grandma, but I don't want to _____ my best friend's birthday party.

Listen & Talk 1 B

M: Junsu, are you okay? _____ _____ _____?

B: Hello, Mr. Smith. I have a problem.

M: What _____?

B: You know Jaewoo, Yunho, and I are best friends, right? They _____ _____ _____, and now I'm _____ _____ the middle. I don't know _____ _____ _____.

M: That sounds hard. Do you know _____ they had a fight?

B: Yes, but it doesn't sound like a _____ _____ to me. I guess they had _____ kind of _____.

M: _____ _____ you all meet together and talk about it? I think they'll listen to you.

B: That's a good idea. They're both good friends of mine. I _____ _____ _____.

M: I understand. I hope everything _____ _____.

Listen & Talk 1 C

B: Hey, Mandy. _____ _____ _____?

G: I don't know what to do, Nick. My brother _____ _____ _____ _____ _____ with his homework this Wednesday, but I told him I can't. I have so many things to do that day.

B: What do you have to do this Wednesday?

G: I need to go to the library to _____ _____ _____. Then I have to meet you to work on our _____. After that, I have to _____ for an exam at night.

소녀: 엄마, 우리에게 문제가 생겼어요.
여성: 무슨 일이니?
소녀: 이번 주 토요일에 할머니와 저녁 식사를 하기로 했잖아요, 그렇죠? 그런데 수진이의 생일 파티가 토요일 저녁이라는 것을 방금 깨달았어요. 수진이는 저의 가장 친한 친구예요. 저 어떡하죠?
여성: 결정하기 힘든 문제인 것 같구나. 네 아빠와 함께 이야기해 보자.
소녀: 네, 엄마. 할머니를 정말 뵙고 싶지만, 가장 친한 친구의 생일 파티에 빠지고 싶지는 않아요.

남자: 준수야, 괜찮니? 무슨 일이야?
소년: 안녕하세요, Smith 선생님. 저에게 문제가 생겼어요.
남자: 무슨 일인데?
소년: 재우와 윤호, 그리고 제가 서로 가장 친한 사이라는 거 아시죠, 그렇죠? 그 둘이 싸웠고, 저는 이제 중간에 끼어버린 상태예요. 어떻게 해야 할지 모르겠어요.
남자: 힘들겠구나. 그 둘이 왜 싸웠는지는 아니?
소년: 네, 하지만 제가 보기에는 그다지 대단한 일도 아닌 것 같아요. 아무래도 그 둘 사이에 어떤 오해가 생긴 것 같아요.
남자: 너희 모두 다 같이 만나서 그것에 대해 이야기해 보는 게 어떠니? 그 둘이 네 말은 들을 것 같구나.
소년: 그거 좋은 생각이네요. 두 명 모두 저에게는 좋은 친구들이에요. 저는 누구의 편도 들 수 없어요.
남자: 이해한단다. 모두 잘 해결되기를 바란다.

남: 어이, Mandy. 무슨 일이야?
여: 어떻게 해야 할지 모르겠어, Nick. 내 동생이 이번 주 수요일에 숙제를 도와달라고 했는데, 도와줄 수 없다고 했어. 나는 그날 해야 할 일이 너무 많아.
남: 이번 주 수요일에 무엇을 해야 하는데?
여: 책을 반납하러 도서관에 가야 해. 그런 다음 우리의 발표 준비를 위해 너를 만나야 하고. 그다음에, 밤에는 시험 준비를 해야 해.

B: Oh, you _____ have a lot to do.

G: Yes. But my brother seemed _____ _____, so I feel bad.

B: Well, then _____ _____ _____ on Thursday instead for our presentation? Then you can do _____ and also _____ your brother on Wednesday.

G: That would _____ _____ _____ so much! Thanks for understanding, Nick!

남: 아, 너 정말로 할 일이 많구나.

여: 응. 하지만 내 동생이 실망한 것처럼 보여서, 기분이 좋지가 않아.

남: 음, 그럼 우리 발표를 위해 목요일에 대신 만나는 건 어때? 그러면 너는 수요일에 모든 일을 하고 네 동생도 도와줄 수 있어.

여: 그러면 정말 큰 도움이 될 거야! 이해해 줘서 고마워, Nick!

Listen & Talk 2 A

G: _____ _____ is coming. How do you want to help out?

B: I want to take photos for Sports Day.

G: That's great. You are really _____ _____ _____ _____. I _____ _____ _____ _____ you will take some wonderful pictures.

여: 곧 있으면 운동회야. 어떻게 돕고 싶니?

남: 나는 운동회 날 사진을 찍고 싶어.

여: 그거 좋다. 너는 정말 사진을 잘 찍잖아. 나는 네가 운동회 날에 멋진 사진들을 찍을 것이라는 것을 확신해.

Listen & Talk 2 B

B: In the Send Our Stories project, we are going to make a picture book for children in other countries. We've _____ everyone _____ three groups. Each group will _____ _____ _____ a different task. Group A will _____ a Korean story into English. Group B will make drawings for the book and _____ it. After copies of the book are printed, Group C will be _____ _____ _____ sending them to the children. It won't be easy, but _____ _____ _____ _____ _____ the children _____ receive these books will really enjoy them.

남: Send Our Stories 프로젝트에서 우리는 외국의 아이들을 위한 그림책을 만들 예정입니다. 우리는 모두를 세 그룹으로 나누었습니다. 각 그룹은 서로 다른 작업을 담당할 것입니다. A 그룹은 한국어 이야기를 영어로 번역할 것입니다. B 그룹은 이 책의 그림을 그리고 편집을 할 것입니다. 책들이 인쇄되면, C 그룹은 이 책들을 아이들에게 보내는 일을 맡게 될 것입니다. 쉽지는 않겠지만, 저는 이 책을 받는 어린이들이 이 책을 정말로 좋아할 것이라고 확신합니다.

Listen & Talk 2 C

B: I'm so _____ about our museum _____ _____.

G1: Me too. Let's check our tasks. Yen, what are you _____ _____ _____?

G2: I'm in charge of _____ _____.

G1: Okay. Sejin, are you going to do _____ _____ on the museum?

B: Yes, I am. Are you going to _____ _____ _____ _____ _____, Emma?

G1: That's right. I think we're ready.

G2: Good. I _____ _____ _____ _____ our project will _____ _____ well.

남: 우리의 박물관 견학이 정말 기대돼.

여1: 나도 그래. 각자 맡은 일을 확인해 보자. Yen, 너는 무엇을 담당하지?

여2: 나는 사진 촬영 담당이야.

여1: 그래. 세진아, 너는 박물관 조사를 할 거지?

남: 응, 맞아. 너는 견학 보고서를 작성할 거지, Emma?

여1: 맞아. 이제 우리는 준비가 된 것 같아.

여2: 좋아. 우리 프로젝트가 잘될 거라는 데 의심의 여지가 없어.

[01~02] 다음 대화를 읽고 물음에 답하시오.

Sejin: I'm so excited about our museum field trip.

Emma: (A)Me too. Let's check our tasks. Yen, what are you in charge of?

Yen: I'm in charge of taking pictures.

Emma: Okay. Sejin, are you going to do some research on the museum?

Sejin: Yes, I am. Are you going to write our field trip report, Emma?

Emma: That's right. I think we're ready.

Yen: Good. I have no ___(B)___ that our project will turn out well.

01 위 대화의 밑줄 친 (A)와 바꾸어 쓸 수 있는 것은?

① So do I.　　② So am I.　　③ Neither do I.

④ Neither am I.　　⑤ Me neither.

02 위 대화의 빈칸 (B)에 알맞은 말을 쓰시오.

➡ _____

03 다음 대화의 내용과 일치하지 <u>않는</u> 것은?

Jisu: Mom, we've got a problem.

Mom: What's the matter?

Jisu: We're going to have dinner with Grandma this Saturday, right? But I just realized that Sujin's birthday party is on Saturday evening. She's my best friend. What should I do?

Mom: That sounds like a difficult decision. Let's talk about it with your dad.

Jisu: Okay, Mom. I'd love to see Grandma, but I don't want to miss my best friend's birthday party.

① 지수는 이번 주 토요일에 할머니와 저녁을 먹을 예정이다.
② 지수의 가장 친한 친구의 생일 파티가 토요일 저녁에 있다.
③ 지수는 할머니도 보고 싶고, 친구의 생일 파티도 놓치고 싶지 않다.
④ 엄마는 지수에게 아빠와 이야기해 볼 것을 조언했다.
⑤ 토요일에 지수는 할머니와의 저녁식사 대신 수진이의 생일 파티에 참석할 것이다.

[01~02] 다음 대화를 읽고 물음에 답하시오.

Jisu: Mom, we've got a problem.

Mom: (A)What's the matter?

Jisu: We're going to have dinner with Grandma this Saturday, right? But I just realized that Sujin's birthday party is on Saturday evening. She's my best friend. What should I do?

Mom: That sounds like a difficult decision. Let's talk about it with your dad.

Jisu: Okay, Mom. I'd love to see Grandma, but I don't want to miss my best friend's birthday party.

01 위 대화의 밑줄 친 (A)와 바꾸어 쓸 수 있는 것은?

① How are you doing?

② Where have you been?

③ Is there something wrong?

④ Can you tell me how to do it?

⑤ How were your holidays?

02 위 대화를 읽고 대답할 수 없는 것은?

① When is Jisu going to have dinner with her grandma?

② When is Sujin's birthday party?

③ What's the matter with Jisu?

④ What are Jisu and her mom going to talk about with her dad?

⑤ What is Jisu going to do on Saturday?

서답형

03 다음 대화에서 밑줄 친 우리말을 〈보기〉에 주어진 단어를 모두 배열하여 영작하시오.

G: Sports Day is coming. How do you want to help out?

B: I want to take photos for Sports Day.

G: That's great. You are really good at taking photos. 나는 네가 멋진 사진들을 찍을 것이라는 것을 확신해.

┤ 보기 ├

wonderful / no / that / I / you / some / will / have / pictures / doubt / take

➡ _____

[04~06] 다음 대화를 읽고 물음에 답하시오.

Mr. Smith: Junsu, are you okay? What's the matter?

Junsu: ⓐ Hello, Mr. Smith. I have a problem.

Mr. Smith: ⓑ What happened?

Junsu: ⓒ You know Jaewoo, Yunho, and I are best friends, right? They had a fight, and now I'm stuck in the middle. I don't know what to do.

Mr. Smith: ⓓ Do you know why they (A)[had a fight / made up with]?

Junsu: ⓔ Yes, but it doesn't sound like a big deal to me. I guess they had some kind of misunderstanding.

Mr. Smith: Why don't you all meet together and talk about it? I think they'll listen to you.

Junsu: That's a good idea. They're both good friends of mine. I can't (B)[take part / take sides].

Mr. Smith: I understand. I hope everything (C)[works out / works on].

04 위 대화의 ⓐ~ⓔ 중 주어진 문장이 들어가기에 가장 적절한 곳은?

That sounds hard.

① ⓐ　　② ⓑ　　③ ⓒ　　④ ⓓ　　⑤ ⓔ

05 위 대화의 (A)~(C)에 알맞은 말이 바르게 짝지어진 것은?

	(A)	(B)	(C)
①	had a fight	take part	works out
②	had a fight	take sides	works on
③	had a fight	take sides	works out
④	made up with	take sides	works on
⑤	made up with	take part	works out

06 위 대화를 읽고 대답할 수 <u>없는</u> 것은?

① What's the matter with Junsu?

② Who are Junsu's best friends?

③ When did Jaewoo and Yunho have a fight?

④ What is Mr. Smith's advice?

⑤ Does Junsu know why Jaewoo and Yunho had a fight?

[07~09] 다음 대화를 읽고 물음에 답하시오.

> **Sejin:** I'm so excited about our museum field trip.
> **Emma:** Me too. Let's check our tasks. Yen, what are you in charge of?
> **Yen:** I'm in charge of taking pictures.
> **Emma:** Okay. Sejin, are you going to do some research on the museum?
> **Sejin:** Yes, I am. Are you going to write our field trip report, Emma?
> **Emma:** That's right. I think we're ready.
> **Yen:** Good. _____

서답형

07 위 대화의 빈칸에 들어갈 말을 〈보기〉에 주어진 단어들을 모두 배열하여 완성하시오.

┌ 보기 ┐

that / out / our / no / I / doubt / project / have / well / will / turn

➡ _____

서답형

08 What is Sejin going to do for the museum field trip?

➡ _____

서답형

09 Who will be in charge of writing the field trip report?

➡ _____
_____

[10~11] 다음 글을 읽고 물음에 답하시오.

> **B:** In the Send Our Stories project, we are going to make a picture book for children in other countries. ⓐUnderline{We've divided} everyone into three groups. Each group will be responsible for a different task. Group A will translate a Korean story into English. Group B will make drawings for the book and ⓑedit it. After copies of the book ⓒprinted, Group C will be in charge of ⓓsending them to the children. It won't be easy, but I have no doubt that the children ⓔwho receive these books will really enjoy them.

10 위 글의 밑줄 친 ⓐ~ⓔ 중 어법상 어색한 것을 골라 바르게 고치시오.

_____ ➡ _____

11 위 글의 내용과 일치하지 <u>않는</u> 것은?

① Send Our Stories 프로젝트에서 외국의 아이들을 위한 그림책을 만들 예정이다.

② 모두를 세 그룹으로 나누어 각 그룹은 서로 다른 작업을 담당할 것이다.

③ A 그룹은 영어 이야기를 한국어로 번역할 것이다.

④ B 그룹은 이 책의 그림을 그리고 편집을 할 것이다.

⑤ C 그룹은 이 책들을 아이들에게 보내는 일을 맡게 될 것이다.

[01~03] 다음 글을 읽고 물음에 답하시오.

B: In the Send Our Stories project, we are going to make a picture book for children in other countries. We've divided everyone into three groups. Each group will be responsible for a different task. Group A will translate a Korean story into English. Group B will make drawings for the book and edit it. After copies of the book are printed, Group C will be in charge of sending them to the children. It won't be easy, but I have no doubt that the children who receive these books will really enjoy them.

01 What are they going to do in the Send Our Stories project?

➡ _____

_____

_____

02 What is Group B in charge of?

➡ _____

_____

03 What do students have to do after copies of the book are printed?

➡ _____

04 다음 대화의 내용과 일치하도록 Mandy의 일기를 완성하시오.

Nick: Hey, Mandy. What's the matter?

Mandy: I don't know what to do, Nick. My brother asked me to help him with his homework this Wednesday,

but I told him I can't. I have so many things to do that day.

Nick: What do you have to do this Wednesday?

Mandy: I need to go to the library to return some books. Then I have to meet you to work on our presentation. After that, I have to prepare for an exam at night.

Nick: Oh, you do have a lot to do.

Mandy: Yes. But my brother seemed let down, so I feel bad.

Nick: Well, then how about meeting on Thursday instead for our presentation? Then you can do everything and also help your brother on Wednesday.

Mandy: That would help me out so much! Thanks for understanding, Nick!

Mandy's Diary

Mon, June 22, 2020
Today, I really appreciated Nick. When my brother asked me to (A)_____ _____ this Wednesday, I said I couldn't help him. My brother seemed (B)_____, so I felt so sorry. In fact, I had lots of things to do this Wednesday. I have to go to the library (C)_____ _____, and (D)_____ _____. After that, (E)_____ _____. When I talked about it to Nick, he suggested putting off our meeting schedule. He understood me, so we decided to meet (F)_____ for our presentation. How kind he was! Thanks to Nick, I can help my brother.

Grammar

① 접속사 if/whether

> • I suddenly started to wonder **if[whether]** these are the only qualities that make a good leader. 나는 갑자기 이것들이 좋은 리더를 만드는 유일한 자질들인지 궁금해하기 시작했다.

■ '~인지 (아닌지)'라는 의미의 접속사로 불확실하거나 의문시되는 사실을 나타낼 때 쓰이며, 'if[whether]+주어+동사'의 형태로, 주로 ask, be not sure, find out, know, see, tell, wonder 등과 같은 동사의 목적어 역할을 하는 명사절을 이끈다. if 뒤에 오는 절은 의문사가 없는 간접의문문이며 문장 마지막에 or not을 함께 써서 '~ 아닌지'의 의미를 확실하게 전달할 수 있다.

• I'm not sure **if** I should take this job. 이 일을 맡아야 할지 모르겠어. 〈목적어〉
• **Whether** he will fight or run away is his option. 싸우거나 도망하거나 그 사람 마음대로다. 〈주어〉
• What is at issue is **whether** she was responsible for her actions. 쟁점이 되고 있는 것은 그녀가 자기 행동에 대해 책임을 져야 했느냐는 점이다. 〈보어〉

■ whether와 if는 보통 다음과 같은 차이가 있다.

(1) whether는 문장의 맨 처음에 나와 주어를 이끌 수 있지만 if는 그럴 수 없다.

• **Whether** he will carry out his plan (or not) is not confirmed. 그가 계획을 실행할지는 확인되지 않는다.

(2) whether는 전치사의 목적어를 이끌 수 있지만 if는 그럴 수 없다.

• Keep track of **whether** the screensaver has become active (or not). 화면 보호기의 활성화 여부를 추적하세요.

(3) whether는 to부정사와 함께 쓰일 수 있지만 if는 그럴 수 없다.

• He seemed to try to decide **whether** to say something or not. 그는 무슨 말을 할까 말까 결정하려는 듯이 보였다.

(4) whether는 'or not'이 바로 뒤에 나올 때 쓰일 수 있지만 if는 그럴 수 없다. 'whether[if] ~ or not'의 형태로는 쓸 수 있다.

• I don't know **whether** or not it was true. 나는 그것이 사실이었는지 아닌지 모른다.
• I don't know **whether[if]** he'll be promoted or not. 나는 그가 승진할지 여부를 모른다.

(5) whether는 be동사의 보어로 쓰일 수 있지만 if는 그럴 수 없다.

• The question is **whether** he is ready for it. 문제는 그가 그것에 준비가 되었느냐는 것이다.

핵심 Check

1. 다음 괄호 안에서 알맞은 말을 고르시오.

(1) Please tell me (if / that) you need anything.

(2) I asked (that / whether) he believed the rumor.

❷ 조동사의 수동태

> • I don't think a person like me **can be called** a leader.
> 나 같은 사람이 리더로 불릴 수 있다고 생각하지 않아.
>
> • She begged that she **should be allowed** to go. 그녀는 가도록 허락해 달라고 간청했다.

■ 수동태는 행위자보다는 행위의 대상에 중점을 두고 말할 때 쓰며, 조동사가 있는 문장의 수동태는 '조동사+be+과거분사'의 형태로 나타내며, 수동태 문장에 조동사의 뜻을 더하여 해석한다.

　• We must take down the sign. 우리는 그 표지판을 치워야 한다.

　　→ The sign **must be taken** down. 그 표지판은 치워져야 한다.

■ 부정문은 '조동사+not+be+과거분사'의 형태로, 의문문은 '조동사+주어+be+과거분사 ~?'의 형태로 쓴다.

　• Applications received after 1 July **will not be counted**. 7월 1일 이후에 접수된 원서는 인정되지 않는다.

　• **Can** it **be proved** that he did commit these offences? 그가 정말 이 범행들을 저질렀다는 것을 입증할 수 있을까요?

cf. 1. 수동태 구문에서 행위자가 일반인이거나 강조할 필요가 없을 때에는 'by+행위자'를 생략하고 쓸 수 있다.

　• This tool **can be used** in a variety of ways. 이 도구는 갖가지 방식으로 이용될 수 있다.

　2. 수동태로 쓰지 않는 동사

　자동사는 목적어가 없으므로 수동태로 쓸 수 없으며 '상태'나 '소유'를 나타내는 타동사도 수동태로 쓰이지 않음에 주의해야 한다.

　• The idea **occurred** to him in a dream. 그 아이디어는 꿈속에서 그에게 떠오른 것이었다.

　The idea was occurred to him in a dream. (×)

　• She **has** a good singing voice. 그녀는 노래하는 목소리가 곱다.

　A good singing voice is had by her. (×)

핵심 Check

2. 다음 우리말과 일치하도록 주어진 어휘를 이용하여 빈칸에 알맞게 쓰시오.

(1) 그 회의는 Glasgow에서 열릴 것이다. (will, hold)

➡ The conference _____ _____ _____ in Glasgow.

(2) 그것은 조심스럽게 처리되어야 한다. (should, handle)

➡ It _____ _____ _____ carefully.

01 다음 우리말에 맞게 빈칸에 알맞은 것을 고르시오.

> 그가 집에 있을지 모르겠다.
> = I wonder _____ he is at home.

① that   ② what   ③ which

④ if   ⑤ unless

02 다음 문장을 수동태로 고쳤을 때 알맞은 것은?

> We can purchase uniforms from the school.

① Uniforms can be purchased from the school.

② Uniforms are purchased from the school.

③ Uniforms be purchased from the school.

④ Uniforms can purchase from the school.

⑤ Uniforms can are purchased from the school.

03 다음 중 어법상 <u>어색한</u> 것은?

① Please check if the rumor is true.

② I wonder if she likes me.

③ I was not sure that she would come.

④ Will you ask him if he will participate in the party?

⑤ I don't know whether there is a library around here.

04 다음 괄호 안의 어휘를 바르게 배열하시오.

(1) The letter (tomorrow, by me, sent, be, will).

➡ _____

(2) The pain of the victims (forgotten, be, not, must).

➡ _____

(3) How else (it, done, can, be)?

➡ _____

01 다음 중 어법상 올바른 것은?

① I don't want to know that something happened.

② I wonder if we can win the soccer game.

③ Matthew asked Vivian if or not she wanted to go back home.

④ I'm not sure that Ted won the speech contest.

⑤ Let me know if she brings some food.

02 다음 중 어법상 바르지 않은 것은?

① The cloth should be laid flat on the table.

② This essay will have to completely rewritten.

③ Nothing could be done without her help.

④ This problem must be solved right now.

⑤ The money will be used to help babies.

03 다음 대화의 빈칸에 들어갈 말로 알맞은 것은?

> M: I want to take photos for Sports Day.
> B: That's great. Some wonderful pictures _____.

① take   ② are take

③ will take   ④ will taken

⑤ will be taken

서답형

04 다음 괄호 안에서 알맞은 말을 고르시오.

(1) Please let me know (if / that) you will make it or not.

(2) He should decide (whether / that) he will run or not.

(3) It remains to be seen (if / whether) or not this idea can be put into practice.

(4) I doubt if she (is / will be) present at the meeting tomorrow.

(5) They (can are / can be) cooked separately.

(6) I (will be not / will not be) finished for another hour.

(7) The cartoon characters should only (appear / be appeared) on healthy foods.

(8) So many hotels (resemble / are resembled) each other.

서답형

05 다음 우리말에 맞게 괄호 안에 주어진 어휘를 이용하여 영작하시오.

> 나는 그녀가 이탈리아의 음식을 좋아하는지 아닌지 모른다. (she, know, Italian food, if, or, like, not)

➡ _____

서답형

06 다음 우리말과 일치하도록 빈칸에 알맞게 쓰시오. (어휘가 주어진 경우, 그 어휘를 활용할 것.)

(1) 그는 나에게 자기가 암에 걸렸다고 생각하느냐고 물었다.

➡ He asked me _____ I thought he had cancer.

(2) 우화는 여러 가지 관점에서 이해될 수 있다. (can, understand)

➡ Fables _____ _____ _____ on various levels.

(3) 그녀가 반드시 그 규칙을 지키게 해야 한다. (must, make)

➡ She _____ _____ _____ to comply with the rules.

중요

07 다음 빈칸에 알맞은 말이 바르게 짝지어진 것은?

• Will you see _____ you can pick me out in this photo?
• Schools should _____ only on exam results.

① that – not be judged
② if – be not judged
③ if – not be judged
④ whether – be not judged
⑤ whether – judged not be

08 다음 우리말에 맞도록 빈칸에 들어갈 알맞은 것은?

그것은 쉽게 끝마칠 수 있다.
= It _____ with ease.

① can be finished ② can finish
③ can finished ④ finishes
⑤ can be finish

09 다음 우리말을 바르게 영작한 것을 고르시오.

나는 비가 오는지 눈이 오는지 궁금해하고 있었다.

① I was wondering that it was raining or snowing.
② I was wondering whether raining or snowing.
③ I was wondering whether it was raining or snowing.
④ I was wondering if raining or snowing.
⑤ I was wondering if it was raining and snowing.

서답형

10 주어진 어휘를 이용하여 다음 우리말을 영작하시오.

그 계획은 비용 때문에 연기되어야만 했다. (the plan, cost, had, because, postpone, to, of)

➡ _____

_____

중요

11 다음 두 문장을 한 문장으로 연결할 때 가장 적절한 것은?

• Would you please check?
• Did I fill out this card right?

① Would you please check if I filled out this card right?
② Would you please check if or not I filled out this card right?
③ Would you please check how I filled out this card right?
④ Would you please check that I filled out this card right?
⑤ Would you please check what I filled out this card right?

12 다음 문장을 수동태로 바르게 바꾼 것을 고르시오.

> We may change the prices without prior notice.

① We may be changed the prices without prior notice.
② We may have changed the prices without prior notice.
③ The prices may change without prior notice.
④ The prices may have changed without prior notice.
⑤ The prices may be changed without prior notice.

13 다음 빈칸에 들어갈 말이 나머지와 다른 하나는?

① Check _____ the seat is set at the right height.
② Do you know _____ she has any personal problems?
③ They can decide _____ they like it or not.
④ I am not sure _____ or not he will come tonight
⑤ John asked Peter _____ he could close the window.

14 다음 문장의 빈칸에 들어갈 말로 알맞은 말은?

> Jake wanted to know _____ Angelina liked to watch a movie with him.

① which   ② what   ③ that
④ if   ⑤ unless

15 다음 중 어법상 어색한 것을 고르시오. (2개)

① Personal calls must be taken outside of the office area.
② Very little of the house may be remained after the fire.
③ Art may be used as a vehicle for advertisements.
④ Do you know if will Cathy come home soon?
⑤ Can you tell me if you are going shopping tonight?

서답형

16 다음 문장에서 어법상 어색한 것을 바르게 고쳐 다시 쓰시오.

(1) Joan asked that I want to go to the party.
➡ _____
_____

(2) It depends on if it applies directly to your job.
➡ _____
_____

(3) You'll have to choose if to buy it or not.
➡ _____
_____

(4) The beautiful clothes will put on right now.
➡ _____
_____

(5) Problems will be occurred as a result of human life.
➡ _____
_____

01 다음을 수동태 문장으로 바꿔 쓰시오.

(1) About a million people may watch the final match.

➡ _____

_____

(2) We should not underestimate the value of regular exercise.

➡ _____

_____

(3) We can make the robots work faster in the future.

➡ _____

_____

(4) No one can solve this math problem.

➡ _____

_____

02 주어진 두 문장을 〈보기〉처럼 하나의 문장으로 쓰시오.

┌─ 보기 ─┐
• He asked me.
• He didn't know if Jane had been to Rome.
→ He asked me if[whether] Jane had been to Rome.
└────────┘

• Ask her.
• You don't know if she watches TV every night.

➡ _____

_____

03 그림을 보고, 주어진 어휘를 이용하여 빈칸을 알맞게 채우시오.

(1)

Susan wonders _____

better than her. (a picture, Jake, draw)

(2)

I have no doubt that some wonderful pictures for Sports Day _____.
(will, take)

04 괄호 안에 주어진 말을 이용하여 어법에 맞게 문장을 완성하시오.

(1) I wonder _____ this food. (like, you)

(2) I don't know _____.
(I, respond, should, how)

05 를 이용하여 다음 두 문장을 한 문장으로 바꿔 쓰시오.

(1) • I want to know.

• Are my study plans effective?

➡ _____

_____

(2) • I want to check.

• Can I view the content of the site?

➡ _____

_____

(3) • I'm not sure.

• Does she run fast enough?

➡ _____

_____

06 다음 문장에서 어법상 어색한 것을 바르게 고쳐 다시 쓰시오.

(1) If I believe you or not is important.

➡ _____

_____

(2) My heart raced, not knowing if or not my son was alive.

➡ _____

_____

(3) He seemed undecided if to go or stay.

➡ _____

_____

(4) My lost card might use illegally.

➡ _____

_____

(5) Ghosts can be appeared in visible form in the world of the living.

➡ _____

_____

(6) The tree was had to saw down.

➡ _____

_____

07 다음에 주어진 어휘를 이용하여 문장을 완성하시오.

(1) (may, affect)

➡ Manufacturing processes _____ by the purpose of the product.

(2) (will, release)

➡ The new model _____ in July.

08 다음 우리말에 맞게 주어진 단어에 한 단어를 추가하여 바르게 배열하시오.

(1) 그는 내가 그의 가방을 봤는지 나에게 물어보았다. (he, his, I, me, backpack, asked, saw)

➡ _____

_____

(2) 아무도 그가 진심인지 아닌지 알 수 없다. (he, one, can, is, tell, no, not, serious, or)

➡ _____

_____

(3) 저 집에 누가 살고 있는지 보자. (let's, anyone, lives, see, that house, in)

➡ _____

_____

(4) 그 방은 오후 2시까지는 청소되지 않을 것이다. (won't, cleaned, until 2 p.m., the room)

➡ _____

_____

(5) 여기서 그들의 목소리를 들을 수 있다. (heard, voices, can, here, their, from)

➡ _____

_____

(6) 우리 모두 그분이 그리울 겁니다. (shall, be, missed, he, us all)

➡ _____

_____

Reading

We Are All Leaders

Brian: The election is coming up. Why don't you run for class
= How[What] about running

representative, Yumi?

Yumi: No way. I'm not the right person for that position. I've never
= Definitely not. = Never.

thought about running.
현재완료 용법(경험), 현재완료 경험은 주로 ever. never. before. once 등의 부사와 함께 쓰인다.

Brian: Why not?
Why?(×)

Yumi: Come on, Brian. Leaders have special qualities. I don't think a

person like me can be called a leader.
조동사 can을 써서 나타낸 조동사의 수동태 문장.

Brian: What do you mean? I think you have very good leadership
think와 you 사이에 접속사 that이 생략되어 있음.

qualities. You're really friendly and outgoing. You also help

people get along. I have no doubt that you will be elected if you
= to get   조건을 나타내는 접속사: 만약 ~한다면

run.

Brian told me this afternoon that I have good leadership qualities.
접속사(생략가능)
No one has ever told me that before. Why does he think so? Maybe he
= I have good leadership qualities.   = I have good leadership qualities.
was just trying to be nice. When he said that to me, however, I started
= I have good leadership qualities.
to think. Can I really become a leader?
= thinking

election 선거

run (선거에) 입후보하다

representative 대표(자)

quality 질. 우수함. 자질

leadership 지도력. 리더십

outgoing 외향적인. 사교적인

get along 잘 지내다. 어울려 지내다

확인문제

● 다음 문장이 본문의 내용과 일치하면 T, 일치하지 않으면 F를 쓰시오.

1 Yumi says that she is not the right person for class representative. ☐

2 Yumi thinks she has special qualities. ☐

3 Brian thinks Yumi has very good leadership qualities. ☐

4 Brian has no doubt that Yumi will be elected if she runs. ☐

5 Brian told Yumi this afternoon that he has good leadership qualities. ☐

I don't know. I think leaders should have a vision, clear goals, and the ability to motivate others. I don't have any of those things.
= I have none of those things. not ~ any: 아무것도 … 아니다(전체 부정)

Then I suddenly started to wonder if these are the only qualities
접속사: ~인지 아닌지

that make a good leader. Maybe I'm wrong. Maybe there are other
선행사 'the only qualities'를 수식하는 주격 관계대명사. 선행사에 the only가 있으면 주로 관계대명사로 that을 쓴다.

leadership qualities. So I decided to do some research online.
decide는 to부정사를 목적어로 취한다.

Here's what I found!
= the thing which[that]

GREEN LEADERS: "Team Builders"

• Ensure that the team feels valued
= Make sure

• Create a positive environment
↔ negative

• Are friendly and easy to talk to
to talk(×)

RED LEADERS: "Logical Analysts"

• Have good reasoning skills

• Analyze problems and situations

• Think of the most effective ways to achieve the team's goals
형용사적 용법의 to부정사

PURPLE LEADERS: "Hands-Off Managers"

• Allow others to work on their own
allow+목적어+to부정사   on one's own: 혼자서, 단독으로

• Do not try to control people
try to 부정사: ~하려고 노력하다

• Give advice only when it is needed
= advice

vision 시력, 비전
clear 명확한, 뚜렷한
goal 목적, 목표
motivate 동기를 부여하다
ensure 반드시 ~하게 하다, 보장하다
valued 귀중한, 존중 받는
logical 논리적인, 타당한
reasoning 추리, 추론
analyze 분석하다
effective 효과적인
achieve 성취하다, 이루다
hands-off 불간섭주의의, 자유방임의

📎 **확인문제**

● 다음 문장이 본문의 내용과 일치하면 T, 일치하지 않으면 F를 쓰시오.

1 Yumi thinks leaders should have a vision, clear goals, and the ability to motivate others. ☐

2 Green leaders are "logical analysts." ☐

3 Green leaders make sure that the team feels valued. ☐

4 Red leaders are friendly and easy to talk to. ☐

5 Purple leaders allow others to work on their own. ☐

6 Purple leaders give advice at any time. ☐

ORANGE LEADERS: "Strict Directors"

• Make everyone's role clear
  clearly(×)
• Make sure everything is finished on time
  = Ensure   시간을 어기지 않고, 정각에
• Ensure each step is done properly
  = Make sure

YELLOW LEADERS: "Quiet Supporters"

• Lead by example

• Let the team members shine instead
                    to shine(×)
• Meet the team members' needs
  = Satisfy

BLUE LEADERS: "Creative Thinkers"

• Approach problems in new ways
  Approach to(×)
• Come up with fresh ideas

• Deal with tasks differently from others
  = Treat = Handle

I was surprised that there are actually many different leadership styles, but soon I realized the reason.

We belong to many different groups, and many different situations
   are belonged to(×)
can come up in our lives. They all call for different leadership styles.
         = Many different groups and (many different) situations
Each group's unique situation determines the best leadership style.

"I am a part of many different groups, and I have different responsibilities in each group."

After reading everything, I became more confident. I discovered that
      = I read
I have some of the qualities of a "green leader." If my classmates think
                              조건을 나타내는 접속사: 만약 ~한다면
a green leader would make our class better, they might pick me to be class representative! Okay, let's try it!

properly 적절히, 제대로
lead by example 솔선수범하다
approach 접근하다
come up with 찾아내다, 내놓다
deal with 다루다, 처리하다
belong to ~에 속하다
come up 나오다, 발생하다
call for ~을 필요로 하다
determine 결정하다, 결심하다
responsibility 책임, 의무
confident 자신 있는
discover 발견하다, 찾다

📎 **확인문제**

● 다음 문장이 본문의 내용과 일치하면 T, 일치하지 않으면 F를 쓰시오.

1 Orange leaders ensure everything is finished on time. ☐

2 Blue leaders let the team members shine instead. ☐

3 The writer was surprised that there are actually many different leadership styles. ☐

4 Many different situations all call for the same leadership styles. ☐

5 Each group's unique situation determines the best leadership style. ☐

6 After reading everything, the writer lost confidence. ☐

• 우리말을 참고하여 빈칸에 알맞은 말을 쓰시오.

1 _____ _____ _____ Leaders

2 Brian: The election is _____ _____ .

3 _____ _____ _____ run for class representative, Yumi?

4 Yumi: _____ _____ .

5 I'm not the _____ _____ for that position.

6 I've never _____ _____ running.

7 Brian: _____ _____ ?

8 Yumi: _____ _____ , Brian.

9 Leaders have _____ _____ .

10 I don't think a person like me _____ _____ _____ a leader.

11 Brian: _____ do you mean?

12 I think you have very _____ _____ _____ .

13 You're really _____ and _____ .

14 You also help people _____ _____ .

15 I have no doubt that you _____ _____ _____ if you run.

16 Brian told me this afternoon that I have _____ _____ _____ .

17 No one _____ _____ _____ me that before.

18 _____ does he think so?

19 Maybe he was just _____ _____ _____ nice.

20 When he said that to me, _____ , I started to think.

---

1 우리는 모두 리더들이다

2 Brian: "선거가 다가오고 있어.

3 유미야, 반 대표에 입후보하는 게 어때?"

4 유미: "아니.

5 나는 그 자리에 적절한 사람이 아니야.

6 나는 입후보하는 것에 대해 생각해 본 적이 없어."

7 Brian: "왜?"

8 유미: "이봐, Brian.

9 리더들은 특별한 자질을 갖추고 있어.

10 나 같은 사람이 리더로 불릴 수 있다고 생각하지 않아."

11 Brian: "무슨 말이야?

12 내 생각에 너는 매우 좋은 지도력 자질들을 갖추고 있어.

13 너는 정말 친절하고 외향적이잖아.

14 또 너는 사람들이 어울리도록 도와주기도 해.

15 만약 네가 입후보한다면 당선될 거라고 믿어 의심치 않아."

16 Brian은 오늘 오후에 내게 내가 좋은 지도력 자질들을 갖추고 있다고 말했다.

17 이전에는 아무도 내게 그런 말을 한 적이 없었다.

18 왜 그는 그렇게 생각했을까?

19 아마도 그는 그저 친절하려고 했을 것이다.

20 그러나 그가 내게 그렇게 말했을 때, 나는 생각하기 시작했다.

21 Can I really _____ _____ _____?

22 I _____ _____.

23 I think leaders should have _____ _____, clear goals, and the ability _____ _____ _____.

24 I don't have _____ _____ _____ _____.

25 Then I suddenly started to _____ _____ these are the only qualities that make a good leader.

26 Maybe I'm _____.

27 Maybe there are _____ _____ _____.

28 So I decided to _____ _____ _____ _____.

29 Here's _____ I found!

30 **GREEN LEADERS:** "Team _____"

31 Ensure that the team _____ _____

32 Create a _____ _____

33 Are friendly and easy _____ _____ _____

34 **RED LEADERS:** "_____ _____"

35 Have good _____ _____

36 _____ problems and situations

37 Think of the most effective ways to _____ _____ _____ _____

38 **PURPLE LEADERS:** "_____ _____"

39 Allow others to work _____ _____ _____

40 Do not _____ _____ _____ people

41 Give advice only when _____ _____ _____

21	내가 정말 리더가 될 수 있을까?
22	나는 모르겠다.
23	나는 리더가 비전, 명확한 목표, 그리고 다른 사람에게 동기를 부여할 능력을 가지고 있어야 한다고 생각한다.
24	나는 그러한 것들 중 어느 것도 가지고 있지 않다.
25	그때 나는 갑자기 이것들이 좋은 리더를 만드는 유일한 자질들인지 궁금해하기 시작했다.
26	아마도 내가 틀린지도 모른다.
27	어쩌면 다른 지도력 자질들이 있는지도 모른다.
28	그래서 나는 온라인으로 조사해 보기로 결심했다.
29	여기에 내가 찾은 것이 있다!
30	〈녹색 리더〉 '팀 조직자'
31	팀이 반드시 가치 있다고 느끼게 한다
32	긍정적인 환경을 조성한다
33	친절하고 말을 걸기 쉽다
34	〈빨간색 리더〉 '논리적 분석가'
35	좋은 추론 기술을 갖고 있다
36	문제와 상황들을 분석한다
37	팀의 목표를 성취하는 가장 효과적인 방법들을 생각한다
38	〈보라색 리더〉 '방임적 관리자'
39	다른 사람들이 스스로 일하도록 해 준다
40	사람들을 통제하려고 하지 않는다
41	필요할 때만 조언한다

42 ORANGE LEADERS: "_____ _____"

43 Make _____ _____ clear

44 Make sure everything is finished _____ _____

45 Ensure _____ _____ is done properly

46 YELLOW LEADERS: "_____ _____"

47 Lead _____ _____

48 Let the team members _____ _____

49 _____ the team members' _____

50 BLUE LEADERS: "_____ _____"

51 _____ problems in new ways

52 _____ _____ _____ fresh ideas

53 Deal with tasks _____ _____ others

54 I was surprised that there are actually many different leadership styles, but soon I _____ _____ _____.

55 We _____ _____ many different groups, and many different situations can _____ _____ in our lives.

56 They all _____ _____ different leadership styles.

57 Each group's _____ _____ determines the best leadership style.

58 "I am a part of many different groups, and I have _____ _____ in each group."

59 After reading everything, I became _____ _____.

60 I discovered that I have _____ _____ _____ _____ of a "green leader."

61 If my classmates think a green leader would make our class better, they might _____ _____ to be class representative!

62 Okay, _____ _____ it!

42 〈주황색 리더〉 '엄격한 감독관'

43 모두의 역할을 분명하게 해 준다

44 모든 일을 제때 끝날 것을 확실히 한다

45 각 단계가 적절히 이행되도록 한다

46 〈노란색 리더〉 '조용한 지지자'

47 솔선수범한다

48 팀원들이 대신 빛나도록 해 준다

49 팀원들의 요구 사항을 충족한다

50 〈파란색 리더〉 '창조적 사상가'

51 새로운 방식으로 문제들에 접근한다

52 신선한 아이디어를 떠올린다

53 다른 사람들과 다르게 일을 처리한다

54 나는 실제로 서로 다른 많은 지도력 유형들이 있어서 놀랐지만, 곧 그 이유를 깨달았다.

55 우리는 서로 다른 여러 집단에 속하고, 우리 인생에서 서로 다른 많은 상황들이 발생할 수 있다.

56 그것들은 모두 서로 다른 지도력 유형들을 요구한다.

57 각 집단의 독특한 상황이 최고의 지도력 유형을 결정한다.

58 "나는 서로 다른 많은 집단의 일부이고, 각 집단에서 각각 다른 책임을 갖고 있어."

59 모든 것을 읽고 나서, 나는 더 자신감이 생겼다.

60 나는 '녹색 리더'의 자질들 중 일부를 가지고 있다는 것을 알게 되었다.

61 만약 나의 반 친구들이 녹색 리더가 우리 학급을 더 좋게 만들 거라고 생각한다면, 그들은 학급 대표로 나를 뽑을지도 모른다!

62 좋아, 시도해 보자!

● 우리말을 참고하여 본문을 영작하시오.

1 우리는 모두 리더들이다
➡ _____

2 Brian: "선거가 다가오고 있어.
➡ _____

3 유미야, 반 대표에 입후보하는 게 어때?"
➡ _____

4 유미: "아니.
➡ _____

5 나는 그 자리에 적절한 사람이 아니야.
➡ _____

6 나는 입후보하는 것에 대해 생각해 본 적이 없어."
➡ _____

7 Brian: "왜?"
➡ _____

8 유미: "이봐, Brian.
➡ _____

9 리더들은 특별한 자질을 갖추고 있어.
➡ _____

10 나 같은 사람이 리더로 불릴 수 있다고 생각하지 않아."
➡ _____

11 Brian: "무슨 말이야?
➡ _____

12 내 생각에 너는 매우 좋은 지도력 자질들을 갖추고 있어.
➡ _____

13 너는 정말 친절하고 외향적이잖아.
➡ _____

14 또 너는 사람들이 어울리도록 도와주기도 해.
➡ _____

15 만약 네가 입후보한다면 당선될 거라고 믿어 의심치 않아."
➡ _____

16 Brian은 오늘 오후에 내게 내가 좋은 지도력 자질들을 갖추고 있다고 말했다.
➡ _____

17 이전에는 아무도 내게 그런 말을 한 적이 없었다.
➡ _____

18 왜 그는 그렇게 생각했을까?
➡ _____

19 아마도 그는 그저 친절하려고 했을 것이다.
➡ _____

20 그러나 그가 내게 그렇게 말했을 때, 나는 생각하기 시작했다.
➡ _____

21 내가 정말 리더가 될 수 있을까?

➡ _____

22 나는 모르겠다.

➡ _____

23 나는 리더가 비전, 명확한 목표, 그리고 다른 사람들에게 동기를 부여할 능력을 가지고 있어야 한다고 생각한다.

➡ _____

24 나는 그러한 것들 중 어느 것도 가지고 있지 않다.

➡ _____

25 그때 나는 갑자기 이것들이 좋은 리더를 만드는 유일한 자질들인지 궁금해하기 시작했다.

➡ _____

26 아마도 내가 틀린지도 모른다.

➡ _____

27 어쩌면 다른 지도력 자질들이 있는지도 모른다.

➡ _____

28 그래서 나는 온라인으로 조사해 보기로 결심했다.

➡ _____

29 여기에 내가 찾은 것이 있다!

➡ _____

30 〈녹색 리더〉 '팀 조직자'

➡ _____

31 팀이 반드시 가치 있다고 느끼게 한다

➡ _____

32 긍정적인 환경을 조성한다

➡ _____

33 친절하고 말을 걸기 쉽다

➡ _____

34 〈빨간색 리더〉 '논리적 분석가'

➡ _____

35 좋은 추론 기술을 갖고 있다

➡ _____

36 문제와 상황들을 분석한다

➡ _____

37 팀의 목표를 성취하는 가장 효과적인 방법들을 생각한다

➡ _____

38 〈보라색 리더〉 '방임적 관리자'

➡ _____

39 다른 사람들이 스스로 일하도록 해 준다

➡ _____

40 사람들을 통제하려고 하지 않는다

➡ _____

41 필요할 때만 조언한다

➡ _____

42 〈주황색 리더〉 '엄격한 감독관'
➡ _____

43 모두의 역할을 분명하게 해 준다
➡ _____

44 모든 일을 제때 끝날 것을 확실히 한다
➡ _____

45 단계가 적절히 이행되도록 한다
➡ _____

46 〈노란색 리더〉 '조용한 지지자'
➡ _____

47 솔선수범한다
➡ _____

48 팀원들이 대신 빛나도록 해 준다
➡ _____

49 팀원들의 요구 사항을 충족한다
➡ _____

50 〈파란색 리더〉 '창조적 사상가'
➡ _____

51 새로운 방식으로 문제들에 접근한다
➡ _____

52 신선한 아이디어를 떠올린다
➡ _____

53 다른 사람들과 다르게 일을 처리한다
➡ _____

54 나는 실제로 서로 다른 많은 지도력 유형들이 있어서 놀랐지만, 곧 그 이유를 깨달았다.
➡ _____

55 우리는 서로 다른 여러 집단에 속하고, 우리 인생에서 서로 다른 많은 상황들이 발생할 수 있다.
➡ _____

56 그것들은 모두 서로 다른 지도력 유형들을 요구한다.
➡ _____

57 각 집단의 독특한 상황이 최고의 지도력 유형을 결정한다.
➡ _____

58 "나는 서로 다른 많은 집단의 일부이고, 각 집단에서 각각 다른 책임을 갖고 있어."
➡ _____

59 모든 것을 읽고 나서, 나는 더 자신감이 생겼다.
➡ _____

60 나는 '녹색 리더'의 자질들 중 일부분을 가지고 있다는 것을 알게 되었다.
➡ _____

61 만약 나의 반 친구들이 녹색 리더가 우리 학급을 더 좋게 만들 거라고 생각한다면, 그들은 학급 대표로 나를 뽑을지도 모른다!

62 좋아, 시도해 보자!
➡ _____

[01~03] 다음 글을 읽고 물음에 답하시오.

> Brian: The election is coming up. Why (A)[do / don't] you run for class representative, Yumi?
>
> Yumi: No way. I'm not the right person for that position. ⓐI've never thought about running.
>
> Brian: (B)[Why / Why not]?
>
> Yumi: Come on, Brian. Leaders have special qualities. I don't think a person like me can be called a leader.
>
> Brian: What do you mean? I think you have very good leadership qualities. You're really friendly and outgoing. You also help people get along. I have no doubt that you will be elected (C)[if / whether] you run.

서답형

01 위 글의 괄호 (A)~(C)에서 문맥이나 어법상 알맞은 낱말을 골라 쓰시오.

➡ (A) _____ (B) _____ (C) _____

02 아래 〈보기〉에서 위 글의 밑줄 친 문장 ⓐ에 쓰인 현재완료와 용법이 같은 것의 개수를 고르시오.

┌─── 보기 ───┐
> ① How long have you studied English?
> ② She has just finished doing her homework.
> ③ How many times have you read the book?
> ④ Yumi has been sick since yesterday.
> ⑤ Have you ever met each other before?
└──────────┘

① 1개 ② 2개 ③ 3개 ④ 4개 ⑤ 5개

03 According to the passage, which is NOT true?

> ① Brian proposes that Yumi should run for class representative.
> ② Yumi rejects Brian's proposal saying that she isn't the right person for class representative.
> ③ Yumi has never thought about running for class representative.
> ④ Brian doesn't think a person like him can be called a leader.
> ⑤ Brian thinks Yumi has very good leadership qualities.

[04~06] 다음 글을 읽고 물음에 답하시오.

> I was surprised that there are actually many different leadership styles, but soon I realized the reason.
>
> We belong to many different groups, and many different situations can come up in our lives. They all ⓐcall for different leadership styles. Each group's unique situation determines the best leadership style.
>
> "I am a part of many different groups, and I have different responsibilities in each group."
>
> ⓑAfter reading everything, I became more confident. I discovered that I have some of the qualities of a "green leader." If my classmates think a green leader would make our class better, they might pick me to be class representative! Okay, let's try it!

04 위 글의 밑줄 친 ⓐcall for와 바꿔 쓸 수 <u>없는</u> 말을 고르시오.

① require   ② stand for
③ need   ④ demand
⑤ want

서답형

05 위 글의 밑줄 친 ⓑ를 다음과 같이 바꿔 쓸 때 빈칸에 들어갈 알맞은 말을 두 단어로 쓰시오.

➡ After ＿＿＿＿ ＿＿＿＿ everything

서답형

06 What determines the best leadership style? Fill in the blanks with suitable words.

> The ＿＿＿＿ ＿＿＿＿ of each group determines it.

[07~10] 다음 글을 읽고 물음에 답하시오.

(A)Here's which I found!
GREEN LEADERS: " ⓐ **"**
• Ensure that the team feels valued
• Create a positive environment
• Are friendly and easy to talk to
RED LEADERS: "Logical Analysts"
• Have good reasoning skills
• Analyze problems and situations
• Think of the most effective ways to achieve the team's goals
PURPLE LEADERS: "Hands-Off Managers"
• Allow others to work on their own
• Do not try to control people
• Give advice only when it is needed

07 위 글의 빈칸 ⓐ에 들어갈 알맞은 말을 고르시오.

① Strict Directors ② Team Builders
③ Quiet Supporters ④ Creative Thinkers
⑤ Carefree Directors

서답형

08 위 글의 밑줄 친 (A)에서 어법상 틀린 부분을 찾아 고치시오.

＿＿＿＿＿ ➡ ＿＿＿＿＿

서답형

09 What can we call the leaders who analyze problems and situations? Fill in the blanks with suitable words.

> They are ＿＿＿＿ ＿＿＿＿ .

➡ ＿＿＿＿＿＿ 또는 ＿＿＿＿＿＿

서답형

10 다음 빈칸 (A)~(C)에 알맞은 단어를 넣어 '보라색 리더들'의 특징을 완성하시오.

> They let others work (A)＿＿＿ ＿＿＿ ＿＿＿ , don't try to (B)＿＿＿ people, and give advice only when (C)＿＿＿ ＿＿＿ ＿＿＿ .

[11~13] 다음 글을 읽고 물음에 답하시오.

Brian told me this afternoon that I have good leadership qualities. No one has ever told me that before. Why does he think so? Maybe he was just trying to be nice. When he said that to me, ＿ⓐ＿ , I started to think. ⓑCan I really become a leader? ⓒI don't know. I think leaders should have a vision, clear goals, and the ability to motivate others. I don't have any of those things.

Then I suddenly started to wonder if these are the only qualities that make a good leader. Maybe I'm wrong. Maybe there are other leadership qualities. So I decided to do some research online.

11 위 글의 빈칸 ⓐ에 들어갈 알맞은 말을 고르시오.

① for example ② in addition
③ furthermore ④ however
⑤ that is

서답형

12 위 글의 밑줄 친 ⓑ와 ⓒ를 합쳐 다음과 같이 한 문장으로 고칠 때 빈칸에 들어갈 알맞은 단어를 쓰시오.

➡ I don't know _____ I can really become a leader.

13 위 글의 주제로 알맞은 것을 고르시오.

① the best way to be a good leader
② the chance to strengthen leadership
③ a program for leadership qualities
④ a crisis that requires strong leadership
⑤ the qualities leaders should have

[14~17] 다음 글을 읽고 물음에 답하시오.

Here's what I found!
ORANGE LEADERS: "(A)Strict Directors"
• Make everyone's role clear
• Make sure everything is finished on time
• Ensure each step is done properly
YELLOW LEADERS: "Quiet Supporters"
• Lead by example
• (B)Let the team members to shine instead
• Meet the team members' needs
BLUE LEADERS: "Creative Thinkers"
• Approach problems in new ways
• Come up ⓐ fresh ideas
• Deal ⓑ tasks differently from others

서답형

14 위 글의 빈칸 ⓐ와 ⓑ에 공통으로 들어갈 알맞은 전치사를 쓰시오.

➡ _____

15 위 글의 밑줄 친 (A)Strict와 바꿔 쓸 수 없는 말을 고르시오.

① Stern
② Easy-going
③ Severe
④ Rigid
⑤ Rigorous

서답형

16 위 글의 밑줄 친 (B)에서 어법상 틀린 부분을 찾아 고치시오.

_____ ➡ _____

서답형

17 다음 '주황색 리더들'의 특징에 대한 설명 중, 위 글의 내용과 다른 부분을 찾아서 고치시오.

> They are strict directors who make everyone's role clear, don't mind whether everything is finished on time, and make sure each step is done properly.

_____ ➡ _____

[18~21] 다음 글을 읽고 물음에 답하시오.

I was surprised that there are actually many different leadership styles, but soon I realized the reason.

We belong ⓐ many different groups, and many different situations can come up in our lives. They all call for different leadership styles. Each group's unique situation determines the best leadership style.

"I am a part of many different groups, and I have different responsibilities in each group."

After reading everything, I became more ⓑ . I discovered that I have some of the qualities of a "green leader." If my classmates think a green leader would make our class better, they might pick me to be class representative! Okay, let's try it!

18 위 글의 빈칸 ⓐ에 알맞은 전치사를 쓰시오.

➡ _____

19 위 글의 빈칸 ⓑ에 들어갈 알맞은 말을 고르시오.

① generous   ② modest

③ confident   ④ anxious

⑤ selfish

서답형

20 Why are there actually many different leadership styles? Fill in the blanks (A)~(C) with suitable words.

> That's because many different situations which call for (A)_____ _____ _____ can come up in our lives, and the (B)_____ situation of each group we are in determines the (C)_____ _____ _____.

21 위 글의 제목으로 알맞은 것을 고르시오.

① How Many Leadership Styles Are There?

② Which Group Do You Want to Choose?

③ Many Different Situations Can Happen in Our Lives

④ Wow! I Have the Qualities of a "Green Leader!"

⑤ The Best Leadership Style Depends on the Situation

[22~24] 다음 글을 읽고 물음에 답하시오.

Brian told me this afternoon that I have good leadership qualities. No one has ever told me that before. Why does he think so? Maybe he was just trying to be nice. (①) When he said that to me, however, I started to think. (②) Can I really become a leader? (③) I think leaders should have a vision, clear goals, and the ability to motivate others. (④) I don't have any of ⓐthose things. (⑤)

Then I suddenly started to wonder if these are the only qualities that make a good leader. Maybe I'm wrong. Maybe there are other leadership qualities. So I decided to do some research online.   <I: Yumi>

22 위 글의 흐름으로 보아, 주어진 문장이 들어가기에 가장 적절한 곳은?

> I don't know.

①   ②   ③   ④   ⑤

서답형

23 위 글의 밑줄 친 ⓐthose things가 가리키는 것을 본문에서 찾아 쓰시오.

➡ _____

_____

24 위 글의 뒤에 올 내용으로 가장 알맞은 것을 고르시오.

① the reason why Brian told Yumi to run for class representative

② Brian's thought about Yumi's leadership qualities

③ some research Yumi did online about leadership qualities

④ the importance of searching for the necessary information online

⑤ the effective way to do some research online

[25~27] 다음 글을 읽고 물음에 답하시오.

Brian: The election is coming up. Why don't you (A)run for class representative, Yumi?

Yumi: No way. (B)나는 그 자리에 적절한 사람이 아니야. I've never thought about running.

Brian: Why not?

Yumi: Come on, Brian. Leaders have special qualities. I don't think a person like me can be called a leader.

Brian: What do you mean? I think you have very good leadership qualities. You're really friendly and outgoing. You also help people get along. I have no doubt that you will ___ⓐ___ if you run.

서답형

25 위 글의 빈칸 ⓐ에 elect를 알맞은 형태로 쓰시오.

➡ _____

26 위 글의 밑줄 친 (A)run과 같은 의미로 쓰인 것을 고르시오.

① Why did you run for the doctor?
② The buses run every ten minutes.
③ When did he run a factory?
④ She wanted to run in the election.
⑤ The show had a record-breaking run in the London theatre.

서답형

27 위 글의 밑줄 친 (B)의 우리말에 맞게 주어진 어휘를 이용하여 8 단어로 영작하시오.

right, position

➡ _____

[28~31] 다음 글을 읽고 물음에 답하시오.

Here's what I found!
ORANGE LEADERS: "Strict Directors"
• Make everyone's role clear
• (A)Make sure everything is finished on time
• Ensure each (B)step is done properly

YELLOW LEADERS: "Quiet ___ⓐ___ "
• Lead by example
• Let the team members shine instead
• Meet the team members' needs
BLUE LEADERS: "Creative Thinkers"
• Approach problems in new ways
• Come up with fresh ideas
• Deal with tasks differently from others

28 위 글의 빈칸 ⓐ에 들어갈 알맞은 말을 고르시오.

① Competitors   ② Opponents
③ Supporters   ④ Challengers
⑤ Rivals

서답형

29 위 글의 밑줄 친 (A)Make sure와 바꿔 쓸 수 있는 말을 본문에서 찾아 쓰시오.

➡ _____

중요

30 위 글의 밑줄 친 (B)step과 같은 의미로 쓰인 것을 고르시오.

① He took a step towards the door.
② She walked with a quick light step.
③ Why did you step on my foot?
④ When you complete the first stage, you can move on to step 2.
⑤ He sat on the bottom step.

서답형

31 다음 빈칸 (A)~(C)에 알맞은 단어를 넣어 '파란색 리더들'의 특징을 완성하시오.

Blue leaders are "(A)_____ _____" who approach problems in new ways, think of (B)_____ _____, and treat tasks (C)_____ others.

[01~03] 다음 글을 읽고 물음에 답하시오.

Brian: The election is coming up. ⓐWhy don't you run for class representative, Yumi?

Yumi: No way. I'm not the right person for ⓑ that position. I've never thought about running.

Brian: Why not?

Yumi: Come on, Brian. Leaders have special qualities. I don't think a person like me can be called a leader.

Brian: What do you mean? I think you have very good leadership qualities. You're really friendly and outgoing. You also help people get along. I have no doubt that you will be elected if you run.

01 위 글의 밑줄 친 ⓐ를 다음과 같이 바꿔 쓸 때 빈칸에 들어갈 알맞은 말을 두 단어로 쓰시오.

➡ _____ _____ running for class representative, Yumi?

02 위 글의 밑줄 친 ⓑthat position이 가리키는 것을 본문에서 찾아 쓰시오.

➡ _____

03 본문의 내용과 일치하도록 다음 빈칸 (A)와 (B)에 알맞은 단어를 쓰시오.

> Yumi says that leaders have (A)_____ _____ and that she is not a suitable person for (B)_____ _____.

[04~06] 다음 글을 읽고 물음에 답하시오.

Here's what I found!

ORANGE LEADERS: "Strict Directors"
- Make everyone's role (A)[clear / clearly]
- Make sure everything is finished on time
- Ensure each step is done (B)[proper / properly]

YELLOW LEADERS: "Quiet Supporters"
- Lead by example
- Let the team members shine instead
- Meet the team members' needs

BLUE LEADERS: "Creative Thinkers"
- (C)[Approach / Approach to] problems in new ways
- Come up with fresh ideas
- Deal with tasks differently from others

04 위 글의 괄호 (A)~(C)에서 문맥이나 어법상 알맞은 낱말을 골라 쓰시오.

➡ (A) _____ (B) _____ (C) _____

05 다음 빈칸 (A)~(C)에 알맞은 단어를 넣어 주황색 리더들의 특징을 완성하시오.

> Orange leaders are "(A)_____ _____" who make everyone's role clear, make sure everything is finished (B)_____ _____, and ensure each step is done (C)_____.

06 다음 '노란색 리더들'의 특징에 대한 설명 중, 위 글의 내용과 다른 부분을 찾아서 고치시오.

> They are creative thinkers who lead by example, let the team members shine instead, and meet the team members' needs.

_____ ➡ _____

[07~09] 다음 글을 읽고 물음에 답하시오.

Brian told me this afternoon that I have good leadership qualities. No one has ever told me that before. Why does he think so? Maybe he was just trying to be nice. When he said that to me, however, I started to think. Can I really become a leader? I don't know. I think leaders should have a vision, clear goals, and the ability to motivate others. ⓐI don't have any of those things.

ⓑThen I suddenly started to wonder that these are the only qualities that make a good leader. Maybe I'm wrong. Maybe there are other leadership qualities. So I decided to do some research online.   <I: Yumi>

07 위 글의 밑줄 친 ⓐ를 다음과 같이 바꿔 쓸 때 빈칸에 들어갈 알맞은 단어를 쓰시오.

➡ I have _____ of those things.

08 위 글의 밑줄 친 ⓑ에서 어법상 틀린 부분을 찾아 고치시오.

_____ ➡ _____

09 What qualities does Yumi think leaders should have? Answer in English in a full sentence.

➡ _____

_____

[10~12] 다음 글을 읽고 물음에 답하시오.

I was surprised that there are actually many different leadership styles, but soon I realized the reason.

We belong to many different groups, and many different situations can come up in our lives. They all call for different leadership styles. ⓐ각 집단의 독특한 상황이 최고의 지도력 유형을 결정한다.

"I am a part of many different groups, and I have different responsibilities in each group."

After reading everything, I became more confident. I discovered that I have some of the qualities of a "green leader." If my classmates think a green leader would make our class better, they might pick me to be class representative! Okay, let's try it!   <I: Yumi>

10 위 글의 밑줄 친 ⓐ의 우리말에 맞게 주어진 어휘를 이용하여 9 단어로 영작하시오.

each, unique situation, determines, style

➡ _____

_____

11 After reading everything, what did Yumi discover about her leadership style? Fill in the blanks with suitable words.

She discovered that she has some of the qualities of a "_____ _____."

12 주어진 영영풀이에 해당하는 단어를 본문에서 찾아 쓰시오.

a person who has been chosen to act or make decisions on behalf of another person or a group of people

➡ _____

Presentation Time Step 3

Our group chose tasks to prepare for our class birthday party. I will buy a
<u>부정사의 형용사적 용법(tasks 수식) (부사적 용법으로 볼 수도 있음.)</u>

cake. Woojin and Taeho will decorate the classroom. Yeji will play birthday

party songs. I have no doubt that our birthday party will be a lot of fun!
접속사(동격의 명사절을 이끔)   = much

구문해설 ・ **prepare**: 준비하다[시키다] ・ **decorate**: 장식하다, 꾸미다
・ **doubt**: 의심, 의혹; 의심하다, 의문[의혹]을 갖다, 확신하지 못하다
・ **make[have] no doubt of[that]**: ～을 확신하다, 틀림없이 ～하다

해석

우리 모둠은 우리 학급 생일 파티를 준비하기 위한 과제를 선정했다. 나는 케이크를 살 것이다. 우진이와 태호는 교실을 장식할 것이다. 예지는 생일 파티 노래를 연주할 것이다. 나는 우리의 생일 파티가 아주 재미있을 것이라고 확신한다.

After You Read B

1. Hi, I'm Jennifer. I try to lead by example and take care of others' needs. The
                                                              = care for
   important thing is that the members of my team shine.
                          보어를 이끄는 접속사
2. Hello, I'm Heejin. I enjoy approaching problems in new ways. I try my best
                               to approach(×)
   to come up with new ideas.
   to부정사의 부사적 용법(목적)
3. Hi, I'm Chris. I analyze my team's problems and situations, and then I

   look for the most effective ways to achieve our goals.
   ～을 찾다   to부정사의 형용사적 용법

구문해설 ・ **take care of**: 돌보다 ・ **shine**: 빛나다 ・ **approach**: 접근하다 ・ **come up with**: 생각해 내다
・ **analyze**: 분석하다 ・ **effective**: 효과적인 ・ **achieve**: 성취하다

1. 안녕, 나는 Jennifer야. 나는 솔선수범하며 다른 사람들의 요구를 해결하려고 노력해. 중요한 것은 우리 팀 구성원들이 빛나는 거야.

2. 안녕, 나는 희진이야. 나는 문제에 새로운 방법으로 접근하는 것이 즐거워. 나는 최선을 다해서 새로운 아이디어를 제시해.

3. 안녕, 나는 Chris야. 나는 우리 팀의 문제점과 상황을 분석해. 그런 다음 우리의 목표를 달성하기 위한 가장 효과적인 방법들을 찾아.

Do it Yourself B

Brian: Why don't you run for class representative, Yumi?
          ～하는 게 어때? = How about ～? = What about ～?

Yumi: No way. I've never thought about running.
                   have p.p.: 현재완료

Brian: Why not?

Yumi: Leaders have special qualities. I don't think a person like me can be
                                                              = ～처럼(전치사)
   called a leader.

Brian: What do you mean? You're really friendly and outgoing. You also help

   people get along. I have no doubt that you will be elected if you run.
   = 어울리다

구문해설 ・ **representative**: 대표 ・ **run**: 입후보하다 ・ **quality**: 자질 ・ **outgoing**: 외향적인

Brian: 유미야, 반 대표에 입후보하는 게 어때?

Yumi: 아니. 나는 입후보하는 것에 대해 생각해 본 적이 없어.

Brian: 왜?

Yumi: 리더들은 특별한 자질을 갖추고 있어. 나 같은 사람이 리더로 불릴 수 있다고 생각하지 않아.

Brian: 무슨 말이야? 너는 정말 친절하고 외향적이잖아. 또 너는 사람들이 어울리도록 도와주기도 해. 만약 네가 입후보한다면 당선될 거라고 믿어 의심치 않아.

01 다음 짝지어진 단어의 관계가 같도록 빈칸에 알맞은 말을 쓰시오.

> understanding : misunderstanding
> = logical : _____

02 다음 영영풀이가 가리키는 것을 고르시오.

> to come close to someone or something

① edit
② discover
③ realize
④ return
⑤ approach

03 다음 중 밑줄 친 부분의 뜻풀이가 바르지 않은 것은?

① After many attempts, he finally won the election. (선거)
② Jennie will run for student president. (입후보하다)
③ Jason is a representative of our science club. (대표자)
④ We should focus on the supporters' qualities. (자질)
⑤ She's a really bright and outgoing person. (밖으로)

04 다음 우리말에 맞게 빈칸에 알맞은 말을 쓰시오.

(1) 나는 그림 그리기를 담당한다.
➡ I'm _____ drawing pictures.
(2) 그들은 나의 좋은 친구들이기 때문에 편을 들 수 없다.
➡ I can't _____ because they are my good friends.

(3) Emma는 영화 편집을 잘한다.
➡ Emma _____ editing the movies.

05 다음 우리말을 주어진 단어를 이용하여 영작하시오.

(1) 그녀와 나는 다른 그룹에 속한다. (belong, different)
➡ _____

(2) 이 작업은 높은 수준의 지식을 요구한다. (work, call)
➡ _____

(3) 나는 그들의 필요를 충족시켜 주기 위해 최선을 다했다. (try, meet)
➡ _____

06 다음 짝지어진 대화가 어색한 것은?

① A: I think we're ready.
B: Good. I have no doubt that our project will turn out well.
② A: What do you want to do for our class?
B: I want to take photos of our classmates.
③ A: What's the matter with you?
B: I need to prepare for an exam this Thursday, but I also have to go to band practice.
④ A: What's wrong with you?
B: That would help me out so much.
⑤ A: I'm in charge of making the presentation materials.
B: I have no doubt that it will be very helpful for us.

[07~08] 다음 대화를 읽고 물음에 답하시오.

Sujin: What's the matter? You look worried.

Minsu: You know I'm going to be giving a presentation on our team's research. But I feel very nervous when I talk in front of many people.

Sujin: Oh, I didn't know that you got nervous. Actually, I also have a problem.

Minsu: What's wrong?

Sujin: I'm in charge of making the presentation materials, but I'm not good at it.

Minsu: You're not? I thought you were good at (A)it.

Sujin: No, I'm not. Hey, then what about switching roles? I've given presentations many times before, so I don't get nervous at all.

Minsu: Really? That would be great. I think I am good at making presentation materials, and I like making (B)them!

Sujin: That's good. Let's talk to the other team members.

Minsu: Cool. I feel so relieved now.

07 위 대화의 밑줄 친 (A)와 (B)가 가리키는 것을 찾아 각각 쓰시오.

➡ (A) _____

(B) _____

08 위 대화의 내용과 일치하지 <u>않는</u> 것은?

① 민수는 팀의 조사에 대한 발표를 할 예정이었다.

② 민수는 여러 사람들 앞에서 이야기할 때 긴장을 많이 한다.

③ 수진이는 발표 자료를 만드는 일을 맡았다.

④ 수진이는 민수에게 역할을 바꿀 것을 제안했다.

⑤ 민수는 발표 자료 만드는 것을 잘하지 못한다.

[09~11] 다음 대화를 읽고 물음에 답하시오.

Mr. Smith: Junsu, are you okay? What's the matter?

Junsu: Hello, Mr. Smith. I have a problem.

Mr. Smith: What happened?

Junsu: You know Jaewoo, Yunho, and I are best friends, right? They had a fight, and now I'm ⓐstuck in the middle. I don't know what ⓑto do.

Mr. Smith: That sounds hard. Do you know why they had a fight?

Junsu: Yes, but it doesn't sound like a big deal to me. I guess they had some kind of ⓒmisunderstand.

Mr. Smith: Why don't you all meet together and talk about it? I think they'll listen to you.

Junsu: That's a good idea. They're both good friends of ⓓmine. I can't _____ (A) _____.

Mr. Smith: I understand. I hope everything ⓔworks out.

09 위 대화의 빈칸 (A)에 '편을 들다'의 의미를 나타내는 숙어를 두 단어로 쓰시오.

➡ _____

10 위 대화의 밑줄 친 ⓐ~ⓔ 중 어법상 <u>틀린</u> 것을 찾아 바르게 고치시오.

_____ ➡ _____

11 위 대화의 내용과 일치하지 <u>않는</u> 것은?

① 재우, 윤호, 그리고 준수는 서로 가장 친한 사이이다.

② 재우와 윤호가 싸워 준수는 그들 사이에 끼어버린 상태이다.

③ 준수가 보기에 재우와 윤호는 심각한 일로 싸웠다.

④ 준수는 재우와 윤호 사이에 어떤 오해가 생긴 것이라 생각한다.

⑤ Smith 선생님은 준수에게 모두 모여 함께 이야기해 볼 것을 조언한다.

[12~14] 다음 대화를 읽고 물음에 답하시오.

> Nick: Hey, Mandy. What's the matter?
>
> Mandy: I don't know what to do, Nick. My brother asked me to help him with his homework this Wednesday, but I told him I can't. I have so many things to do that day.
>
> Nick: ⓐ What do you have to do this Wednesday?
>
> Mandy: ⓑ I need to go to the library to return some books. Then I have to meet you to work on our presentation. After that, I have to prepare for an exam at night.
>
> Nick: ⓒ Oh, you do have a lot to do.
>
> Mandy: ⓓ Yes. (A)But my brother seemed let down, so I feel bad.
>
> Nick: ⓔ Then you can do everything and also help your brother on Wednesday.
>
> Mandy: That would help me out so much! Thanks for understanding, Nick!

12 위 대화의 ⓐ~ⓔ 중 주어진 문장이 들어가기에 적절한 곳은?

> Well, then how about meeting on Thursday instead for our presentation?

① ⓐ   ② ⓑ   ③ ⓒ   ④ ⓓ   ⑤ ⓔ

13 위 대화의 밑줄 친 (A)로부터 알 수 있는 Mandy의 동생의 기분으로 적절한 것은?

① lonely   ② disappointed   ③ satisfied
④ excited   ⑤ amused

14 위 대화를 읽고 대답할 수 없는 것은?

① What's the problem with Mandy?
② What did Mandy's brother ask her?
③ What does Mandy have to do this Wednesday?
④ Why does Mandy need to go to the library on Wednesday?
⑤ What exam does Mandy have to prepare for?

15 다음 대화의 빈칸에 들어갈 말로 나머지와 의미가 <u>다른</u> 것은?

> G: Sports Day is coming. How do you want to help out?
>
> B: I want to take photos for Sports Day.
>
> G: That's great. You are really good at taking photos. _____

① I have no doubt that you will take some wonderful pictures.
② I'm sure that you will take some wonderful pictures.
③ I bet that you will take some wonderful pictures.
④ I'm certain that you will take some wonderful pictures.
⑤ I doubt that you will take some wonderful pictures.

Grammar

16 다음 빈칸에 알맞은 것은?

> His case _____ into account next week.

① takes   ② be taken   ③ will take
④ will taken   ⑤ will be taken

17 다음을 수동태 문장으로 바꿔 쓸 때 빈칸에 알맞은 말을 쓰시오.

> Anybody who wants the puppy can adopt it.
>
> → The puppy _____ by anybody who wants it.

18 다음 빈칸에 들어갈 말이 나머지와 <u>다른</u> 하나는?

① She was of two minds about _____ to go to the party.

② The man asked _____ he could borrow the woman's calculator.

③ I want to know _____ dogs can understand human emotions.

④ Every now and again she checked to see _____ he was still asleep.

⑤ The market will decide _____ the TV station has any future.

19 다음 ⓐ~ⓕ 중 어법상 옳은 것을 <u>모두</u> 고르시오.

ⓐ I'll check if the president can meet with you now.

ⓑ I'm not sure that you will like the food.

ⓒ I wonder whether we'll have good weather tomorrow.

ⓓ Beauty cannot be measured by any absolute standard.

ⓔ He said the pain of the victims must not forget.

ⓕ The file will be deleted by the police officer.

➡ _____

Reading

[20~21] 다음 대화를 읽고 물음에 답하시오.

Brian: The election is coming up. Why don't you run ⓐ class representative, Yumi?

Yumi: No way. I'm not the right person ⓑ that position. I've never thought about running.

Brian: ⓒUnderline Why not?

Yumi: Come on, Brian. Leaders have special qualities. I don't think a person like me can be called a leader.

Brian: What do you mean? I think you have very good leadership qualities. You're really friendly and outgoing. You also help people get along. I have no doubt that you will be elected if you run.

20 위 대화의 빈칸 ⓐ와 ⓑ에 공통으로 들어갈 알맞은 전치사를 고르시오.

① to   ② for   ③ at
④ about   ⑤ in

21 위 대화의 밑줄 친 ⓒWhy not?에 생략된 말을 넣어 문장을 다시 쓰시오.

➡ _____

[22~24] 다음 글을 읽고 물음에 답하시오.

I was surprised that there are ⓐactually many different leadership styles, but soon I realized the reason.

We belong to many different groups, and many different situations can come up in our lives. ⓑThey all call for different leadership styles. Each group's unique situation determines the best leadership style.

After reading everything, I became more confident. I discovered that I have some of the qualities of a "green leader." ⓒ만약 나의 반 친구들이 녹색 리더가 우리 학급을 더 좋게 만들 거라고 생각한다면, they might pick me to be class representative! Okay, let's try it!

22 위 글의 밑줄 친 ⓐactually와 바꿔 쓸 수 있는 말을 <u>모두</u> 고르시오.

① of course   ② in fact
③ in addition   ④ instead
⑤ as a matter of fact

23 위 글의 밑줄 친 ⓑThey가 가리키는 것을 본문에서 찾아 쓰시오.

➡ _____

24 위 글의 밑줄 친 ⓒ의 우리말에 맞게 주어진 어휘를 알맞게 배열하시오.

> our class / make / think / a green leader / better / my classmates / if / would

➡ _____

_____

[25~27] 다음 글을 읽고 물음에 답하시오.

Here's what I found!
ORANGE LEADERS: "Strict Directors"
• Make everyone's role clear
• Make sure everything is finished on time
• Ensure each step is done properly
YELLOW LEADERS: "Quiet Supporters"
• Lead by example
• Let the team members shine instead
• Meet the team members' needs
BLUE LEADERS: "Creative Thinkers"
• Approach problems in new ways
• Come up with fresh ideas
• ⓐDeal with tasks differently from others

25 위 글의 밑줄 친 ⓐDeal with와 바꿔 쓸 수 있는 말을 <u>모두</u> 고르시오.

① Treat   ② Attend to   ③ Carry
④ Handle   ⑤ Deal in

26 What is Chris's leadership style? Fill in the blank with a suitable word.

> Hi, I'm Chris. I try to lead by example and care for others' needs. The important thing is that the members of my team shine.

➡ Chris's leadership style is _____ leader.

27 According to the passage, which is NOT true?

① Orange leaders make everyone's role clear.
② Orange leaders are 'Strict Directors' who ensure everything is finished on time.
③ Yellow leaders are 'Quiet Supporters' who satisfy the team members' needs.
④ Blue leaders approach problems in the same ways.
⑤ Blue leaders are 'Creative Thinkers' who handle tasks differently from others.

[28~29] 다음 글을 읽고 물음에 답하시오.

> **Yuna: A Wonderful Leader**
> I think my partner Yuna is a yellow leader because ⓐshe leads the group by example. I noticed it last Friday when we were cleaning the classroom. No one wanted to separate the recycling, but Yuna came over and separated it ⓑherself. I was impressed, so I started helping her. I think she is a wonderful leader.

28 위 글의 밑줄 친 ⓐ의 예를 본문에서 찾아 우리말로 쓰시오.

➡ _____

_____

29 위 글의 밑줄 친 ⓑherself와 문법적 쓰임이 같은 것을 고르시오.

① She absented <u>herself</u> from school.
② I went there by <u>myself</u>.
③ I <u>myself</u> did it.
④ She finished the work for <u>herself</u>.
⑤ He talked to <u>himself</u>.

출제율 90%

01 다음 문장의 빈칸에 들어갈 말을 〈보기〉에서 골라 올바른 형태로 쓰시오.

┌─── 보기 ───┐
approach / confident / determine / wonder / properly
└──────────┘

(1) This machine works _____ with solar power.

(2) The referee was _____ the player.

(3) I _____ who the Nobel Prize winner is.

(4) What _____ the price of service in a market?

(5) Be _____ in your potential.

출제율 95%

02 다음 대화가 자연스럽게 이어지도록 순서대로 배열하시오.

> Sejin: I'm so excited about our museum field trip.
> (A) Okay. Sejin, are you going to do some research on the museum?
> (B) That's right. I think we're ready.
> (C) I'm in charge of taking pictures.
> (D) Yes, I am. Are you going to write our field trip report, Emma?
> (E) Me too. Let's check our tasks. Yen, what are you in charge of?

➡ _____

[03~05] 다음 대화를 읽고 물음에 답하시오.

> Sujin: What's the matter? You look worried.
> Minsu: ⓐ You know I'm going to be giving a presentation on our team's research. But I feel very nervous when I talk in front of many people.

> Sujin: ⓑ Oh, I didn't know that you got nervous. Actually, I also have a problem.
> Minsu: ⓒ What's wrong?
> Sujin: I'm in charge of making the presentation materials, but I'm not good at it.
> Minsu: You're not? I thought you were good at it.
> Sujin: ⓓ No, I'm not. Hey, then what about switching roles? I've given presentations many times before, so I don't get nervous at all.
> Minsu: ⓔ I think I am good at making presentation materials, and I like making them!
> Sujin: That's good. Let's talk to the other team members.
> Minsu: Cool. I feel so ___(A)___ now.

출제율 95%

03 위 대화의 ⓐ~ⓔ 중 주어진 문장이 들어가기에 적절한 곳은?

> Really? That would be great.

① ⓐ   ② ⓑ   ③ ⓒ   ④ ⓓ   ⑤ ⓔ

출제율 90%

04 위 대화의 빈칸 (A)에 들어갈 말로 적절한 것은?

① relieved   ② worried   ③ nervous
④ disappointed   ⑤ upset

출제율 100%

05 위 대화를 읽고 대답할 수 없는 것은?

① What's wrong with Minsu?
② What is Minsu in charge of?
③ What isn't Sujin good at?
④ What is Sujin's suggestion?
⑤ How many times has Sujin given presentations?

B: In the Send Our Stories project, we are going to make a picture book for children in other countries. ⓐ Each group will be (A)[responded / responsible] for a different task. ⓑ Group A will (B)[translate / transfer] a Korean story into English. ⓒ Group B will make drawings for the book and edit it. ⓓ After copies of the book are printed, Group C will be in charge of sending them to the children. ⓔ It won't be easy, but I have no doubt that the children who (C)[send / receive] these books will really enjoy them.

출제율 100%

06 위 글의 ⓐ~ⓔ 중 주어진 문장이 들어가기에 적절한 곳은?

We've divided everyone into three groups.

① ⓐ ② ⓑ ③ ⓒ ④ ⓓ ⑤ ⓔ

출제율 90%

07 위 글의 (A)~(C)에 들어갈 말이 바르게 짝지어진 것은?

	(A)	(B)	(C)
①	responded	translate	send
②	responded	transfer	receive
③	responsible	translate	receive
④	responsible	transfer	send
⑤	responsible	translate	send

[08~10] 다음 대화를 읽고 물음에 답하시오.

Nick: Hey, Mandy. What's the matter?

Mandy: I don't know what to do, Nick. My brother asked me to help him with his homework this Wednesday, but I told him I can't. I have so many things to do that day.

Nick: What do you have to do this Wednesday?

Mandy: I need to go to the library to return some books. Then I have to meet you to work on our presentation. After that, I have to prepare for an exam at night.

Nick: Oh, you do have a lot to do.

Mandy: Yes. But my brother seemed let down, so I feel bad.

Nick: Well, then how about meeting on Thursday instead for our presentation? Then you can do everything and also help your brother on Wednesday.

Mandy: That would help me out so much! Thanks for understanding, Nick!

출제율 95%

08 What did Mandy's brother ask her to do this Wednesday?

➡ _____

출제율 90%

09 What was Mandy supposed to do after going to the library this Wednesday?

➡ _____

_____

출제율 90%

10 What did Nick suggest for their presentation?

➡ _____

_____

출제율 95%

11 다음 빈칸에 알맞은 말이 순서대로 짝지어진 것은?

- Before you leave, you should check _____ you turned off the light.
- These books must _____ by next Tuesday.

① that – returned ② if – return
③ if – be returned ④ whether – returning
⑤ whether – have returned

12 다음 중 어법상 올바른 문장은? _{출제율 95%}

① They will check that stores in school zones sell unhealthy food to children.

② I was anxious about if I failed the exam or not.

③ Try this product for a week and decide if or not you want to buy it.

④ The judge is going to decide if he is guilty or not.

⑤ I wonder that you are going to attend the meeting.

13 수동태로 바꾼 문장 중 틀린 것은? _{출제율 95%}

① They might pick me to be class representative.
→ I might be picked to be class representative by them.

② We will belong to many different groups.
→ Many different groups will be belonged by us.

③ The girl must wear a black skirt with white spots.
→ A black skirt with white spots must be worn by the girl.

④ They will fix the elevator this afternoon.
→ The elevator will be fixed this afternoon.

⑤ You can order the lunch special only from 11 a.m. to 1 p.m.
→ The lunch special can be ordered only from 11 a.m. to 1 p.m.

[14~15] 다음 글을 읽고 물음에 답하시오.

Brian told me this afternoon that I have good leadership qualities. No one has ever told me that before. Why does he think so? Maybe he was just trying to be nice. When he said that to me, however, I started to think. Can I really become a leader? I don't know. I think leaders should have a vision, clear goals, and the ability to motivate others. ⓐ나는 그러한 것들 중 어느 것도 가지고 있지 않다.

Then I suddenly started to wonder if these are the only qualities that make a good leader. Maybe I'm wrong. Maybe there are other leadership qualities. So I decided to do some research online.   <I: Yumi>

14 위 글의 밑줄 친 ⓐ의 우리말에 맞게 7 단어로 영작하시오. _{출제율 90%}

➡ _____

15 According to the passage, which is NOT true? _{출제율 100%}

① This afternoon, Brian told Yumi that she has good leadership qualities.

② Brian was the first person that told Yumi that she has good leadership qualities.

③ Yumi thinks she can't become a leader.

④ Yumi thinks that there may be other leadership qualities.

⑤ Yumi decided to do some research on leadership qualities online.

[16~18] 다음 글을 읽고 물음에 답하시오.

Here's what I found!
ORANGE LEADERS: "Strict Directors"
• Make everyone's role clear
• Make sure everything is finished on time
• Ensure each step is done properly

YELLOW LEADERS: "Quiet Supporters"
• Lead by example
• Let the team members shine instead
• ⓐMeet the team members' needs
BLUE LEADERS: "Creative Thinkers"
• Approach problems in new ways
• Come up with fresh ideas
• Deal with tasks differently from others

16 위 글의 밑줄 친 ⓐMeet와 같은 의미로 쓰인 것을 고르시오.

① Maybe we'll <u>meet</u> again some time.
② Where does this road <u>meet</u> the highway?
③ Others didn't <u>meet</u> similar problems.
④ I will <u>meet</u> your wishes.
⑤ Did you <u>meet</u> anyone in town?

17 What is Jennifer's leadership style? Fill in the blank with a suitable word.

> Hello, I'm Jennifer. I try my best to think of new ideas and I treat tasks in a different way from others.

➡ Jennifer's leadership style is _____ leader.

18 위 글을 읽고 답할 수 <u>없는</u> 질문을 고르시오.

① How do orange leaders make everyone's role clear?
② What can we call the leaders who make sure that each step is done properly?
③ Do yellow leaders lead by example?
④ What is another name for blue leaders?
⑤ How do blue leaders approach problems?

[19~21] 다음 글을 읽고 물음에 답하시오.

I was surprised that there are actually many different leadership styles, but soon I realized the reason. (①)
We belong to many different groups, and many different situations can come up in our lives. (②) Each group's unique situation determines the best leadership style. (③)
After reading everything, I became more confident. (④) I discovered that I have some of the qualities of a "green leader." (⑤) If my classmates think a green leader would make our class better, they might pick me to be class representative! Okay, let's try it! <I: Yumi>

19 위 글의 흐름으로 보아, 주어진 문장이 들어가기에 가장 적절한 곳은?

> They all call for different leadership styles.

①　　②　　③　　④　　⑤

20 위 글의 주제로 알맞은 것을 고르시오.

① There are many different leadership styles.
② We belong to many different groups.
③ Many different situations can come up in our lives.
④ The unique situation of each group determines the best leadership style.
⑤ Yumi has some of the qualities of a "green leader."

21 Why was Yumi surprised? Answer in English beginning with "Because".

➡ _____

_____

[01~03] 다음 대화를 읽고 물음에 답하시오.

> **Mr. Smith:** Junsu, are you okay? What's the matter?
>
> **Junsu:** Hello, Mr. Smith. I have a problem.
>
> **Mr. Smith:** What happened?
>
> **Junsu:** You know Jaewoo, Yunho, and I are best friends, right? They had a fight, and now I'm stuck in the middle. I don't know what to do.
>
> **Mr. Smith:** That sounds hard. Do you know why they had a fight?
>
> **Junsu:** Yes, but it doesn't sound like a big deal to me. I guess they had some kind of misunderstanding.
>
> **Mr. Smith:** Why don't you all meet together and talk about it? I think they'll listen to you.
>
> **Junsu:** That's a good idea. They're both good friends of mine. I can't take sides.
>
> **Mr. Smith:** I understand. I hope everything works out.

01 Why did Jaewoo and Yunho have a fight?

➡ _____

02 What does Mr. Smith recommend Junsu to do?

➡ _____
_____

03 Why can't Junsu take sides?

➡ _____
_____

04 다음 문장을 수동태는 능동태로, 능동태는 수동태로 바꾸어 쓰시오.

(1) People must make reservations through the online system.

➡ _____
_____

(2) They can use this item in a variety of ways.

➡ _____
_____

(3) Who can make the most beautiful clothes for me?

➡ _____
_____

(4) Some diseases cannot be cured by medicine.

➡ _____
_____

(5) They can be seen only by wise people.

➡ _____
_____

05 if를 이용하여 다음 두 문장을 한 문장으로 바꿔 쓰시오.

(1) • Before you leave, you should check.
    • Did you turn off the tap?

➡ _____
_____

(2) • My mom asked me.
    • Will you have dinner?

➡ _____
_____

(3) • I don't know.
    • Is he strong?

➡ _____
_____

06 다음 문장에서 어법상 틀린 부분을 찾아 바르게 고쳐 다시 쓰시오.

> I want to know if or not I will get taller.

➡ _____

_____

[07~09] 다음 대화를 읽고 물음에 답하시오.

> Brian: The election is coming up. Why don't you run for class representative, Yumi?
>
> Yumi: _____ⓐ_____ I'm not the right person for that position. I've never thought about running.
>
> Brian: Why not?
>
> Yumi: Come on, Brian. Leaders have special qualities. ⓑ나 같은 사람이 리더로 불릴 수 있다고 생각하지 않아.
>
> Brian: What do you mean? I think you have very good leadership qualities. You're really friendly and outgoing. You also help people get along. I have no doubt that you will be elected if you run.

07 위 대화의 빈칸 ⓐ에 주어진 영영풀이에 해당하는 어구를 두 단어로 쓰시오.

> definitely not, never

➡ _____

08 위 대화의 밑줄 친 ⓑ의 우리말에 맞게 주어진 어휘를 알맞게 배열하시오.

> a leader / like / called / I / be / a person / don't / me / can / think

➡ _____

_____

09 위 대화의 내용과 일치하도록 다음 빈칸 (A)와 (B)에 알맞은 단어를 쓰시오.

> Brian is sure that Yumi will (A)_____ _____ if she runs for class representative because he thinks Yumi has very good (B)_____ _____.

[10~11] 다음 글을 읽고 물음에 답하시오.

> Here's what I found!
> **GREEN LEADERS:** "Team Builders"
> • Ensure that the team feels valued
> • Create a positive environment
> • Are friendly and easy to talk to
> **RED LEADERS:** "Logical Analysts"
> • Have good reasoning skills
> • Analyze problems and situations
> • Think of the most effective ways to achieve the team's goals
> **PURPLE LEADERS:** "Hands-Off Managers"
> • Allow others to work on their own
> • Do not try to control people
> • Give advice only when ⓐit is needed

10 위 글의 밑줄 친 ⓐit이 가리키는 것을 본문에서 찾아 쓰시오.

➡ _____

11 What do we call the leaders who let others work on their own? Fill in the blanks with suitable words.

> They are _____ _____.

➡ _____ 또는 _____

01 다음 대화의 내용과 일치하도록 준수의 일기를 완성하시오.

> Mr. Smith: Junsu, are you okay? What's the matter?
>
> Junsu: Hello, Mr. Smith. I have a problem.
>
> Mr. Smith: What happened?
>
> Junsu: You know Jaewoo, Yunho, and I are best friends, right? They had a fight, and now I'm stuck in the middle. I don't know what to do.
>
> Mr. Smith: That sounds hard. Do you know why they had a fight?
>
> Junsu: Yes, but it doesn't sound like a big deal to me. I guess they had some kind of misunderstanding.
>
> Mr. Smith: Why don't you all meet together and talk about it? I think they'll listen to you.
>
> Junsu: That's a good idea. They're both good friends of mine. I can't take sides.
>
> Mr. Smith: I understand. I hope everything works out.

> Today I was worried about Jaewoo and Yunho. They had a fight, so I was (A)_____ in the middle. I didn't know (B)_____, so I talked about it with Mr. Smith. I knew the reason why they had a fight. It didn't sound like a big deal to me, but I guessed (C)_____. After listening to me, Mr. Smith advised me to (D)_____. I agreed with him, so I decided to do so soon. Because (E)_____, I couldn't take sides. I hope everything works out soon.

02 다음 그림을 보고, 괄호 안에 주어진 어휘를 배열하여 능동태의 문장을 쓰고 그것을 수동태의 문장으로 바꿔 쓰시오.

(the boxes / they / be / unpacking / will)

(1) _____ (능동태)

(2) _____ (수동태)

단원별 모의고사

01 다음 짝지어진 단어의 관계가 같도록 빈칸에 알맞은 말을 쓰시오.

> wide : narrow = negative : _____

02 다음 영영풀이가 가리키는 것을 고르시오.

> to deeply study every piece of something to understand it

① analyze   ② translate   ③ return

④ prepare   ⑤ motivate

03 다음 우리말에 맞게 주어진 단어를 사용하여 영작하시오.

(1) 학생들을 향한 그의 메시지는 매우 명확했다. (clear, very)

➡ _____

(2) 나의 목표는 그저 경주를 마치는 것이다. (just, to)

➡ _____

(3) 선생님은 우리에게 동기를 부여하기 위해 어떤 이야기를 해주셨다. (told, us)

➡ _____

[04~06] 다음 대화를 읽고 물음에 답하시오.

Jisu: (A) Mom, we've got a problem.

Mom: (B) What's the matter?

Jisu: (C) We're going to have dinner with Grandma this Saturday, right? But I just realized that Sujin's birthday party is on Saturday evening. She's my best friend. What should I do?

Mom: (D) Let's talk about it with your dad.

Jisu: (E) Okay, Mom. I'd love to see Grandma, but I don't want to miss my best friend's birthday party.

04 위 대화의 (A)~(E) 중 주어진 문장이 들어가기에 적절한 곳은?

> That sounds like a difficult decision.

① (A)   ② (B)   ③ (C)   ④ (D)   ⑤ (E)

05 What doesn't Jisu want to miss?

➡ _____
_____

06 What does Jisu's mom advise her to do?

➡ _____

[07~09] 다음 대화를 읽고 물음에 답하시오.

Mr. Smith: Junsu, are you okay? What's the matter?

Junsu: Hello, Mr. Smith. I have a problem.

Mr. Smith: What happened?

Junsu: You know Jaewoo, Yunho, and I are best friends, right? They had a fight, and now (a)저는 중간에 끼어버린 상태예요. I don't know what to do.

Mr. Smith: That sounds hard. Do you know why they had a fight?

Junsu: Yes, but it doesn't sound like a big deal to me. I guess they had some kind of misunderstanding.

Mr. Smith: _____ (A) _____ I think they'll listen to you.

Junsu: That's a good idea. They're both good friends of mine. I can't take sides.

Mr. Smith: I understand. I hope everything works out.

07 위 대화의 빈칸 (A)에 들어갈 말로 적절하지 <u>않은</u> 것은?

① How about meeting all together and talking about it?

② Why don't you all meet together and talk about it?

③ I think you all should meet together and talk about it.

④ I advise you all to meet together and talk about it.

⑤ I doubt if you all should meet together and talk about it.

08 위 대화의 밑줄 친 (a)의 우리말을 5 단어를 사용하여 영작하시오.

➡ _____

09 위 대화에서 나타난 준수의 심경 변화로 적절한 것은?

① excited → confused

② worried → relieved

③ lonely → worried

④ relaxed → horrified

⑤ relieved → excited

[10~12] 다음 대화를 읽고 물음에 답하시오.

> Nick: Hey, Mandy. (A)<u>What's the matter?</u>
>
> Mandy: I don't know what to do, Nick. My brother asked me to help him with his homework this Wednesday, but I told him I can't. I have so many things to do that day.
>
> Nick: What do you have to do this Wednesday?
>
> Mandy: I need to go to the library to return some books. Then I have to meet you to work on our presentation. After that, I have to prepare for an exam at night.

> Nick: Oh, you do have a lot to do.
>
> Mandy: Yes. But (B)<u>내 동생이 실망한 것처럼 보였어</u>(seem, let), so I feel bad.
>
> Nick: Well, then how about meeting on Thursday instead for our presentation? Then you can do everything and also help your brother on Wednesday.
>
> Mandy: That would help me out so much! Thanks for understanding, Nick!

10 위 대화의 밑줄 친 (A)와 바꾸어 쓰기가 <u>어색한</u> 것은?

① Is there something bothering you?

② Is something worrying you?

③ What are you worried about?

④ What's wrong?

⑤ How do you like the matter?

11 위 대화의 밑줄 친 우리말 (B)를 주어진 단어를 활용하여 영작하시오.

➡ _____

12 위 대화의 내용과 일치하지 <u>않는</u> 것은?

① Mandy의 남동생이 이번 주 수요일에 그의 숙제를 도와 달라고 했다.

② Mandy는 수요일에 책을 반납하러 도서관에 가야 한다.

③ Mandy는 수요일 밤에 시험 준비를 해야 한다.

④ Mandy와 Nick은 함께 발표 준비를 할 예정이다.

⑤ Mandy는 남동생의 숙제를 목요일에 도와줄 예정이다.

13 다음 중 어법상 올바른 문장을 <u>모두</u> 고르시오.

① I want to know that there are ghosts in the world.

② I doubt whether the new computer will be any better.

③ Some friends have asked me if or not I'd write a novel.

④ Membership fees should be pay to the secretary.

⑤ The boy group's title song will be released tonight.

14 다음 중 어법상 어색한 것을 고르시오.

① He wants to know if the meeting is canceled.

② Before you leave, you should check if you cleaned the living room.

③ Jack may know if or not Andy will come to the meeting.

④ The teacher tried to check whether his students understood the question.

⑤ Your body temperature can differ by two or three degrees, depending on whether you wear a tie.

15 다음 밑줄 친 부분 중 어법상 어색한 것은?

① They announced that the flight <u>would be delayed</u>.

② The button <u>should be pushed</u> right now.

③ Girls <u>will be allowed</u> to wear shorts and pants starting this year.

④ Everything <u>can't be had</u> only by you.

⑤ This artwork <u>may not be touched</u>.

16 다음 우리말을 괄호 안에 주어진 어휘를 이용하여 영작하시오.

(1) 너는 화요일까지 그 일을 해야만 한다. (the job, by Tuesday, must, do, 9 단어)

➡ _____

(2) 이 책은 모든 사람이 읽어야 한다. (this book, should, everyone, 7 단어)

➡ _____

(3) 나는 네가 입후보하면 당선될 것이라고 믿어 의심치 않는다. (I, doubt, elect, run, will, have, that, no, if, 12 단어)

➡ _____

_____

(4) 나는 우리가 이 쿠폰을 쓸 수 있는지 잘 모르겠다. (sure, can, this coupon, if, 9 단어)

➡ _____

_____

(5) 당신은 그 기계가 작동하는지 어떻게 알 수 있나요? (the machine, tell, work, whether, how, 9 단어)

➡ _____

_____

(6) 그 소년은 그 괴물이 살았는지 죽었는지 확인하고 싶었다. (alive or dead, the boy, the monster, want, check, if, 12 단어)

➡ _____

_____

17 다음 중 어법상 올바르지 <u>않은</u> 것을 <u>모두</u> 고르시오.

① I suddenly started to wonder if these are the only qualities that make a good leader.

② I wonder if you've seen my backpack.

③ You should check if or not you locked the door.

④ Beth wants to know if the problem can solve.

⑤ I was wondering if this cake can be sent to my house.

[18~19] 다음 글을 읽고 물음에 답하시오.

Brian told me this afternoon that I have good leadership qualities. No one has ever told me ⓐthat before. Why does he think ⓑso? Maybe he was just trying to be nice. When he said ⓒthat to me, however, I started to think. Can I really become a leader? I don't know. I think leaders should have a vision, clear goals, and the ability to motivate others. I don't have any of ⓓthose things.

Then I suddenly started to wonder if ⓔthese are the only qualities (A)that make a good leader. Maybe I'm wrong. Maybe there are ⓕother leadership qualities. So I decided to do some research online. <I: Yumi>

18 위 글의 밑줄 친 ⓐ~ⓕ 중에서 가리키는 것이 서로 다른 것을 고르시오.

① ⓐ – ⓑ   ② ⓐ – ⓒ   ③ ⓑ – ⓒ
④ ⓓ – ⓔ   ⑤ ⓔ – ⓕ

19 위 글의 밑줄 친 (A)that과 문법적 쓰임이 다른 것을 고르시오.

① It's the best novel that I've ever read.
② The watch that you gave me keeps perfect time.
③ The people that I spoke to were very helpful.
④ The rumor that the actress was married wasn't right.
⑤ Where's the book that you bought yesterday?

[20~23] 다음 글을 읽고 물음에 답하시오.

Here's what I found!
GREEN LEADERS: "Team Builders"
• Ensure that the team feels valued

• Create a positive environment
• Are friendly and easy to talk to
RED LEADERS: "Logical Analysts"
• Have good reasoning skills
• Analyze problems and situations
• Think of the most effective ways (A)to achieve the team's goals
PURPLE LEADERS: "Hands-Off Managers"
• Allow others to work on their own
• Do not try to control people
• Give advice only when it ___ⓐ___

20 위 글의 빈칸 ⓐ에 need를 알맞은 형태로 쓰시오.

➡ _____

21 위 글의 밑줄 친 (A)to achieve와 to부정사의 용법이 같은 것을 고르시오.

① You must work hard to achieve the team's goals.
② He is the only person to achieve the team's goals.
③ Is it difficult to achieve the team's goals?
④ Teamwork is needed to achieve the team's goals.
⑤ I don't know how to achieve the team's goals.

22 다음 빈칸 (A)~(C)에 알맞은 단어를 넣어 '녹색 리더들'의 특징을 완성하시오.

Green leaders are "(A)_____ _____" who make sure that the team feels valued, create a (B)_____ _____, and are (C)_____ and easy to talk to.

23 다음 '빨간색 리더들'의 특징에 대한 설명 중, 위 글의 내용과 <u>다른</u> 부분을 찾아서 고치시오.

> They are logical analysts who have good reasoning skills and think of the most impressive ways to achieve the team's goals.

_____ ➡ _____

[24~25] 다음 글을 읽고 물음에 답하시오.

I was surprised that there are actually many different leadership styles, but soon I realized the reason.

We belong ___ⓐ___ many different groups, and many different situations can come up in our lives. They all call ___ⓑ___ different leadership styles. Each group's unique situation determines the best leadership style.

"I am a part of many different groups, and I have different responsibilities in each group."

After reading everything, I became more confident. I discovered that I have some of the qualities of a "green leader." If my classmates think a green leader would make our class better, they might pick me to be class representative! Okay, let's try it! <I: Yumi>

24 위 글의 빈칸 ⓐ와 ⓑ에 들어갈 전치사가 바르게 짝지어진 것은?

ⓐ ⓑ	ⓐ ⓑ
① to – for	② in – on
③ to – on	④ in – to
⑤ on – for	

25 According to the passage, which is NOT true?

① Yumi was surprised that there are actually many different leadership styles.

② Yumi couldn't realize the reason why there are actually many different leadership styles.

③ Lots of different situations can come up in our lives.

④ The best leadership style is determined by each group's unique situation.

⑤ After Yumi read everything, she became more confident.

[26~27] 다음 글을 읽고 물음에 답하시오.

Sumin: A Wonderful Leader

I think my partner Sumin is an orange leader because ⓐ<u>he gave the other classmates clear roles</u>. I noticed ⓑ<u>it</u> last Wednesday when we were all enjoying our school sports day. After the event was over, no one knew what to do to clean up, but Sumin gave each of us a different cleaning task after the event. I was grateful, so I started to pick up the trash around us. I think Sumin is a wonderful leader.

26 위 글의 밑줄 친 ⓐ의 예를 본문에서 찾아 쓰시오.

➡ _____

_____

27 위 글의 밑줄 친 ⓑit이 가리키는 것을 본문에서 찾아 쓰시오.

➡ _____

MEMO

Environmental Innovations

🎙 의사소통 기능

- 의견 표현하기

  In my opinion, taking care of the environment starts with the little things.

- 희망 · 기대 표현하기

  I can't wait to see it!

🎙 언어 형식

- to부정사의 의미상 주어

  It is important **for us** to find ways to protect the environment.

- 관계부사

  Cancun is a city **where** 4.8 million tourists travel every year.

Words & Expressions

Key Words

- **additional** [ədíʃənl] 휑 추가적인
- **architect** [áːrkətèkt] 명 건축가
- **architecture** [áːrkitèktʃər] 명 건축(술)
- **artwork** [ártwərk] 명 (예술적) 작품
- **attract** [ətrǽkt] 동 끌다, 매혹시키다
- **awareness** [əwɛ́ərnis] 명 인식, 의식
- **bright** [brait] 휑 영리한, 똑똑한
- **chemical** [kémikəl] 명 화학물질
- **climate** [kláimit] 명 기후
- **company** [kʌ́mpəni] 명 회사
- **contain** [kəntéin] 동 포함하다
- **creative** [kriéitiv] 휑 창의적인
- **damage** [dǽmidʒ] 동 손상시키다
- **design** [dizáin] 동 설계하다
- **direct** [dirékt] 휑 직접적인, 직행의
- **disappear** [dìsəpíər] 동 사라지다
- **eco-friendly** [ékoufréndli] 휑 친환경적인
- **encourage** [inkɔ́ːridʒ] 동 격려하다, 장려하다
- **environment** [inváiərənmənt] 명 환경
- **explanation** [èksplənéiʃən] 명 설명
- **flow** [flou] 명 흐름
- **goal** [goul] 명 목표, 목적
- **grain** [grein] 명 곡물, 알곡
- **greenery** [gríːnəri] 명 푸른 잎, 푸른 나무
- **hopefully** [hóupfəli] 휑 바라건대
- **incredible** [inkrédəbl] 휑 믿기 힘든, 굉장한
- **innovation** [ìnəvéiʃən] 명 혁신
- **instead** [instéd] 휑 대신에
- **material** [mətíəriəl] 명 자료, 소재, 재료
- **natural** [nǽtʃərəl] 휑 자연적인
- **opinion** [əpínjən] 명 의견
- **place** [pleis] 동 두다
- **plastic bag** 비닐봉지
- **pollution** [pəlúːʃən] 명 오염
- **prevent** [privént] 동 예방하다, 막다, 방지하다
- **properly** [prápərli] 휑 적절하게
- **protect** [prətékt] 동 보호하다, 지키다
- **provide** [prəváid] 동 제공하다
- **quality** [kwáləti] 명 품질, 질
- **realize** [ríːəlàiz] 동 깨닫다
- **reduce** [ridjúːs] 동 줄이다
- **remind** [rimáind] 동 상기시키다
- **resource** [ríːsɔːrs] 명 자원
- **reusable** [riúzəbəl] 휑 재사용할 수 있는
- **ride** [raid] 명 탑승, 타기
- **separate** [sépərèit] 동 분리하다
- **seriously** [síəriəsli] 휑 심각하게, 진지하게
- **shade** [ʃeid] 명 그늘
- **statue** [stǽtʃuː] 명 조각, 조각상
- **structure** [strʌ́ktʃər] 명 구조(물)
- **suggestion** [səgdʒéstʃən] 명 제안
- **support** [səpɔ́ːrt] 동 지지[지원]하다, (필요한 것을 제공하여) 존재하게[살게] 하다
- **surface** [sə́ːrfis] 명 표면
- **theme** [θiːm] 명 주제
- **throughout** [θruːáut] 전 내내, 줄곧, 가로질러
- **underwater** [ʌndərwɔ́tər] 명 수중, 해저 휑 물속의, 수중의
- **unique** [juːníːk] 휑 유일무이한, 독특한
- **unwanted** [ʌnwántid] 휑 원치 않는, 불필요한
- **waste** [weist] 명 낭비 동 낭비하다

Key Expressions

- **a variety of** 다양한
- **be bored with** ~에 지루해하다
- **be made of** ~로 만들어지다
- **break down** 무너지다, 고장 나다, (썩어서) ~이 되다
- **come up with** ~을 생각해 내다
- **contribute to** ~에 기여하다, (~의) 원인이 되다
- **get better** 회복하다, 좋아지다
- **have a point** 일리가 있다
- **hold a contest** 대회를 개최하다
- **in harmony with** ~와 조화하여
- **in addition to** ~ 이외에도
- **in my opinion** 내 생각에는
- **make a suggestion about** ~에 대하여 제안하다
- **raise awareness** 인식을 높이다
- **take care of** ~을 돌보다
- **take the stairs** 계단을 이용하다
- **That's why ~.** 그것이 바로 ~한 이유이다.
- **throw ~ away** ~을 버리다
- **Why don't you/we ~ ?** ~하는 것이 어떠니?
- **would like to** ~하고 싶다
- **You have a point.** 네 말이 일리가 있다.

Word Power

※ 서로 비슷한 뜻을 가진 어휘

☐ **awareness** 인식, 의식 : **perception** 지각

☐ **creative** 창의적인 : **original** 독창적인

☐ **goal** 목적, 목표 : **target** 목표

☐ **opinion** 의견 : **idea** 생각

☐ **provide** 제공하다 : **supply** 공급하다

☐ **company** 회사 : **corporation** 회사

☐ **damage** 손상시키다 : **harm** 해를 끼치다

☐ **incredible** 믿기 힘든 : **unbelievable** 믿을 수 없는

☐ **properly** 적절하게 : **suitably** 적절하게

☐ **reduce** 줄이다 : **cut down** 줄이다

※ 서로 반대의 뜻을 가진 어휘

☐ **bright** 영리한 ↔ **dull** 우둔한

☐ **disappear** 사라지다 ↔ **appear** 나타나다

☐ **incredible** 믿기 힘든 ↔ **credible** 믿을 만한

☐ **direct** 직접적인 ↔ **indirect** 간접적인

☐ **encourage** 격려하다 ↔ **discourage** 의욕을 꺾다

☐ **natural** 자연적인 ↔ **artificial** 인공적인

※ 명사 – 형용사

☐ **addition** 추가 – **additional** 추가적인

☐ **environment** 환경 – **environmental** 환경적인

☐ **nature** 자연 – **natural** 자연적인

☐ **creation** 창조 – **creative** 창의적인

☐ **innovation** 혁신 – **innovative** 혁신적인

☐ **reuse** 재사용 – **reusable** 재사용할 수 있는

※ 동사 – 명사

☐ **add** 더하다 – **addition** 추가

☐ **encourage** 격려하다 – **encouragement** 격려

☐ **innovate** 혁신하다 – **innovation** 혁신

☐ **protect** 보호하다 – **protection** 보호

☐ **separate** 분리하다 – **separation** 분리

☐ **attract** 끌다 – **attraction** 매력

☐ **explain** 설명하다 – **explanation** 설명

☐ **prevent** 예방하다 – **prevention** 예방

☐ **reduce** 줄이다 – **reduction** 감소

☐ **suggest** 제안하다 – **suggestion** 제안

English Dictionary

☐ **architect** 건축가
→ a person who designs buildings 건물을 설계하는 사람

☐ **artwork** (예술적) 작품
→ something created to be beautiful by a painter, sculptor, etc. 화가, 조각가 등에 의해서 아름답도록 만들어진 것

☐ **climate** 기후
→ the general weather of a region
어느 지역의 전체적인 날씨

☐ **damage** 손상시키다
→ to harm something 어떤 것에 해를 끼치다

☐ **disappear** 사라지다
→ to no longer be seen 더 이상 보이지 않다

☐ **explanation** 설명
→ information to help people understand something
사람들이 어떤 것을 이해하도록 돕기 위한 정보

☐ **greenery** 푸른 잎, 푸른 나무
→ plants or vegetation 식물 또는 초목

☐ **opinion** 의견
→ one's beliefs, ideas, thoughts, and assumptions about a matter 어떤 문제에 관한 믿음, 아이디어, 생각 및 추정

☐ **reusable** 재사용할 수 있는
→ capable of being used more than once
한 번 이상 사용될 수 있는

☐ **surface** 표면
→ the top layer of something 사물의 꼭대기 층

☐ **underwater** 수중에, 해저에
→ below the water 수면 아래

01 다음 짝지어진 단어의 관계가 같도록 빈칸에 알맞은 말을 쓰시오.

> direct : indirect = appear : _____

02 다음 영영풀이가 가리키는 것을 고르시오.

> a person who designs buildings

① architect　　② artist
③ greenery　　④ artwork
⑤ protector

03 다음 중 밑줄 친 부분의 뜻풀이가 바르지 <u>않은</u> 것은?

① Using <u>reusable</u> cloth bags is a great way to protect our environment. (재사용할 수 있는)
② Did you have any <u>suggestion</u> to improve your school? (자원)
③ What method is used to <u>separate</u> oil from water? (분리하다)
④ The campaign <u>encourages</u> people to save water. (격려하다)
⑤ The songs <u>remind</u> me of my grandmother. (상기시키다)

서답형

04 다음 문장의 빈칸에 들어갈 말을 〈보기〉에서 골라 쓰시오.

> ┌─ 보기 ─┐
> support / materials / additional / unique / artwork

(1) Can we use other _____ instead of plastics?

(2) Artists should be able to _____ themselves without any help.
(3) If you require _____ information, please let me know.
(4) The _____ was originally created by a British artist.
(5) This tower has a _____ view of Seoul.

05 다음 주어진 문장의 밑줄 친 bright와 같은 의미로 쓰인 것은?

> Sujin is one of the <u>bright</u> students in her class.

① I really like your <u>bright</u> yellow dress.
② My brother is watching a <u>bright</u> star shining in the sky.
③ The boy gave me a <u>bright</u> smile.
④ I noticed that his eyes were <u>bright</u> with excitement.
⑤ I chose her as the leader because she is <u>bright</u>, kind, and humorous.

중요

06 다음 문장에 공통으로 들어갈 말을 고르시오.

> • They are living together _____ harmony by helping each other.
> • _____ addition to teaching English, my teacher aims to motivate them.
> • _____ my view, this book would be helpful to study English grammar.

① in[In]　　② to[To]　　③ of[Of]
④ for[For]　　⑤ by[By]

01 다음 짝지어진 단어의 관계가 같도록 빈칸에 알맞은 말을 쓰시오.

> encourage : discourage = credible : _____

02 다음 문장의 빈칸에 들어갈 말을 〈보기〉에서 골라 쓰시오.

> ┤ 보기 ├
> surface / statue / explanation / damage / prevent

(1) Despite her careful _____, we are still confused.

(2) The dust can _____ your eyes.

(3) There are ways to _____ plastic from getting to the ocean.

(4) You can see a small black dot on the sun's _____.

(5) The _____ of Mr. Ban welcomes visitors at the entrance.

03 다음 우리말에 맞게 빈칸에 알맞은 말을 쓰시오. (철자가 주어진 것은 그 철자로 시작할 것.)

(1) 우리는 처음으로 요리 대회를 개최할 것입니다.
➡ We'll _____ _____ _____ _____ for the first time.

(2) 나는 이 캠페인이 어린이 교육의 중요성에 대한 인식을 높일 수 있기를 희망한다.
➡ I hope this campaign will r_____ a_____ of the importance of children's education.

(3) 나는 사진 대회에 대해 제안을 하고 싶습니다.
➡ I would like to _____ _____ _____ about the photo contest.

(4) 만약 이 책을 읽는 것이 지루해지면, 내게 알려주세요.
➡ If you get b_____ _____ reading this book, let me know please.

04 다음 우리말과 일치하도록 주어진 단어를 모두 배열하여 완성하시오.

(1) 한옥은 나무로 만들어진 한국의 전통적인 구조물이다.
(a / of / made / Korean / *hanok* / structure / wood / is / traditional)
➡ _____
_____

(2) 우리는 어떻게 물의 흐름의 방향이 바뀌었는지 배울 것이다.
(to / going / changed / learn / how / the / direction / has / we / of / water / are / flow)
➡ _____
_____

(3) 창의성과 혁신은 성공의 열쇠이다.
(creativity / keys / success / innovation / to / and / are)
➡ _____
_____

(4) 거리에 쓰레기를 버리지 마세요.
(throw / trash / away / don't / the / the / street / on)
➡ _____
_____

Conversation

① 의견 표현하기

> • In my opinion, taking care of the environment starts with the little things.
> 내 생각에는, 환경을 보호하는 것은 작은 것들부터 시작한다고 생각해.

■ 자신의 생각이나 의견을 말하고자 할 때 많이 사용하는 표현으로 'In my opinion'이 있다. 우리말로는 '내 (개인적) 생각은'이라는 뜻으로 문장의 맨 앞에 사용하고 이 표현 뒤에는 콤마(,)를 찍는다. 'In my opinion, ~'과 유사 표현으로는 'In my view, ~', 'I think ~', 'I believe ~', 'I feel ~' 등이 있고 'It seems to me ~'를 쓸 수도 있다.

■ 동사 seem을 사용하여 'It seems (to me) that ~'이라고 하는 것은 '내 생각은 ~이다'라는 뜻으로 자신의 의견을 완곡하게 이야기할 때 사용하는 표현이다. 또한 'It seems to ~' 혹은 'It seems like ~' 등의 형태로 사용하여 '~인 것처럼 보인다, ~하는 것처럼 보인다'라는 의미로 자신의 의견을 나타낸다.

■ '내가 알기로는 ~'이라는 뜻으로 'as far as I know', 'as far as I'm concerned' 등에 이어서 원하는 내용을 덧붙여 자신의 의견을 표현하거나 'I'm convinced that ~ (나는 ~라고 확신한다.)'를 통해서도 자신의 의견을 표현하는 것이 가능하다.

의견 제시하기

- In my opinion/view, ~ 내 견해/의견으로는
- It seems to me that ~ 나에게는 ~인 것 같다
- As far as I know, 내가 알기로는
- I think/feel/believe ~ 내 생각은/느낌에는/내가 믿기로는
- I'm sure ~ 분명 ~이다
- I'm convinced that ~ 나는 ~라고 확신한다

의견을 물을 때 쓰는 여러 표현

- What do you think (of/about) ~? ~에 대해서 어떻게 생각해?
- How do you feel about ~ ? ~에 대한 너의 느낌은 어떠니?
- What is your view/opinion? 너의 견해/의견은 무엇이니?

핵심 Check

1. 다음 대화의 밑줄 친 우리말을 주어진 단어를 사용하여 영작하시오.

   B: I think we're using too many plastic bags.

   G: I agree. It's not good for the environment.
   How can we reduce our use of plastic bags?

   B: 내 생각에는 물건을 사러 갈 때 재사용할 수 있는 가방을 가져 가야 해. (opinion, reusable, bring, go)

   ➡ _____

② 희망 · 기대 표현하기

> • I can't wait to see it! 나도 어서 그것을 보고 싶다!

■ 'I can't wait to ~!(너무 기대된다!, 빨리 ~하고 싶어!)'는 원하던 일이 다가오고 있을 때, 빨리 하고 싶은 기대감을 나타내는 표현이며, 직역의 의미는 '~하는 것을 기다릴 수 없다'이고, 보통 '당장 ~하고 싶다, 빨리 ~했으면 좋겠다.'로 해석한다. 'I can't wait'는 뒤에 to부정사가 올 수 있고, 명사가 올 때는 전치사 for와 함께 써서 'I can't wait to+동사원형' 또는 'I can't wait for+명사/동명사'의 구조가 된다.

■ 말하는 사람의 기대 · 희망을 표현할 때는 '기대하다'라는 의미의 'expect'를 써서 'I'm expecting to+동사원형 ~'이라고 하거나 '열망하다'는 의미의 동사 'long'을 사용하여 'I'm longing to+동사원형, I'm longing for+명사'라고 하고, 형용사 'eager(열망하는)'를 써서 'I'm eager to+동사원형, I'm eager for+명사'의 형태로 나타내기도 한다

■ 앞으로 일어날 일이나 하고 싶은 일에 대하여 희망 · 기대를 표현할 때 'I am looking forward to ~.'나 'I look forward to ~.'같은 표현을 사용하기도 한다. 'look forward to'는 '기대하다'의 의미이다. 희망을 나타낼 때는 'I hope to ~', 'I want to ~', 'I wish to ~'라고 할 수 있다.

■ 'look forward to'에서 to는 전치사이기 때문에 뒤에 명사나 동명사가 와서 'look forward to+명사[동명사]'가 되어야 한다. hope, want, expect는 모두 to부정사를 목적어로 가지기 때문에 'want/hope/expect to+동사원형'이 되어야 한다.

희망 · 기대 표현하기

• I can't wait to+동사원형/for+명사 ~.   빨리 ~하고 싶다.
• I'm looking forward to+동명사/명사(구) ~.   ~하기를 기대한다.
• I am expecting to+동사원형 ~.   ~하기를 기대한다.
• I am eager for+명사/to+동사원형 ~.   ~하기를 기대한다.

핵심 Check

2. 다음 밑줄 친 (A)의 우리말을 영어로 가장 적절하게 표현한 것은?

G: I want to buy a new bag. I'm bored with my old bags.

B: Then how about using old clothes to make a new bag? You can find out how to do it online.

G: Oh, that sounds interesting! (A)어서 나만의 가방을 만들고 싶어!

① I'm looking forward to make my own bag!   ② I hope making my own bag!
③ I can't wait to make my own bag!   ④ I'm longing make my own bag!
⑤ I'm eager to making my own bag!

Listen & Talk 1 B

G: Jiho, hurry up! The elevator is going up soon.

B: The science room is just on the third floor. ❶Why don't we take the stairs?

G: I don't want to walk all the way up there.

B: Come on. Elevators use lots of energy. We need to save energy to ❷protect the environment.

G: But one elevator ❸ride doesn't use ❹that much energy.

B: That's true, but the energy from all the elevator rides ❺adds up over time. ❻In my opinion, taking care of the environment starts with the little things.

G: ❼You have a point. Let's take the stairs.

여: 지호야, 서둘러! 엘리베이터가 곧 올라간다.

남: 과학실은 겨우 3층에 있잖아. 우리 계단을 오르는 건 어때?

여: 그 모든 계단을 올라서 가고 싶진 않아.

남: 잘 생각해 봐. 엘리베이터는 전기를 많이 쓰잖아. 우리는 환경을 보호하려면 에너지를 아껴야 해.

여: 하지만 엘리베이터를 한 번 탄다고 그렇게 많은 에너지를 사용하진 않잖아.

남: 그렇지. 하지만 엘리베이터를 타면서 사용하는 에너지는 시간이 흐르면서 누적될 거야. 내 생각에는, 환경을 보호하는 것은 작은 것부터 시작한다고 생각해.

여: 네 말이 일리가 있네. 계단을 이용하자.

❶ Why don't we ~? = How about ~? = What about ~? = ~하는 게 어때? ❷ protect: 보호하다 ❸ ride: 탑승
❹ that은 부사로 '그렇게, 그 정도로'를 뜻한다. ❺ add up: 합산하다 ❻ In my opinion: 내 생각은 = In my view
❼ You have a point.: 네 말이 일리가 있다.

Check(√) True or False

(1) The girl and the boy are going up to the 3rd floor. T ☐ F ☐

(2) The boy didn't want to take the elevator because one elevator ride uses a lot of energy. T ☐ F ☐

 Listen & Talk 2 B

G: I read a cool article today.

B: What was ❶it about?

G: It was about a new bag. ❷It just looks like a ❸plastic bag, but ❹ it's made mostly of corn.

B: That sounds really amazing.

G: Yes, but there's more. The bag ❺breaks down in soil in only three months and disappears in about three minutes in warm water!

B: Wow! That will help us reduce plastic waste ❻by a lot!

G: I know! The company will start selling the bag sometime this year. ❼I can't wait to use it!

여: 오늘 굉장한 기사를 읽었어.

남: 무엇에 대한 기사였니?

여: 새로운 봉지에 관한 기사였어. 그것은 비닐봉지처럼 생겼지만, 대부분 옥수수로 만든 거야.

남: 그것 참 놀랍구나.

여: 응, 하지만 놀라운 게 더 있어. 그 봉지는 흙 속에서 3달 만에 분해되고 따뜻한 물속에서는 3분 만에 사라져!

남: 와! 그건 우리가 플라스틱 쓰레기를 줄이는 데 많이 도움이 되겠구나!

여: 내 말이 그 말이야! 그 회사는 올해 중으로 그 봉지를 팔기 시작할 거야. 어서 사용하고 싶어!

❶ it은 a cool article을 가리킨다. ❷ It은 a new bag을 가리킨다. ❸ plastic bag: 비닐봉지
❹ be made of: ~로 만들어지다 ❺ break down: 분해되다 ❻ by a lot: 많이
❼ I can't wait to ~: '너무 기대된다, 빨리 ~하고 싶어'라는 의미로 원하던 일이 다가오고 있을 때, 빨리하고 싶은 기대감을 나타내는 표현이다.

Check(√) True or False

(3) The article the girl read is about the new bag made mostly of corns. T ☐ F ☐

(4) The new bags break down in only three months in warm water. T ☐ F ☐

Listen & Talk 1 A

B: I think we're using too many ❶plastic bags.

G: ❷I agree. It's not good for the environment. How can we reduce our use of plastic bags?

B: ❸In my opinion, we should bring ❹reusable bags when we go shopping.

❶ plastic bag: 비닐봉지
❷ 상대방의 의견에 동의하는 표현으로 'I can't agree with you more.' 등으로 바꾸어 쓸 수 있다.
❸ 자신의 의견을 나타내는 표현으로 'I think ~' 또는 'In my view, ~,' 등으로 바꾸어 표현할 수 있다.
❹ reusable: 재사용할 수 있는

Listen & Talk 1 C

B: Today, ❶I'd like to ❷make a suggestion about the trash problem at our school. I've found that many students just ❸throw things away instead of recycling them. As you know, however, recycling is very important because ❹it saves resources and helps protect the environment. So, in my opinion, we need to reduce the number of ❺trash cans at school to encourage recycling. Why don't we ❻place four different colored recycling bins on every floor instead? This will remind students to ❼ separate the paper, glass, plastic, and cans properly.

❶ I'd like to ~: ~하고 싶다   ❷ make a suggestion: 제안하다
❸ throw ~ away: ~을 버리다   ❹ it은 recycling을 가리킨다.
❺ trash can: 쓰레기통   ❻ place: 놓다, 두다
❼ separate: 분리하다

Listen & Talk 2 A

B: Our club is ❶holding a photo contest next week.

G: What kinds of photos will be in ❷it?

B: The ❸theme is pollution around the world. We are holding this contest to ❹ raise students' awareness of environmental problems.

G: That sounds nice. I can't wait to see it!

❶ hold a contest: 대회를 열다
❷ it은 a photo contest를 가리킨다.
❸ theme: 주제
❹ raise awareness: 인식을 높이다

Listen & Talk 2 C

B: What are we going to do this weekend, Mihee?

G: ❶Why don't we go to the sheep park near my house?

B: A sheep park? How interesting! Are there really sheep in the park?

G: Yes. They are there to protect the environment.

B: How can they help the environment?

G: You know, people usually use ❷chemicals to kill ❸unwanted plants. The sheep in the park eat those plants, so the chemicals ❹are not needed.

B: ❺What a bright idea! I can't wait to visit the park!

❶ Why don't we ~?: '~하는 게 어때?'라고 제안하는 표현으로 'Let's ~'로 바꾸어 표현할 수 있다.
❷ chemical: 화학물질
❸ unwanted plants: 잡초
❹ be+p.p. 형태로 수동태이다.
❺ 감탄문으로 'What+a(n)+형용사+명사(+주어+동사)!' 순서로 이어진다.

Do It Yourself

G: I want to buy a new bag.

B: You already have too many bags. In my opinion, you don't need any more.

G: But ❶I'm bored with my old bags.

B: Then how about using old clothes to make a new bag? You can find out ❷how to do it online.

G: Oh, that sounds interesting! I can't wait to make my own bag.

❶ be bored with: ~에 지루해하다
❷ how to ~ : ~하는 방법

● 다음 우리말과 일치하도록 빈칸에 알맞은 말을 쓰시오.

Listen & Talk 1 A

B: I think we're using too many _____ _____.

G: I agree. It's not good for the _____. How can we reduce our use of _____ _____?

B: _____ _____ _____, we should bring _____ _____ when we go shopping.

해석

남: 내 생각엔 우리는 비닐봉지를 너무 많이 쓰는 것 같아.

여: 내 생각도 그래. 그건 환경에 좋지 않아. 우리 비닐봉지 사용을 어떻게 줄일 수 있을까?

남: 내 생각에는 물건을 사러 갈 때 재사용할 수 있는 가방을 가져 가야 해.

Listen & Talk 1 B

G: Jiho, hurry _____! The elevator is _____ _____ soon.

B: The science room is just on the third floor. Why don't we _____ _____ _____?

G: I don't want to walk _____ _____ _____ up there.

B: Come on. Elevators use lots of energy. We need to _____ energy to _____ _____ _____.

G: But _____ _____ _____ doesn't use that much energy.

B: That's true, but the energy from all the elevator rides _____ _____ over time. _____ _____ _____, _____ _____ _____ the environment starts with the little things.

G: You _____ _____ _____. Let's take the stairs.

여: 지호야, 서둘러! 엘리베이터가 곧 올라간다.

남: 과학실은 겨우 3층에 있잖아. 우리 계단을 오르는 건 어때?

여: 그 모든 계단을 올라서 가고 싶진 않아.

남: 잘 생각해 봐. 엘리베이터는 전기를 많이 쓰잖아. 우리는 환경을 보호하려면 에너지를 아껴야 해.

여: 하지만 엘리베이터를 한 번 탄다고 그렇게 많은 에너지를 사용하진 않잖아.

남: 그렇지, 하지만 엘리베이터를 타면서 사용하는 에너지는 시간이 흐르면서 누적될 거야. 내 생각에는, 환경을 보호하는 것은 작은 것부터 시작한다고 생각해.

여: 네 말이 일리가 있네. 계단을 이용하자.

Listen & Speak 1 C

B: Today, I'd like to _____ _____ _____ about the trash problem at our school. I've found that many students just _____ things _____ instead of _____ them. As you know, however, recycling is very important because it saves _____ and helps _____ the environment. So, _____ _____ _____, we need to reduce the number of _____ _____ at school to encourage recycling. Why don't we _____ four different _____ _____ _____ on every floor instead? This will _____ students to _____ the paper, glass, plastic, and cans properly.

남: 오늘 저는 우리 학교의 쓰레기 문제에 대해 제안을 하나 하고자 합니다. 저는 많은 학생들이 쓰레기를 재활용하는 대신에 그냥 버리는 것을 발견했습니다. 하지만, 여러분도 알다시피, 재활용은 자원을 아낄 수 있고 환경을 보호하는 것을 돕기 때문에 재활용하는 것은 정말 중요합니다. 그래서 제 생각에는 재활용을 권장하기 위해 학교에 있는 쓰레기통의 수를 줄이는 것이 필요하다고 생각합니다. 대신에 모든 층에 각기 색이 다른 4개의 재활용 통을 두는 것이 어떨까요? 이는 학생들이 종이, 유리, 플라스틱, 캔을 적절하게 구분할 수 있도록 상기시킬 것입니다.

Listen & Talk 2 A

B: Our club is _____ a photo contest next week.

G: _____ _____ _____ photos will be in it?

B: The _____ is pollution around the world. We are holding this contest to _____ _____ _____ of environmental problems.

G: That sounds nice. I can't _____ _____ _____ _____!

Listen & Talk 2 B

G: I read a cool _____ today.

B: What was it about?

G: It was about a new bag. It just looks like a _____ _____, but it's _____ mostly _____ corn.

B: That sounds really _____.

G: Yes, but there's more. The bag _____ _____ in _____ in only three months and _____ in about three minutes in warm water!

B: Wow! That will help us _____ _____ _____ by a lot!

G: I know! The _____ will start selling the bag sometime this year. I can't _____ _____ _____ it!

Listen & Talk 2 C

B: What are we going to do this weekend, Mihee?

G: Why don't we go to the _____ _____ near my house?

B: A sheep park? How _____! Are there really sheep in the park?

G: Yes. They are there to _____ _____ _____.

B: _____ _____ they help the environment?

G: You know, people usually use _____ to kill _____ _____. The sheep in the park eat those plants, so the _____ are not needed.

B: What a _____ idea! I can't _____ _____ visit the park!

Do It Yourself

G: I want to buy a new bag.

B: You already have too many bags. _____ _____ _____, you don't need _____ _____.

G: But I'm _____ _____ my old bags.

B: Then how about _____ old clothes to make a new bag? You can find out _____ _____ _____ _____ online.

G: Oh, that sounds _____! I can't wait _____ _____ my own bag.

해석

남: 다음 주에 우리 동아리에서 사진 대회를 개최할 거야.

여: 어떤 종류의 사진들이 출품되니?

남: 주제는 세계의 환경오염이야. 우리는 학생들이 환경 문제에 대해 인식을 높일 수 있도록 이 대회를 개최하는 거야.

여: 그거 참 멋지네. 나도 어서 대회를 보고 싶다!

여: 오늘 굉장한 기사를 읽었어.

남: 무엇에 대한 기사였니?

여: 새로운 봉지에 관한 기사였어. 그것은 비닐봉지처럼 생겼지만, 대부분 옥수수로 만든 거야.

남: 그것 참 놀랍구나.

여: 응, 하지만 놀라운 게 더 있어. 그 봉지는 흙 속에서 3달 만에 분해되고 따뜻한 물속에서는 3분 만에 사라져!

남: 와! 그건 우리가 플라스틱 쓰레기를 줄이는 데 많이 도움이 되겠구나!

여: 내 말이 그 말이야! 그 회사는 올해 중으로 그 봉지를 팔기 시작할 거야. 어서 사용하고 싶어!

남: 이번 주말에 무엇을 할 계획이니, 미희야?

여: 우리 집 근처에 있는 양 공원에 가는 것은 어때?

남: 양 공원? 그것 참 흥미로운데! 공원에 정말로 양이 있는 거야?

여: 응. 양들은 환경을 보호하기 위해 거기에 있어.

남: 그들이 어떻게 환경에 도움을 줄 수 있지?

여: 있지, 사람들은 잡초를 없애기 위해 화학 물질을 사용하잖아. 그 공원에 있는 양들이 그런 잡초들을 먹어서, 화학물질이 필요하지 않게 돼.

남: 그것 참 놀라운 생각이구나! 어서 그 공원에 가보고 싶다!

여: 나 새로운 가방을 사고 싶어.

남: 넌 이미 너무 많은 가방을 가지고 있어. 내 생각에 넌 가방이 더 필요하지 않아.

여: 하지만 난 나의 오래된 가방들에 질렸는걸.

남: 그럼 새로운 가방을 만들기 위해 오래된 옷들을 사용하는 것은 어때? 만드는 방법은 온라인상에서 찾아볼 수 있어.

여: 오, 그것 참 흥미로운데! 어서 나만의 가방을 만들고 싶어!

[01~02] 다음 대화를 읽고 물음에 답하시오.

> Minsu: Our club is holding a photo contest next week.
>
> Sora: What kinds of photos will be in it?
>
> Minsu: The theme is pollution around the world. We are holding this contest to raise students' awareness of environmental problems.
>
> Sora: That sounds nice. (A)I can't wait to see it!

01 위 대화의 밑줄 친 (A)와 바꾸어 쓸 수 있는 말로 적절하지 <u>않은</u> 것은?

① I'm looking forward to seeing it! ② I hope to see it!

③ I'm expecting to see it! ④ I'm eager to see it!

⑤ I'm tired of seeing it!

02 위 대화의 내용과 일치하지 <u>않는</u> 것은?

① 다음 주 동아리에서 사진 대회를 개최할 것이다.

② 동아리 사진 대회의 주제는 세계의 환경오염이다.

③ 학생들이 환경 문제에 대해 인식을 높이기 위해 대회를 개최한다.

④ 소라는 대회를 보는 것에 기대를 나타냈다.

⑤ 소라는 대회를 기다리다 지쳤다.

[03~04] 다음 대화를 읽고 물음에 답하시오.

> Tom: I think we're using too many plastic bags.
>
> Jane: _____(A)_____ It's not good for the environment. How can we reduce our use of plastic bags?
>
> Tom: In my opinion, we should bring reusable bags when we go shopping.

03 위 대화의 빈칸 (A)에 들어갈 말로 나머지와 의도가 <u>다른</u> 것은?

① I agree. ② I can't agree with you more.

③ I disagree with you. ④ That's what I thought.

⑤ I think so, too.

서답형

04 위 대화에서 다음 영영풀이가 나타내는 말을 찾아 쓰시오.

> capable of being used more than once

➡ _____

01 다음 대화가 자연스럽게 이어지도록 순서대로 배열하시오.

> (A) That sounds nice. I can't wait to see it!
> (B) What kinds of photos will be in it?
> (C) Our club is holding a photo contest next week.
> (D) The theme is pollution around the world. We are holding this contest to raise students' awareness of environmental problems.

➡ _____

[02~04] 다음 대화를 읽고 물음에 답하시오.

Sujin: Jiho, hurry up! The elevator is going up soon.

Jiho: The science room is just on the third floor. Why don't we take the stairs?

Sujin: I don't want to walk all the way up there.

Jiho: Come on. Elevators use lots of energy. We need to save energy (A)[protect / to protect] the environment.

Sujin: But one elevator ride doesn't use that much energy.

Jiho: That's true, but the energy from all the elevator rides (B)[add / adds] up over time. In my opinion, (C)[take / taking] care of the environment starts with the little things.

Sujin: (a)You have a point. Let's take the stairs.

02 위 대화의 (A)~(C)에 들어갈 말이 바르게 짝지어진 것은?

① protect – add – take
② protect – adds – taking
③ to pronvect – adds – take
④ to protect – adds – taking
⑤ to protect – add – take

03 위 대화의 밑줄 친 (a)의 의미를 우리말로 쓰시오.

➡ _____

04 위 대화의 내용과 일치하지 <u>않는</u> 것은?

① 과학실은 3층에 있다.
② 지호는 수진에게 엘리베이터를 타고 올라갈 것을 제안했다.
③ 지호는 환경을 보호하려면 에너지를 아껴야 한다고 생각한다.
④ 수진은 엘리베이터를 한 번 탄다고 그렇게 많은 에너지를 사용하지는 않는다고 생각한다.
⑤ 지호는 엘리베이터를 타면서 사용하는 에너지가 시간이 흐르면서 누적될 것이라고 생각한다.

[05~06] 다음 글을 읽고 물음에 답하시오.

B: Today, I'd like to make a suggestion about the trash problem at our school. I've found that many students just throw things away instead of recycling them. As you know, ___(A)___, recycling is very important because it saves resources and helps protect the environment. So, in my opinion, we need to reduce the number of trash cans at school to encourage recycling. Why don't we place four different colored recycling bins on every floor instead? This will remind students to separate the paper, glass, plastic, and cans properly.

05 위 글의 빈칸 (A)에 들어갈 말로 적절한 것은?

① however   ② moreover
③ in addition   ④ furthermore
⑤ therefore

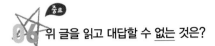 위 글을 읽고 대답할 수 <u>없는</u> 것은?

① What problem is the boy talking about?
② Why is recycling important?
③ What does the boy suggest?
④ How many different colors of recycling bins does the boy need?
⑤ What color recycling bin should the students throw away the paper in?

[07~09] 다음 대화를 읽고 물음에 답하시오.

Emily: I read a cool article today.
Brian: What was it about?
Emily: ⓐIt was about a new bag. It just looks like a plastic bag, but ⓑit's made mostly of corn.
Brian: That sounds really (A)[amazing / amazed].
Emily: Yes, but there's more. The bag breaks down in soil in only three months and (B)[disappear / disappears] in about three minutes in warm water!
Brian: Wow! That will help us (C)[reduce / reducing] plastic waste by a lot!
Emily: I know! The company will start selling the bag sometime this year. I can't wait to use it!

서답형

07 위 대화의 밑줄 친 ⓐ와 ⓑ가 가리키는 것을 찾아 쓰시오.

➡ ⓐ ＿＿＿＿＿＿＿ ⓑ ＿＿＿＿＿＿＿

08 위 대화의 괄호 (A)~(C)에 알맞은 말이 바르게 짝지어진 것은?

① amazing – disappear – reduce
② amazing – disappears – reducing
③ amazing – disappears – reduce
④ amazed – disappears – reducing
⑤ amazed – disappear – reduce

09 위 대화의 내용과 일치하지 <u>않는</u> 것은?

① Emily는 새로운 봉지에 관한 기사를 읽었다.
② 새로운 봉지는 비닐봉지처럼 생겼지만, 대부분 옥수수로 만들어졌다.
③ 새로운 봉지는 흙 속에서 3달 만에 분해되고 따뜻한 물속에서는 3시간 만에 사라진다.
④ 새로운 봉지는 플라스틱 쓰레기를 줄이는 데 도움이 될 것이다.
⑤ 회사는 올해 중으로 새로운 봉지를 팔기 시작할 것이다.

[10~11] 다음 대화를 읽고 물음에 답하시오.

Minsu: Our club is holding a photo contest next week.
Sora: What kinds of photos will be in it?
Minsu: The theme is (A)[pollute / pollution] around the world. We are holding this contest to (B)[rise / raise] students' awareness of environmental problems.
Sora: That sounds nice. I (C)[can / can't] wait to see it!

10 위 대화의 (A)~(C)에 들어갈 말이 바르게 짝지어진 것은?

① pollute – rise – can
② pollute – raise – can't
③ pollution – raise – can
④ pollution – raise – can't
⑤ pollution – rise – can

11 위 대화를 읽고 알 수 <u>없는</u> 것은?

① 사진 대회 개최 시기
② 사진 대회의 주제
③ 사진 대회의 개최 목적
④ 사진 대회의 주관 동아리
⑤ 사진 대회 개최 장소

01 다음 대화의 내용과 일치하도록 빈칸을 완성하시오.

> Minsu: Our club is holding a photo contest next week.
>
> Sora: What kinds of photos will be in it?
>
> Minsu: The theme is pollution around the world. We are holding this contest to raise students' awareness of environmental problems.
>
> Sora: That sounds nice. I can't wait to see it!

> Sora is looking forward to (A)_____ _____. It will be held by (B)_____ next week. The theme is pollution around the world. It is planned to (C)_____ _____ .

[02~05] 다음 대화를 읽고 물음에 답하시오.

> Emily: I read a cool article today.
>
> Brian: What was it about?
>
> Emily: It was about a new bag. It just looks like a plastic bag, but it's made mostly of corn.
>
> Brian: That sounds really amazing.
>
> Emily: Yes, but there's more. The bag breaks down in soil in only three months and disappears in about three minutes in warm water!
>
> Brian: Wow! That will help us reduce plastic waste by a lot!
>
> Emily: I know! The company will start selling the bag sometime this year. I can't wait to use it!

02 What is the new bag mostly made of?

➡ _____

03 How long does it take for the new bag to break down in soil?

➡ _____

04 How does the new bag help protect the environment?

➡ _____
_____

05 위 대화의 내용과 일치하지 않는 것을 찾아 바르게 고치시오.

Get the Incredible Bag!

a. It's made mostly of corn.

b. It breaks down in soil in three months.

c. It disappears in about three minutes in cold water.

_____ ➡ _____

06 다음 대화가 자연스럽게 이어지도록 순서대로 배열하시오.

> Sujin: Jiho, hurry up! The elevator is going up soon.
>
> Jiho: The science room is just on the third floor. Why don't we take the stairs?
>
> (A) But one elevator ride doesn't use that much energy.
>
> (B) I don't want to walk all the way up there.
>
> (C) Come on. Elevators use lots of energy. We need to save energy to protect the environment.
>
> (D) You have a point. Let's take the stairs.
>
> (E) That's true, but the energy from all the elevator rides adds up over time. In my opinion, taking care of the environment starts with the little things.

➡ _____

Grammar

교과서

- It is important **for us** to find ways to protect the environment.
  우리가 환경을 보호할 수 있는 방법을 찾는 것은 중요하다.

- It was very smart **of him** not to miss the chance.
  그는 아주 약빠르게도 그 기회를 놓치지 않았다

■ **쓰임과 형태**
- 쓰임: to부정사가 행하는 동작 또는 상태의 주체를 나타낼 때 쓴다.
- 형태: 'for+목적격+to부정사'

■ **to부정사의 의미상의 주어**

to부정사의 동작을 실제로 하는 주체를 to부정사의 의미상의 주어라고 하며 그 행위의 주체가 문장의 주어나 목적어와 다를 때 to부정사 바로 앞에 'for+목적격'으로 나타낸다.

- I want **him** to go there. 나는 그가 그곳에 가기를 바란다. (그가 to go there의 의미상의 주어임)
- It is important **for him** to attend the meeting every day. 그가 매일 회의에 참석하는 것이 중요하다.
  (그가 to attend의 의미상의 주어임)

■ 이때 사람의 성격이나 성품을 나타내는 형용사(kind, nice, polite, rude, smart, stupid, wise 등)가 보어로 쓰일 때는 'of+목적격'의 형태로 나타낸다.

- It is nice **of you** to show me the way. 길을 가르쳐 주셔서 감사합니다.
- It was so rude **of you** to send her away empty. 그녀를 빈손으로 돌려보내다니 넌 무례했다.

■ to부정사의 의미상의 주어가 일반적인 사람일 경우는 보통 생략한다. 또한 to부정사의 부정은 to부정사 앞에 not이나 never를 써서 'not[never]+to부정사'로 나타낸다.

- Air is necessary **(for us)** to live. 공기는 (우리가) 살아가는 데 필수적이다.

 핵심 Check

1. 빈칸에 알맞은 말을 어법에 맞게 쓰시오.

(1) It was necessary _____ help the young children.

(2) It'll take time _____ her to recover from the illness.

(3) It was wise _____ you to keep out of debt.

② 관계부사

> • Cancun is a city **where** 4.8 million tourists travel every year.
> 칸쿤은 매년 480만 명의 관광객이 여행하는 도시이다.
>
> • There was a time **when** computers were very rare. 컴퓨터가 아주 희귀한 시대가 있었다.

■ 관계부사는 두 문장을 연결하는 접속사의 역할과 부사구의 역할을 동시에 한다. 관계부사 앞에 오는 수식을 받는 명사를 선행사라 하고, 그 선행사에 따라 관계부사 when(시간), where(장소), why(이유), how(방법)를 쓴다.

   • There was a time **when** things were very different. 상황이 아주 달랐던 때가 있었지.

   • I know a place **where** the food is first-class. 음식이 최고인 곳을 한 군데 알아.

■ 선행사에 따른 관계부사

	선행사	관계부사	전치사+관계대명사
때	the day, the time 등	when	in/on/at which
장소	the place, the country 등	where	in/on/at which
이유	the reason	why	for which
방법	the way	how	in which

■ 관계부사 how는 선행사 the way와 함께 쓰지 않고 반드시 둘 중의 하나만 써야 하며 the way that이나 the way in which를 쓸 수 있다. 다른 관계부사의 경우 선행사가 'the time', 'the place', 'the reason'처럼 일반적인 뜻을 나타낼 때, 선행사나 관계부사 중 하나를 생략할 수 있다.

   • The way how he acts really makes me mad.　　　(×) 그의 행동 방식은 나를 화나게 만든다.

   • **The way**[또는 **How**] he acts really makes me mad. (○)

■ 관계부사는 '전치사+관계대명사(which)'로 바꿔 쓸 수 있으며, which를 쓸 때는 전치사를 which 바로 앞에 쓰거나 관계사절의 끝에 쓴다.

   • We visited the house **where** Shakespeare was born. 우리는 셰익스피어의 생가를 방문했다.

   = We visited the house **in which** Shakespeare was born.

   = We visited the house **which** Shakespeare was born **in**.

■ 주의: 관계대명사는 관계사절에서 주어나 목적어의 역할을 하므로 주어나 목적어가 빠진 불완전한 절이 나오지만 관계부사는 부사 역할을 하므로 완전한 절이 나온다.

핵심 Check

2. 다음 괄호 안에서 알맞은 말을 고르시오.

(1) He cares for the children on the days (when / where) he's not working.

(2) The house (when / where) I live was built at the turn of the century.

(3) I'd like to know the reason (why / how) you're so late.

01 다음 빈칸에 알맞은 것을 고르시오.

> It is not easy _____.

① him to find out the answer　　② he finds out the answer

③ he to find out the answer　　④ for him to find out the answer

⑤ of him to find out the answer

02 다음 중 어법상 <u>어색한</u> 문장은?

① I remember the day when we went to the beach.

② Is this the place where the accident happened?

③ I don't like the way how he talks.

④ Give me one good reason why I should help you.

⑤ Galileo's ideas were well in advance of the age in which he lived.

03 다음 ①～⑤ 중 생략할 수 있는 것은?

> ①A good <u>educational background</u> can make ②<u>it</u> easier ③<u>for</u> people ④<u>to develop</u> ⑤<u>good social contacts</u>.

①　　　　②　　　　③　　　　④　　　　⑤

04 다음 괄호 안에서 알맞은 말을 고르시오.

(1) It took three hours for me (write / to write) the report.

(2) It is possible for (she / her) to memorize the poem in ten minutes.

(3) It is necessary (for / of) us to prepare for the winter.

(4) Do you know the reason (how / why) Lisa called me?

(5) George grew up in a village (when / where) there was no electricity.

(6) I remember the day (when / where) I met you.

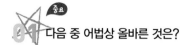

01 다음 중 어법상 올바른 것은?

① It was very kind for you to meet me.

② It is easy catches a disease in winter.

③ It's good for children do things on their own sometimes.

④ It's time for them to wake up.

⑤ That was great for Kevin to rest for a week.

02 다음 중 어법상 어색한 것은?

① I vividly remember the day when we first met.

② This is the reason how I'm here.

③ People gathered around the hotel where he was staying.

④ Explain how you solved the question.

⑤ The age at which a person can begin driving varies from state to state.

03 다음 빈칸에 알맞은 말이 바르게 짝지어진 것은?

- 2010 was the year _____ he published his first novel.
- It is difficult _____ Jackson to work out early in the morning.

① how – of

② how – for

③ when – for

④ when – of

⑤ that – of

서답형

04 다음 괄호 안에서 알맞은 말을 고르시오.

(1) It was not easy (wake / to wake) him up this morning.

(2) It is impossible (of / for) us to emphasize safety training too much.

(3) It is considerate (of / for) you to advise me.

(4) I don't know the reason (when / why) I didn't remember anything during the exam.

(5) Thursday is traditionally the day (which / when) the British go to vote.

(6) This is the house (which / where) Yun Bonggil was born in.

(7) He showed me (the way how / how) he packed his suitcase.

서답형

05 다음 두 문장을 한 문장으로 바꿔 쓸 때 빈칸에 들어갈 알맞은 말을 쓰시오.

- The author has moved his family to a small town.
- He now writes his awesome novels in the town.

→ The author has moved his family to a small town _____ he now writes his awesome novels.

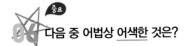

06 다음 중 어법상 어색한 것은?

① It is very important of me to make the fans happy.
② It's dangerous for kids to walk home alone.
③ It's impossible to hold a conversation with all this noise.
④ It was silly of me to want to marry Ann.
⑤ It is difficult for him to get around without a cane.

07 밑줄 친 부분의 쓰임이 주어진 문장과 같은 것은?

Sep. 23 is the day when I got married to Jake.

① When did she promise to meet him?
② It was a magic moment when the two sisters were reunited after 30 years.
③ Since when did you get interested in collecting stamps?
④ He told me the when and the where of the event.
⑤ When he goes out, he takes his dog with him.

08 다음 우리말을 바르게 영작한 것을 고르시오.

이곳은 내가 예전에 살았던 집이다.

① This is the house when I used to live.
② This is the house why I used to live.
③ This is the house which I used to live.
④ This is the house where I used to live in.
⑤ This is the house where I used to live.

서답형

09 주어진 어휘를 이용하여 다음 우리말을 영작하시오.

그들에게 김치를 만드는 것은 어려웠다.
(Gimchi, them, make, hard, it, to)

➡ _____

10 다음 두 문장을 한 문장으로 바르게 연결한 것은?

• My family will go to the beach.
• My parents first met at the beach.

① My family will go to the beach how my parents first met.
② My family will go to the beach why my parents first met.
③ My family will go to the beach when my parents first met.
④ My family will go to the beach where my parents first met.
⑤ My family will go to the beach which my parents first met.

서답형

11 다음 우리말과 일치하도록 빈칸에 알맞은 단어로 묶은 것은?

우리가 환경을 보호할 수 있는 방법을 찾는 것은 중요하다.
= _____ is important _____ us to find ways to protect the environment.

① That – for   ② That – of
③ It – for   ④ It – of
⑤ This – with

12 다음 빈칸에 들어갈 말로 알맞은 말은?

It was brave _____ to speak on behalf of the people.

① for him   ② for his   ③ of his
④ of he   ⑤ of him

서답형

13 다음 문장에서 생략할 수 있는 것을 찾아 쓰시오.

(1) Now is the time when we have to make a decision.

➡ _____

(2) What is the reason why you removed him from his post?

➡ _____

서답형

14 다음 문장에서 어법상 어색한 것을 바르게 고쳐 다시 쓰시오.

(1) Of him to live without her even for a single day was really hard.

➡ _____
_____

(2) I suppose it was rude for me to listen to a private conversation.

➡ _____
_____

(3) It is very important for him making a decision soon.

➡ _____
_____

(4) We should find a place which we can be safe!

➡ _____
_____

(5) Do you know the reason which John left so early?

➡ _____

(6) I have to say I like the way how he solved the situation.

➡ _____
_____

중요

15 다음 중 어법상 어색한 것을 고르시오. (2개)

① It was very nice of her showing me the way.

② The movie was too difficult for me to understand.

③ It is not easy for Leo to get up early in the morning.

④ We are going to visit the city which my grandparents were born.

⑤ My room is a place where I can relax.

16 다음 각 문장의 밑줄 친 이 어떤 용법으로 쓰였는지 쓰시오.

(1) 가주어 ~ 진주어 구문
(2) It ~ that 강조 구문

ⓐ It was the architect that drew up plans for the new office.

ⓑ It is boring for Junho to watch baseball games.

ⓒ It was impossible for me to understand the system.

ⓓ It is the air that we breathe.

ⓔ How long does it take for the plastic bag to break down in soil?

ⓕ What was it that he wanted you to do?

➡ (1) _____ (2) _____

중요

17 다음 중 빈칸에 들어갈 말로 알맞은 것을 고르시오.

That is the reason _____ I don't like living in the city.

① which ② where ③ how
④ when ⑤ why

01 다음 두 문장의 뜻이 비슷하도록 빈칸에 들어갈 알맞은 말을 쓰시오.

(1) She is rarely seen in public nowadays.
   = It is hard for _____ see her in public nowadays.

(2) They nicely invited us.
   = It was nice _____ invite us.

 다음 우리말에 맞게 주어진 어구를 바르게 배열하시오.

(1) 나는 우리가 어제 차를 마셨던 그 카페를 좋아한다. (I, we, the café, tea, like, had, where, yesterday)

   ➡ _____
   _____

(2) 서울을 떠나기로 결정한 이유를 물어봐도 될까요? (I, you, you, the reason, Seoul, decided, ask, may, why, leave, to)

   ➡ _____
   _____

(3) 그 가방들은 우리가 들고 가기에 너무 무거웠다. (the bags, us, carry, were, too, heavy, for, to)

   ➡ _____
   _____

(4) 인부들이 길을 보수하는 데는 몇 주가 걸렸다. (the workers, the street, weeks, a, it, took, repair, few, for, to)

   ➡ _____
   _____

(5) 그녀가 혼자서 외국에 간 것은 용감했다. (her, it, go, was, abroad, brave, alone, to, of)

   ➡ _____
   _____

03 그림을 보고, 주어진 어휘를 이용하여 빈칸을 알맞게 채우시오.

(1)

She didn't know _____
the problems. (the way, solve, could)

(2)

The Eiffel Tower is the place _____.
(I, want, go)

04 괄호 안에 주어진 말을 이용하여 어법에 맞게 문장을 완성하시오.

(1) It was not easy _____ up early this morning. (me, wake)

(2) It is really thoughtful _____ my birthday. (you, remember)

05 주어진 두 문장을 관계부사를 이용하여 하나의 문장으로 쓰시오.

(1) • They made an underwater museum away from the places.
• Sea life was dying at the places.

➡ _____

_____

(2) • I can't forget the day.
• I won the class election on the day.

➡ _____

_____

(3) • They talked about the way.
• He scored the goal in the final match in the way.

➡ _____

_____

(4) • That is the reason.
• I like documentaries for the reason.

➡ _____

_____

06 다음 문장에서 어법상 어색한 것을 바르게 고치시오.

(1) The cake was big enough of us to share.
_____ ➡ _____

(2) It is very foolish for you to waste your precious time on it!
_____ ➡ _____

(3) It was heartless for him to say such a thing to the sick man.
_____ ➡ _____

(4) It was easy for her to not miss a word.
_____ ➡ _____

07 어법상 어색한 것을 바르게 고치시오.

(1) I still remember the day where my class got first place on Sports Day.

➡ _____

(2) The reason which he did it is not clear to me.

➡ _____

(3) I can recognize him by the way how he walks.

➡ _____

(4) I miss the summers when we used to go to the beach in.

➡ _____

08 다음 우리말을 괄호 안의 지시대로 영작하시오.

(1) 나는 내가 파티를 일찍 떠난 이유를 설명했다.

➡ _____
(관계부사를 써서)

➡ _____
(관계대명사를 써서)

(2) 그는 그가 인생을 살았던 방식을 후회한다.

➡ _____
(관계부사를 생략해서)

➡ _____
(선행사를 생략해서)

➡ _____
(that을 써서)

Join Hands, Save the Earth

It is important for us to find ways to protect the environment. Some people have found creative ways to save the earth. One example is an underwater museum in Cancun, Mexico. Let's meet Dr. Rosa Allison, an art professor, and listen to her explanation about the special museum.

Rosa: Cancun is a city where 4.8 million tourists travel every year. One of the most popular activities to do there is looking at the area's beautiful sea life underwater. However, tourist activities are seriously damaging parts of the sea near Cancun. To prevent this, artists did something interesting. They thought if they attracted tourists to a different part of the sea, the dying areas could have time to get better. They made an underwater museum away from the places where sea life was dying. It's about 14 meters below the surface and contains 500 statues. The statues are made from materials that support sea life. They provide additional places for plants and animals to live on. Over time, many types of sea life will grow on the statues, which will make the artwork unique. The artists want people to see a variety of sea life on the statues.

environment: 환경
creative: 창의적인
underwater: 물속의, 수중의
explanation: 설명
damage: 손상시키다
prevent: 막다, 예방하다
surface: 표면
statue: 조각상
material: 재료, 자료
support: 지원하다
additional: 추가적인

확인문제

● 다음 문장이 본문의 내용과 일치하면 T, 일치하지 않으면 F를 쓰시오.

1 Dr. Rosa Allison doesn't know about art well. ☐

2 The sea near Cancun was protected by tourist activities. ☐

3 Sea life in the sea near Cancun was dying. ☐

4 It will be hard to see various sea creatures at the underwater museum. ☐

If people realize how rich sea life is, they will understand how
간접의문문(의문사+주어+동사): realize의 목적어
important it is to save the sea.
간접의문문의 가주어   진주어

In Singapore, people are using architecture to protect the environment
to부정사의 부사적 용법 중 목적(~하기 위해서)
on land. Let's hear what Rajesh Khan, an architect, says about eco-
관계대명사
friendly buildings.

Rajesh: Singapore is hot throughout the year. Most buildings need air

conditioning, which uses a lot of energy and contributes to climate
air conditioning에 수의 일치   uses와 병렬 연결
change. That's why architects in Singapore have begun to design
That's why+결과   현재완료
eco-friendly buildings that use less air conditioning but are still cool
eco-friendly buildings에 수의 일치   use와 병렬 연결
inside. For example, many buildings in Singapore are designed to

have an open structure. This structure makes it possible for outside
가목적어 it   의미상 주어
air to move throughout a building. This natural air flow is how these
진목적어
buildings stay cool. In addition to making open structures, architects
전치사구(목적어로 동명사구가 나옴)
add large gardens. This greenery provides shade and protects parts of
protect A from B: B로부터 A를 보호하다
the building from direct sunlight, which keeps the building cooler.
앞 문장 전체를 선행사로 취하는 관계대명사
Eco-friendly buildings like these not only help protect the
not only A but also B: A 뿐만 아니라 B도(=B as well as A)
environment, but also provide people with a good quality of life. Those
provide A with B: A에게 B를 제공하다
are the goals of this new style of architecture. Hopefully, architects will

keep coming up with new eco-friendly ideas.
keep Ving: 계속해서 V하다
Every field has different ways of protecting the environment. With
every+단수명사: 단수 취급   동격의 전치사
more innovation, humans and nature will be able to live together in
will can(×)
harmony far into the future.

---

architecture: 건축(술)

architect: 건축가

contribute to: ~에 기여하다.
(~의) 원인이 되다

climate: 기후

structure: 구조(물)

flow: 흐름

greenery: 푸른 잎, 푸른 나무

shade: 그늘

in harmony: 조화를 이루어

확인문제

● 다음 문장이 본문의 내용과 일치하면 T, 일치하지 <u>않으면</u> F를 쓰시오.

1 People in Singapore protect the environment by means of architecture. ☐

2 Using air conditioning can be a factor resulting in climate change. ☐

3 The open structure protects the building from direct sunlight. ☐

4 Eco-friendly buildings are helpful not for humans but for the environment. ☐

● 우리말을 참고하여 빈칸에 알맞은 말을 쓰시오.

Join Hands, Save the Earth

1 It is important _____ _____ _____ _____ _____ to protect the environment.

2 Some people have found _____ ways _____ _____ the earth.

3 One example is an _____ _____ in Cancun, Mexico.

4 Let's _____ Dr. Rosa Allison, an art _____, and _____ _____ her explanation about the special museum.

5 Rosa: Cancun is a city _____ 4.8 million _____ _____ every year.

6 One of _____ _____ _____ activities _____ _____ there _____ looking _____ the area's beautiful sea life underwater.

7 _____, tourist activities _____ seriously _____ _____ of the sea _____ Cancun.

8 _____ _____ _____, artists did _____ _____.

9 They thought _____ they _____ tourists _____ a different part of the sea, the _____ _____ could have time _____ _____ _____.

10 They _____ an _____ museum _____ the places _____ sea life was _____.

11 It's _____ 14 _____ the surface and _____ 500 _____.

12 The statues _____ _____ _____ materials _____ _____ sea life.

13 They _____ additional places _____ plants and animals _____ _____ _____.

14 Over time, many types of sea life _____ _____ _____ the statues, _____ _____ _____ the artwork _____.

15 The artists _____ _____ _____ _____ a variety of sea life _____ the statues.

함께 손잡고, 지구를 구합시다

1 우리가 환경을 보호할 수 있는 방법을 찾는 것은 중요하다.

2 몇몇 사람들은 지구를 구하기 위한 창의적인 방법을 찾았다.

3 한 예로 멕시코 칸쿤에 있는 수중 박물관이 있다.

4 미술학 교수인 Rosa Allison 박사를 만나서 이 특별한 박물관에 대한 설명을 들어보자.

5 Rosa: 칸쿤은 매년 480만 명의 관광객이 여행하는 도시이다.

6 그곳에서 할 수 있는 가장 인기 있는 활동 중 하나는 그 지역의 바닷속의 아름다운 해양 생물을 관찰하는 것이다.

7 하지만, 관광 활동들이 칸쿤 근처의 바다 일부를 심각하게 훼손시키고 있다.

8 이러한 일을 방지하기 위해서, 예술가들이 흥미로운 생각을 해 냈다.

9 그들은 만약 관광객들을 바다의 다른 쪽으로 유인한다면, 그 죽어가는 지역이 호전될 시간을 가질 수 있을 것이라 생각했다.

10 그들은 해양 생물이 죽어가는 지역으로부터 떨어진 해저에 수중 박물관을 만들었다.

11 그 박물관은 해수면에서 14미터 아래에 있으며 500개의 조각상이 있다.

12 그 조각상들은 해양 생물에게 도움이 되는 재료들로 만들어졌다.

13 그것들은 식물과 동물들이 살 수 있는 추가적인 장소를 제공한다.

14 시간이 흐르면, 많은 형태의 바다 생명체들이 그 조각상에서 자라게 될 것이며, 이것이 그 예술 작품을 독특하게 만들 것이다.

15 예술가들은 사람들이 그 조각상들에서 (살고 있는) 다양한 해양 생명체들을 보길 원한다.

16 If people realize _____ _____ _____ _____ _____ , they will understand _____ _____ _____ _____ to save the sea.

17 In Singapore, people are _____ architecture _____ _____ the environment _____ _____ .

18 Let's hear _____ Rajesh Khan, an architect, _____ eco-friendly buildings.

19 Rajesh: Singapore is hot _____ _____ _____ .

20 Most buildings _____ air conditioning, _____ _____ a lot of energy and _____ _____ climate change.

21 _____ _____ architects in Singapore _____ _____ design eco-friendly buildings _____ _____ _____ air conditioning but _____ _____ cool inside.

22 _____ _____ , many buildings in Singapore _____ _____ _____ an open structure.

23 This structure makes _____ possible _____ _____ _____ _____ _____ throughout a building.

24 This _____ air flow is _____ _____ _____ _____ .

25 _____ _____ _____ _____ _____ open structures, architects add large gardens.

26 This greenery _____ shade and _____ parts of the building _____ _____ _____ , which _____ the building cooler.

27 Eco-friendly buildings like these _____ _____ protect the environment, _____ _____ _____ _____ people _____ a good quality of life.

28 Those are the _____ of this _____ of _____ .

29 Hopefully, architects _____ _____ _____ _____ new eco-friendly ideas.

30 _____ _____ _____ different ways of _____ the environment.

31 _____ more innovation, humans and nature _____ _____ _____ _____ _____ in harmony _____ _____ the future.

Reading **145**

---

16 만약 사람들이 해양 생물이 얼마나 풍부한지 깨닫는다면, 그들은 바다를 지키는 것이 얼마나 중요한지 이해할 것이다.

17 싱가포르에서는 사람들이 육지의 환경을 보호하기 위해 건축을 이용하고 있다.

18 건축가인 Rajesh Khan이 친환경 건물에 대해 말하는 것을 들어보자.

19 Rajesh: 싱가포르는 연중 더운 곳이다.

20 대부분의 건물들은 에어컨 가동이 필요한데, 이로 인해 많은 에너지가 사용되고 있으며 기후 변화의 원인이 되고 있다.

21 그것이 싱가포르의 건축가들이 에어컨을 덜 쓰면서도 실내에서 여전히 시원한 느낌이 들 수 있는 친환경적인 건물들을 디자인하기 시작한 이유이다.

22 가령, 싱가포르의 많은 건물들은 개방형 구조를 포함하게 디자인되었다.

23 이러한 구조는 외부 공기가 건물을 관통하는 것을 가능케 한다.

24 이러한 자연적인 공기의 흐름이 이 건물을 시원하게 유지해 주는 방법이다.

25 건축가들은 개방형 구조를 만드는 것 외에도 큰 정원을 더한다.

26 이러한 녹지 공간은 그늘을 제공하고 직사광선으로부터 건물의 부분들을 지켜주어 건물을 시원하게 유지한다.

27 이와 같은 친환경적인 건물들은 환경을 보호하는 것을 도울 뿐만 아니라 사람들에게 양질의 삶을 제공한다.

28 그것들이 바로 이러한 새로운 건축 방식의 목표이다.

29 바라건대, 건축가들은 새로운 친환경 아이디어를 계속해서 생각해 낼 것이다.

30 모든 분야에서 환경을 보호하는 다른 방식이 있다.

31 더 나은 혁신으로 인해 먼 미래에 인간과 자연은 함께 조화를 이루며 살아갈 수 있을 것이다.

● 우리말을 참고하여 본문을 영작하시오.

1 우리가 환경을 보호할 수 있는 방법을 찾는 것은 중요하다.
➡ _____

2 몇몇 사람들은 지구를 구하기 위한 창의적인 방법을 찾았다.
➡ _____

3 한 예로 멕시코 칸쿤에 있는 수중 박물관이 있다.
➡ _____

4 미술학 교수인 Rosa Allison 박사를 만나서 이 특별한 박물관에 대한 설명을 들어보자.
➡ _____

5 Rosa: 칸쿤은 매년 480만 명의 관광객이 여행하는 도시이다.
➡ _____

6 그곳에서 할 수 있는 가장 인기 있는 활동 중 하나는 그 지역의 바닷속의 아름다운 해양 생물을 관찰하는 것이다.
➡ _____

7 하지만, 관광 활동들이 칸쿤 근처의 바다 일부를 심각하게 훼손시키고 있다.
➡ _____

8 이러한 일을 방지하기 위해서, 예술가들이 흥미로운 생각을 해냈다.
➡ _____

9 그들은 만약 관광객들을 바다의 다른 쪽으로 유인한다면, 그 죽어가는 지역이 호전될 시간을 가질 수 있을 것이라 생각했다.
➡ _____
_____

10 그들은 해양 생물이 죽어가는 지역으로부터 떨어진 해저에 수중 박물관을 만들었다.
➡ _____

11 그 박물관은 해수면에서 14미터 아래에 있으며 500개의 조각상이 있다.
➡ _____

12 그 조각상들은 해양 생물에게 도움이 되는 재료들로 만들어졌다.
➡ _____

13 그것들은 식물과 동물들이 살 수 있는 추가적인 장소를 제공한다.
➡ _____

14 시간이 흐르면, 많은 형태의 바다 생명체들이 그 조각상에서 자라게 될 것이며, 이것이 그 예술 작품을 독특하게 만들 것이다.
➡ _____

15 예술가들은 사람들이 그 조각상들에서 (살고 있는) 다양한 해양 생명체들을 보길 원한다.
➡ _____

16 만약 사람들이 해양 생물이 얼마나 풍부한지 깨닫는다면, 그들은 바다를 지키는 것이 얼마나 중요한지 이해할 것이다.

➡ _____

17 싱가포르에서는 사람들이 육지의 환경을 보호하기 위해 건축을 이용하고 있다.

➡ _____

18 건축가인 Rajesh Khan이 친환경 건물에 대해 말하는 것을 들어보자.

➡ _____

19 Rajesh: 싱가포르는 연중 더운 곳이다.

➡ _____

20 대부분의 건물들은 에어컨 가동이 필요한데, 이로 인해 많은 에너지가 사용되고 있으며 기후 변화의 원인이 되고 있다.

➡ _____

21 그것이 싱가포르의 건축가들이 에어컨을 덜 쓰면서도 실내에서 여전히 시원한 느낌이 들 수 있는 친환경적인 건물들을 디자인하기 시작한 이유이다.

➡ _____

_____

22 가령, 싱가포르의 많은 건물들은 개방형 구조를 포함하게 디자인되었다.

➡ _____

23 이러한 구조는 외부 공기가 건물을 관통하는 것을 가능케 한다.

➡ _____

24 이러한 자연적인 공기의 흐름이 이 건물을 시원하게 유지해 주는 방법이다.

➡ _____

25 건축가들은 개방형 구조를 만드는 것 외에도 큰 정원을 더한다.

➡ _____

26 이러한 녹지 공간은 그늘을 제공하고 직사광선으로부터 건물의 부분들을 지켜주어 건물을 시원하게 유지한다.

➡ _____

_____

27 이와 같은 친환경적인 건물들은 환경을 보호하는 것을 도울 뿐만 아니라 사람들에게 양질의 삶을 제공한다.

➡ _____

_____

28 그것들이 바로 이러한 새로운 건축 방식의 목표이다.

➡ _____

29 바라건대, 건축가들은 새로운 친환경 아이디어를 계속해서 생각해 낼 것이다.

➡ _____

30 모든 분야에서 환경을 보호하는 다른 방식이 있다.

➡ _____

31 더 나은 혁신으로 인해 먼 미래에 인간과 자연은 함께 조화를 이루며 살아갈 수 있을 것이다.

➡ _____

[01~02] 다음 글을 읽고 물음에 답하시오.

It is important for us to find ways to protect the environment. Some people have found creative ways to save the earth. One example is an underwater museum in Cancun, Mexico. Let's meet Dr. Rosa Allison, an art professor, and listen to her explanation about (A)the special museum.

01 밑줄 친 (A)에 대한 설명으로 적절한 것은?

① It was built to make Mexico famous.
② Rosa Allison built it.
③ It is under the sea.
④ It is harmful for the environment.
⑤ It was found by Rosa Allison.

서답형
02 다음과 같이 풀이되는 말을 위 글에서 찾아 쓰시오.

a building where a large number of interesting and valuable objects, such as works of art or historical items, are kept, studied, and displayed to the public

➡ _____

[03~05] 다음 글을 읽고 물음에 답하시오.

Rosa: Cancun is a city where 4.8 million tourists travel every year. One of the most popular activities to do there is looking at the area's beautiful sea life underwater. _____(A)_____, tourist activities are seriously damaging parts of the sea near Cancun. To prevent this, artists did something interesting. They thought if they attracted tourists to a different part of

the sea, the dying areas could have time to get better. They made an underwater museum away from the places where sea life was dying. It's about 14 meters below the surface and contains 500 statues.

03 빈칸 (A)에 들어갈 말로 가장 적절한 것은?

① For example   ② Therefore
③ Nevertheless   ④ On the other hand
⑤ However

서답형
04 How many tourists visit Cancun every year? Answer in English.

➡ _____

중요
05 위 글을 읽고 답할 수 있는 것은?

① How can people get to Cancun?
② Why do people travel to Cancun?
③ Where did they make an underwater museum?
④ What was another tourist attraction of Cancun?
⑤ How many artists took part in making the museum?

[06~07] 다음 글을 읽고 물음에 답하시오.

The statues are made from materials ① that support sea life. They provide additional places for plants and animals ②to live on. Over time, many types of sea life will grow ③ on the statues, which will make the artwork ④uniquely. The artists want people to see a variety of sea life on the statues. If people realize ⑤how rich sea life is, they will understand how important it is to save the sea.

06 밑줄 친 ①~⑤ 중 어법상 바르지 <u>않은</u> 것은?

서답형 ①　　② 　　③ 　　④ 　　⑤

07 According to the passage, what do the artists want people to see? Answer in English.

➡ _____

_____

[08~10] 다음 글을 읽고 물음에 답하시오.

In Singapore, people are using architecture to protect the environment on land. Let's hear what Rajesh Khan, an architect, says about eco-friendly buildings.

Rajesh: Singapore is hot throughout the year. ① Most buildings need air conditioning, which uses a lot of energy and contributes to climate change. ② That's why architects in Singapore have begun to design eco-friendly buildings that use less air conditioning but are still cool inside. ③ For example, many buildings in Singapore are designed to have an open structure. ④ This natural air flow is how these buildings stay cool. ⑤

08 ①~⑤ 중 주어진 문장이 들어가기에 가장 적절한 곳은?

This structure makes it possible for outside air to move throughout a building.

①　　② 　　③ 　　④ 　　⑤

09 위 글의 내용과 일치하는 것은?

① Rajesh Khan built many buildings.
② Singapore is hot all year round.
③ Eco-friendly buildings use lots of energy.
④ The environment in Singapore is not damaged.
⑤ Air conditioning is rarely used in Singapore.

10 What do most buildings in Singapore need? Answer in English with seven words.

➡ _____

[11~13] 다음 글을 읽고 물음에 답하시오.

In addition to making open structures, architects add large ___(A)___ . This greenery provides shade and protects parts of the building from direct sunlight, which keeps the building cooler.

Eco-friendly buildings like these not only help protect the environment, but also provide people with a good quality of life. Those are the goals of this new style of architecture. Hopefully, architects will keep coming up with new eco-friendly ideas. (B)모든 분야에서 환경을 보호하는 다른 방식이 있다. With more innovation, humans and nature will be able to live together in harmony far into the future.

11 빈칸 (A)에 들어갈 말로 가장 적절한 것은?

① fans　　② gardens　　③ mirrors
④ roofs　　⑤ refrigerators

12 다음 중 위 글 앞에 나올 내용으로 가장 적절한 것은?

① how to grow plants in buildings
② well known traditional architecture
③ other eco-friendly buildings
④ the ways to protect wild life
⑤ hitting on innovative ideas

서답형
13 주어진 단어를 활용하여 밑줄 친 우리말 (B)를 영어로 쓰시오. (어형 변화 가능.)

(every / ways / of / protect / field)

➡ _____

_____

[14~15] 다음 글을 읽고 물음에 답하시오.

It is important for us ___(A)___ ways to protect the environment. Some people have found creative ways to save the earth. One example is an underwater museum in Cancun, Mexico. Let's meet Dr. Rosa Allison, an art professor, and listen to her explanation about the special museum.

14 빈칸 (A)에 들어갈 동사 find의 형태와 다른 것은?

① I was glad _____ the key.
② She went out _____ something to read.
③ He woke up _____ himself alone.
④ I enjoy _____ various insects.
⑤ We were advised _____ another route.

15 다음 중 위 글을 읽고 알 수 있는 것은?

① Rosa Allison lives in Mexico.
② People find ways to use the earth.
③ Rosa Allison is an environmentalist.
④ People aren't interested in saving the earth.
⑤ The underwater museum was made to protect the environment.

[16~19] 다음 글을 읽고 물음에 답하시오.

Cancun is a city where 4.8 million tourists travel every year. One of the most popular activities to do there is looking at the area's beautiful sea life underwater. However, tourist activities are seriously damaging parts of the sea near Cancun.

To prevent this, artists did something interesting. They thought if they attracted tourists to a different part of the sea, the dying areas could have time to get better. They made an underwater museum away from the places where sea life was dying. It's about 14 meters below the surface and contains 500 statues.

The statues are made from materials that support sea life. They provide additional places for plants and animals to live on. Over time, many types of sea life will grow on the statues, which will make the artwork unique.

The artists want people to see a variety of sea life on the statues. If people realize how rich sea life is, they will understand how important it is to save the sea.

서답형

16 What will grow on the statues over time? Answer in English.

➡ _____

_____

17 According to the passage, what made the sea near Cancun damaged?

① too many artistic activities of artists
② tourist activities
③ various kinds of sea life
④ the limited use of the sea
⑤ the garbage that people threw away

서답형

18 What are the statues in the underwater museum made from? Answer in English.

➡ _____

_____

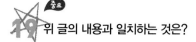 위 글의 내용과 일치하는 것은?

① Cancun is not a well known tourist attraction.

② The underwater museum has nothing to see.

③ There are only a few sea life at the sea of Cancun.

④ The underwater museum is close to the places where sea life was dying.

⑤ The underwater museum was built to distract people from the place which was seriously damaged.

[20~23] 다음 글을 읽고 물음에 답하시오.

In Singapore, people are using architecture to protect the environment ①on land. Let's hear what Rajesh Khan, an architect, says about eco-friendly buildings.

Singapore is ②hot throughout the year. Most buildings need air conditioning, which uses a lot of energy and contributes to climate change. That's why architects in Singapore have begun to design eco-friendly buildings that use ③less air conditioning but are still cool inside. For example, many buildings in Singapore are designed to have an open structure. This structure makes it possible for outside air to move throughout a building. This natural air flow is how these buildings stay cool. _____(A)_____ making open structures, architects add large gardens. This greenery provides shade and protects parts of the building from ④direct sunlight, which keeps the building cooler. Eco-friendly buildings like these not only help protect the environment, but also provide people with a good quality of life. Those are the goals of

(B)this new style of architecture. Hopefully, architects will keep coming up with new eco-friendly ideas.

Every field has different ways of protecting the environment. With more innovation, humans and nature will be able to live together in ⑤isolation far into the future.

20 빈칸 (A)에 들어갈 말로 가장 적절한 것은?

① Instead of   ② In addition to
③ According to   ④ Due to
⑤ Regardless of

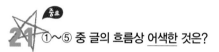 ①~⑤ 중 글의 흐름상 어색한 것은?

①   ②   ③   ④   ⑤

22 밑줄 친 (B)에 대한 설명으로 가장 적절한 것은?

① architecture which is good for animals

② the building structures nobody can imitate

③ architecture good for both nature and human beings

④ the building method helpful for the poor

⑤ the buildings that make people comfortable to live their lives

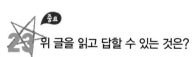 위 글을 읽고 답할 수 있는 것은?

① How many buildings has Rajesh built?

② Why is Singapore hot all year round?

③ When was an eco-friendly building first invented?

④ What makes people innovative in their field?

⑤ What provides people with a good quality of life?

[01~02] 다음 글을 읽고 물음에 답하시오.

(A)우리가 환경을 보호할 수 있는 방법을 찾는 것은 중요하다. Some people have found creative ways to save the earth. One example is an underwater museum in Cancun, Mexico. Let's meet Dr. Rosa Allison, an art professor, and listen to her explanation about the special museum.

중요

01 주어진 어구를 활용하여 밑줄 친 우리말 (A)를 영어로 쓰시오.

(it / to / the environment / ways / protect)

➡ _____

_____

02 Where is Cancun located? Answer in English.

➡ _____

[03~08] 다음 글을 읽고 물음에 답하시오.

Cancun is a city where 4.8 million tourists travel every year. One of the most popular activities to do there is looking at the area's beautiful sea life underwater. However, tourist activities are seriously damaging parts of the sea near Cancun. To prevent (A)this, artists did something interesting. They thought if they attracted tourists to a different part of the sea, the dying areas could have time to get better. They made an underwater museum away from the places where sea life was dying. It's about 14 meters below the surface and contains 500 statues. The statues are made from materials that support sea life. They provide additional places for plants and animals to live on. Over

time, many types of sea life will grow on the statues, which will make the artwork unique. The artists want people to see a variety of sea life on the statues. If people realize how rich sea life is, they will understand how important it is to save the sea.

03 What is one of the most popular activities to do in Cancun? Answer in English with ten words.

➡ _____

_____

중요

04 밑줄 친 (A)가 의미하는 것을 우리말로 쓰시오.

➡ _____

_____

05 What was the purpose of making an underwater museum? Answer in English and use the word 'give.'

➡ _____

고난이도

06 위 글의 내용에 맞게 빈칸에 알맞은 말을 쓰시오.

In addition to being made from _____ _____, the statues provide _____ on which _____ _____.

07 How many statues does the museum contain? Answer in English.

➡ _____

중요

08 According to the passage, what will make the statues unique? Answer in English. (10 words)

➡ _____

[09~14] 다음 글을 읽고 물음에 답하시오.

In Singapore, people are using architecture to protect the environment on land. Let's hear what Rajesh Khan, an architect, says about __(A)__ buildings.

Rajesh: Singapore is hot throughout the year. Most buildings need air conditioning, which uses a lot of energy and contributes to climate change. That's why architects in Singapore have begun to design eco-friendly buildings that use less air conditioning but are still cool inside. For example, many buildings in Singapore are designed to have an open structure. This structure makes it possible for outside air to move throughout a building. This natural air flow is how these buildings stay cool.

In addition to making open structures, architects add large gardens. This greenery provides shade and protects parts of the building from direct sunlight, which keeps the building cooler.

Eco-friendly buildings like (B)these not only help protect the environment, but also provide people with a good quality of life. Those are the goals of this new style of architecture. (C)바라건대, 건축가들은 새로운 친환경 아이디어를 계속해서 생각해 낼 것입니다.

Every field has different ways of protecting the environment. With more innovation, humans and nature will be able to live together in harmony far into the future.

09 빈칸 (A)에 들어갈 말을 위 글에서 찾아 쓰시오.

➡ _____

10 What is the problem of using air conditioning? Answer in English.

➡ _____

_____

11 위 글의 내용에 맞게 빈칸에 알맞은 말을 쓰시오.

An open structure of a building enables _____ to _____.

12 밑줄 친 (B)가 가리키는 것을 우리말로 쓰시오.

➡ _____

13 주어진 단어를 바르게 나열하여 밑줄 친 우리말 (C)를 영어로 쓰시오. (필요하다면 어형을 바꾸시오.)

(will / hopefully / architects / eco-friendly / come / with / keep / up / new / ideas)

➡ _____

_____

14 다음 질문에 대한 답을 위 글의 표현을 활용하여 쓰시오.

Q: What roles do the large gardens of the buildings play?

➡ _____

_____

Listen & Talk 2 D Talk Together

A: Have you heard of edible spoons? They're amazing!
have+p.p.: 현재 완료 시제로 ~해 본 적이 있는지 경험을 묻는다.

B: No, I haven't. Tell me about them.
= edible spoons

A: They are made of grain. They will save resources.
~로 만들어지다

B: That sounds awesome. I can't wait to use them.
= I'm looking forward to using them.

구문해설 · edible: 먹을 수 있는 · grain: 곡물, 낟알 · resource: 자원 · awesome: 멋진, 훌륭한

해석

A: 먹을 수 있는 수저에 대해 들어봤니? 정말 놀라워!

B: 아니, 들어 본 적이 없어. 그것에 대해 이야기해 봐.

A: 수저는 곡물로 만들어져. 그것들은 자원을 절약할 거야.

B: 정말 멋지다. 나는 그것들을 사용하는 게 정말 기다려져.

Presentation Time

How can we make our school eco-friendly? In my opinion, we need a green
5형식 동사(+목적어+목적격보어)

wall. The front wall of our school is a great place for it. A green wall helps to
a green wall

keep the building cool by blocking sunlight. This could reduce the amount of
5형식 동사(목적어+목적격보어)   by+Ving: V함으로써   햇빛을 차단하여 건물을 시원하게 유지하는 것

energy used for air conditioning.

구문해설 · eco-friendly: 친환경적인 · opinion: 의견 · front: 앞 · block: 막다

우리는 어떻게 우리 학교를 친환경적으로 만들 수 있을까요? 제 의견으로는, 우리는 식물로 덮인 벽이 필요합니다. 우리 학교의 앞 벽은 그것을 위한 훌륭한 공간입니다. 식물로 덮인 벽은 햇빛을 차단함으로써 건물을 시원하게 유지하는 것을 돕습니다. 이것은 에어컨을 위해 사용되는 에너지의 양을 줄일 수 있습니다.

Think & Write Step 3

Eat Your Cup and Save the Earth!

Here's an innovative, environmentally friendly item! It is a cookie cup. It's a

cookie that is made in the shape of a cup. After you use the cup, you can just
주격 관계대명사(= which)   시간을 나타내는 접속사

eat it. By doing this, you can save paper or plastic.
by ~ing: ~함으로써 앞 문장의 내용

The cookie cup can change the world.

Be a part of the change!

구문해설 · innovative: 혁신적인 · save: 절약하다

컵을 먹고 지구를 구하세요!

여기 혁신적이며 친환경적인 상품이 있습니다! 이것은 과자컵입니다. 이것은 컵 모양으로 만들어진 과자입니다. 컵을 사용한 후에 그냥 그것을 먹을 수 있습니다. 이렇게 함으로써 종이나 플라스틱을 절약할 수 있습니다.

과자컵은 세상을 바꿀 수 있습니다.

변화의 일부가 되십시오!

Words & Expressions

01 다음 짝지어진 단어의 관계가 같도록 빈칸에 알맞은 말을 쓰시오.

> addition : additional
> = environment : _____

02 다음 영영풀이가 가리키는 것을 고르시오.

> the general weather of a region

① climate   ② state   ③ theme
④ flow   ⑤ quality

03 다음 중 밑줄 친 부분의 뜻풀이가 바르지 <u>않은</u> 것은?

① The study shows a growing <u>awareness</u> of animal rights. (인식)
② He found out something <u>incredible</u> about his wife. (믿을 수 있는)
③ By using fewer plastic bottles, we can <u>protect</u> lots of sea animals. (보호하다, 지키다)
④ These <u>chemicals</u> are mostly used in cleaning products. (화학물질)
⑤ There were many <u>unwanted</u> guests at the ceremony. (원치 않는)

04 다음 우리말에 맞게 빈칸에 알맞은 말을 쓰시오.

(1) 안토니 가우디는 스페인의 유명한 건축가였다.
➡ Antoni Gaudi was a famous _____ from Spain.
(2) 사람들이 프라하에서 즐길 수 있는 것 중 하나는 그곳의 건축이다.
➡ One thing that people can enjoy in Prague is its _____.

(3) 과학 과정은 추가적인 수학 강의와 과학 강의를 포함한다.
➡ The science track includes _____ math and science courses.
(4) 비닐봉지가 물에 떠있다.
➡ The _____ _____ is floating in the water.

05 다음 주어진 문장의 밑줄 친 company와 <u>다른</u> 의미로 쓰인 것은?

> <u>Company</u> profits were 5% lower than last year.

① Mike is working at the largest computer <u>company</u> in the world.
② This deal will be advantageous to your <u>company</u>.
③ We are planning to make a new <u>company</u>.
④ A man is known by the <u>company</u> he keeps.
⑤ The <u>company</u> is investing $9 million to renovate its factories.

06 다음 문장의 빈칸에 공통으로 들어갈 말을 고르시오.

> • It's a ten-minute bus _____ from here to town.
> • Steve gave me a _____ on his motorbike.
> • When I was young, I learned to _____ a bike.

① provide   ② realize   ③ ride
④ remind   ⑤ separate

07 다음 우리말에 맞게 주어진 단어를 사용하여 영작하시오.

(1) 당신 말이 일리가 있네요. (point)

➡ _____

(2) 무엇이 당신의 좋은 건강에 영향을 끼쳤다고 생각하십니까? (contributed, have)

➡ _____

_____

(3) 우리는 다른 사람들과 조화를 이루며 살아야 한다. (harmony, should)

➡ _____

Conversation

[08~09] 다음 대화를 읽고 물음에 답하시오.

July: (A) I want to buy a new bag.

David: (B) You already have too many bags. In my opinion, you don't need any more.

July: (C) But I'm bored with my old bags.

David: (D) You can find out how to do it online.

July: (E) Oh, that sounds interesting! I can't wait to make my own bag.

08 위 대화의 (A)~(E) 중 주어진 문장이 들어가기에 적절한 곳은?

Then how about using old clothes to make a new bag?

① (A)　② (B)　③ (C)　④ (D)　⑤ (E)

09 위 대화의 내용과 일치하지 <u>않는</u> 것은?

① July는 새 가방을 사고 싶어 한다.

② July는 이미 많은 가방을 갖고 있다.

③ July는 오래된 가방에 질렸다.

④ David는 새 가방을 만들기 위해 오래된 옷들을 사용해 볼 것을 조언했다.

⑤ David는 오래된 옷을 사용해 새 가방을 만드는 법을 알고 있다.

[10~11] 다음 대화를 읽고 물음에 답하시오.

Jack: What are we going to do this weekend, Mihee?

Mihee: Why don't we go to the sheep park near my house?

Jack: A sheep park? How ⓐ<u>interesting</u>! Are there really sheep in the park?

Mihee: Yes. They are there ⓑ<u>to protect</u> the environment.

Jack: How can they help the environment?

Mihee: You know, people usually use chemicals to kill ⓒ<u>unwanted</u> plants. The sheep in the park eat those plants, so the chemicals are not ⓓ<u>needing</u>.

Jack: What a bright idea! I can't wait ⓔ<u>to visit</u> the park!

10 위 대화의 밑줄 친 ⓐ~ⓔ 중 어법상 어색한 것을 찾아 바르게 고치시오.

➡ _____

11 위 대화의 내용과 일치하도록 Jack의 일기를 완성하시오.

Saturday, August 26

I went to (A)_____ near Mihee's house. It was fun to see the animals. What's more, they eat (B)_____. This can help reduce the use of (C)_____ to kill those plants.

[12~14] 다음 대화를 읽고 물음에 답하시오.

Minsu: Our club is holding a photo contest next week.

Sora: What kinds of photos will be in it?

Minsu: The theme is pollution around the world. We are holding this contest to raise students' awareness of environmental problems.

Sora: That sounds nice. (A)<u>나는 어서 그것을 보고 싶어</u>!

12 위 대화의 밑줄 친 (A)를 주어진 단어를 사용하여 6 단어로 영작하시오. (wait)

➡ _____

13 What is the subject of the photo contest?

➡ _____

14 Why is Minsu's club holding the photo contest?

➡ _____

_____

[15~16] 다음 대화를 읽고 물음에 답하시오.

Sujin: Jiho, hurry up! The elevator is going up soon.

Jiho: The science room is just on the third floor. Why don't we take the stairs?

Sujin: I don't want to walk all the way up there.

Jiho: Come on. Elevators use lots of energy. We need to save energy to protect the environment.

Sujin: But one elevator ride doesn't use that much energy.

Jiho: That's true, but the energy from all the elevator rides adds up over time. In my opinion, taking care of the environment starts with the little things.

Sujin: You have a point. Let's take the stairs.

15 Why does Jiho suggest that Sujin take the stairs?

➡ _____

_____

_____

16 Where are Sujin and Jiho going to?

➡ _____

Grammar

17 다음 문장의 빈칸에 알맞은 말은?

He knew it was silly _____ to feel so disappointed.

① for he   ② for him
③ for his   ④ of him
⑤ of his

18 다음 그림을 보고, 주어진 어휘를 이용하여 빈칸을 알맞게 채우시오.

He explained to her _____ to carry out the experiment. (way, follow, has to)

19 다음 빈칸에 들어갈 말이 나머지와 <u>다른</u> 하나는?

① It is difficult _____ Juho to study math.
② It's foolish _____ you to think so.
③ It's important _____ you to avoid danger!
④ It was difficult _____ us to visit those historic sites.
⑤ It is boring _____ Yuna to ride a roller coaster.

20 다음 빈칸에 알맞지 <u>않은</u> 것은?

> It's _____ for me to jump that high.

① possible   ② easy   ③ natural

④ brave   ⑤ difficult

21 주어진 두 문장을 관계부사를 이용하여 하나의 문장으로 쓰시오.

(1) • I want to go to a place.

    • I can breathe fresh air there.

➡ _____

_____

(2) • Lunch break at school is the time.

    • Junho can play soccer with his friends at the time.

➡ _____

_____

(3) • I know the reason.

    • The manhole covers are round for the reason.

➡ _____

_____

(4) • My mom doesn't like the way.

    • My sister drives in the way.

➡ _____

_____

Reading

[22~25] 다음 글을 읽고 물음에 답하시오.

Cancun is a city where 4.8 million tourists travel every year. One of the most popular activities to do there is looking at the area's beautiful sea life underwater. ① However, tourist activities are seriously damaging parts of the sea near Cancun. ② To prevent this, artists did something interesting. They thought if they attracted tourists to a different part of the sea, the dying areas could have time (A) to get better. ③ It's about 14 meters below the surface and contains 500 statues. ④ The statues are made from materials that support sea life. They provide additional places for plants and animals to live on. ⑤ Over time, many types of sea life will grow on the statues, which will make the artwork unique. The artists want people to see a variety of sea life on the statues. If people realize _____ ⓐ _____, they will understand how important it is to save the sea.

22 주어진 단어를 바르게 나열하여 빈칸 ⓐ에 들어갈 말을 완성하시오.

> (is / life / rich / sea / how)

➡ _____

23 ①~⑤ 중 주어진 문장이 들어가기에 가장 적절한 곳은?

> They made an underwater museum away from the places where sea life was dying.

①   ②   ③   ④   ⑤

24 밑줄 친 (A)와 쓰임이 같은 것은?

① I called you <u>to say</u> that I love you.

② Jane woke up early <u>to catch</u> the bus.

③ Is there any chance <u>to talk</u> with you?

④ It is necessary <u>to listen</u> carefully.

⑤ My goal is <u>to win</u> the game.

25 다음 중 위 글의 내용과 일치하는 것은?

① Over five million tourists visit Cancun every year.

② The underwater museum is about 14 meters above the sea level.

③ Cancun is famous for its beautiful landscape on countryside.

④ The underwater museum will make various sea life unable to live in the sea.

⑤ The artists want people to realize the importance of saving the sea.

[26~28] 다음 글을 읽고 물음에 답하시오.

In Singapore, people are using architecture to protect the environment on land. Let's hear what Rajesh Khan, an architect, says about eco-friendly buildings.

Rajesh: Singapore is hot throughout the year. Most buildings need air conditioning, which uses ①a lot of energy and contributes to climate change. ②That's because architects in Singapore have begun to design eco-friendly buildings that use less air conditioning but are still ③cool inside. For example, many buildings in Singapore are designed to have an open structure. This structure makes it possible for outside air to move throughout a building. This natural air flow is how these buildings stay cool. In addition to making open structures, architects add large gardens. ④This greenery provides shade and protects parts of the building from direct sunlight, which keeps the building cooler.

Eco-friendly buildings like these not only help protect the environment, but also provide people   (A)   ⑤a good quality of life. Those are the goals of this new style of architecture.

Hopefully, architects will keep coming up   (B)   new eco-friendly ideas.

26 ①~⑤ 중 글의 흐름상 어색한 것을 바르게 고쳐 쓰시오.

_____ ➡ _____

27 빈칸 (A)와 (B)에 공통으로 들어갈 말을 쓰시오.

➡ _____

28 위 글을 읽고 답할 수 있는 것은?

① How large are the gardens?

② How does inside air flow naturally?

③ What does an open structure make possible?

④ Why didn't some buildings have an open structure?

⑤ What is another cause of climate change?

[29~30] 다음 글을 읽고 물음에 답하시오.

_____(A)_____

Here's an innovative, environmentally friendly item! It is a cookie cup. It's a cookie that is made in the shape of a cup. After you use the cup, you can just eat it. By (B)doing this, you can save paper or plastic.

The cookie cup can change the world.

Be a part of the change!

29 주어진 단어를 바르게 나열하여 빈칸 (A)에 들어갈 위 글의 제목을 완성하시오.

(the Earth / and / Eat / Save / Cup / Your)!

➡ _____

30 밑줄 친 (B)가 의미하는 것을 우리말로 쓰시오.

➡ _____

출제율 95%

01 다음 대화가 자연스럽게 이어지도록 순서대로 배열하시오.

> (A) In my opinion, we should bring reusable bags when we go shopping.
> (B) I think we're using too many plastic bags.
> (C) I agree. It's not good for the environment. How can we reduce our use of plastic bags?

➡ _____

출제율 100%

02 다음 중 짝지어진 대화가 어색한 것은?

① A: What causes the environmental problem?
　 B: In my opinion, producing too much waste is one of the causes.

② A: What do you think about the new novel?
　 B: In my view, it is so interesting.

③ A: How can we reduce our use of plastic bags?
　 B: In my opinion, we should bring reusable bags when we go shopping.

④ A: Have you heard about edible spoons? That's amazing!
　 B: That sounds awesome. I can't wait to use them.

⑤ A: How can we make our school eco-friendly?
　 B: That'll be helpful. I can't wait to use it.

[03~04] 다음 대화를 읽고 물음에 답하시오.

Sujin: Jiho, hurry up! The elevator is going up soon.
Jiho: (A) The science room is just on the third floor. Why don't we take the stairs?

Sujin: (B) I don't want to walk all the way up there.
Jiho: (C) Come on. Elevators use lots of energy. We need to save energy to protect the environment.
Sujin: (D) But one elevator ride doesn't use that much energy.
Jiho: (E) In my opinion, taking care of the environment starts with the little things.
Sujin: You have a point. Let's take the stairs.

출제율 90%

03 위 대화의 (A)~(E) 중 주어진 문장이 들어가기에 적절한 곳은?

> That's true, but the energy from all the elevator rides adds up over time.

① (A)　② (B)　③ (C)　④ (D)　⑤ (E)

출제율 100%

04 위 대화를 읽고 대답할 수 없는 것은?

① Where is the science room?
② What do elevators use a lot?
③ What does Jiho suggest to protect the environment?
④ What does taking care of the environment start with?
⑤ How much energy does one elevator ride use?

[05~07] 다음 글을 읽고 물음에 답하시오.

B: Today, I'd like to make a suggestion about the trash problem at our school. I've found that many students just throw things away (A)[instead / instead of] recycling them. As you know, however, (B)[recycle / recycling] is very important because it saves resources and helps protect the environment. So, in my opinion, we need to reduce the number of trash cans at school to encourage recycling. Why don't we place four different colored recycling bins on every floor instead? This will remind students to separate the paper, glass, plastic, and cans (C)[proper / properly].

출제율 90%

05 위 글의 (A)~(C)에 들어갈 말이 바르게 짝지어진 것은?

	(A)	(B)	(C)
①	instead	recycle	proper
②	instead	recycling	properly
③	instead of	recycling	proper
④	instead of	recycling	properly
⑤	instead of	recycle	proper

출제율 100%

06 위 글의 내용과 일치하지 <u>않는</u> 것은?

① 소년은 학교의 쓰레기 문제에 대해 제안을 하고자 한다.

② 학교 학생들이 쓰레기를 재활용하는 대신에 그냥 버리고 있다.

③ 소년은 재활용이 정말 중요하다고 주장한다.

④ 소년은 재활용을 권장하기 위해 학교에 있는 쓰레기통의 개수를 늘리는 것이 필요하다고 생각한다.

⑤ 소년은 학교의 모든 층에 각기 색이 다른 4개의 재활용통을 둘 것을 제안하였다.

출제율 95%

07 위 글에서 다음 영영풀이가 나타내는 말을 찾아 쓰시오.

> to divide things into different parts or groups

➡ _____

[08~09] 다음 대화를 읽고 물음에 답하시오.

Jack: What are we going to do this weekend, Mihee?

Mihee: Why don't we go to the sheep park near my house?

Jack: A sheep park? How interesting! Are there really sheep in the park?

Mihee: Yes. They are there to protect the environment.

Jack: How can they help the environment?

Mihee: You know, people usually use chemicals to kill unwanted plants. The sheep in the park eat those plants, so the chemicals are not needed.

Jack: What a bright idea! (A)I can't wait to visit the park! (looking)

출제율 90%

08 위 대화의 밑줄 친 (A)와 의미가 같도록 주어진 단어를 사용하여 다시 쓰시오.

➡ _____

출제율 95%

09 위 대화의 내용과 일치하지 <u>않는</u> 것은?

① 미희는 Jack에게 주말에 그녀의 집 근처에 있는 양 공원에 갈 것을 제안했다.

② 양들은 환경을 보호하기 위해 공원에 있다.

③ 공원에 있는 양들은 잡초를 먹어 환경을 보호한다.

④ 양 공원에는 잡초를 없애기 위해 많은 화학 물질이 필요하다.

⑤ Jack은 양 공원에 가 보고 싶어 한다.

출제율 90%

10 다음 두 문장이 같도록 할 때 빈칸에 알맞은 말을 쓰시오.

> Ann will never forget the day. Her dog joined her family on the day.
> = Ann will never forget the day _____ her dog joined her family.

출제율 100%

11 다음 중 어법상 적절한 문장은?

① It is easy of children to learn foreign languages.

② This structure makes possible for outside air to move throughout a building.

③ It was boring of her to ride a bike.

④ It was careless of her to open the door for the stranger.

⑤ They don't have enough food to eating.

출제율 95%

12 다음 빈칸에 알맞은 말이 순서대로 짝지어진 것은?

> • We should find the reason _____ our goods didn't sell well at the flea market.
> • It was difficult _____ him to pass the test.

① why – of
② when – of
③ why – for
④ when – for
⑤ which – for

출제율 95%

13 다음 ⓐ~ⓖ 중 어법상 옳은 것을 모두 고르시오.

> ⓐ I want to stop by the café which Felix bought this cupcake.
> ⓑ Autumn is the time where leaves fall.
> ⓒ I will show my classmates how I made peanut sauce.
> ⓓ It is bad of the health to smoke like a chimney.
> ⓔ They had enough food for us to eat.
> ⓕ It is hard for Janet getting along with Tommy.
> ⓖ It is impossible for him to finish the homework by tomorrow.

➡ _____

출제율 95%

14 다음 우리말을 주어진 어휘를 이용하여 영작하시오.

(1) 그는 폭력이 거의 없는 도시에서 성장했다. (a city, violence, grow up, rare)

➡ _____

(2) 내가 그 보고서를 작성하는 데는 세 시간이 걸렸다. (the report, take, write, for, to)

➡ _____

[15~16] 다음 글을 읽고 물음에 답하시오.

> It is important for us to find ways to protect the environment. Some people have found creative ways to save the earth. One example is an underwater museum in Cancun, Mexico. Let's meet Dr. Rosa Allison, an art professor, and listen to her explanation about the special museum.

출제율 90%

15 What creative way to protect the environment is used in Cancun? Answer in English.

➡ _____
_____

출제율 100%

16 위 글에 이어질 내용으로 가장 적절한 것은?

① the records of Rosa Allison's life
② the explanation about an underwater museum
③ how to construct a museum on land
④ the explanation about how to travel Cancun
⑤ the reason why Rosa Allison became an art professor

[17~18] 다음 글을 읽고 물음에 답하시오.

Cancun is a city where 4.8 million tourists travel every year. One of the most popular activities to do there is looking at the area's beautiful sea life underwater. However, tourist activities are seriously damaging parts of the sea near Cancun. To prevent this, artists did something interesting. ⓐThey thought if ⓑthey attracted tourists to a different part of the sea, the dying areas could have time to get better. ⓒThey made (A)an underwater museum away from the places where sea life was dying. It's about 14 meters below the surface and contains 500 statues. The statues are made from materials that support sea life. ⓓThey provide additional places for plants and animals to live on. Over time, many types of sea life will grow on the statues, which will make the artwork unique.

🖉 출제율 95%

17 ⓐ~ⓓ에서 같은 것을 지칭하는 것끼리 바르게 묶은 것은?

① ⓐ – ⓑ, ⓒ, ⓓ 　　② ⓐ, ⓑ – ⓒ, ⓓ

③ ⓑ, ⓒ – ⓐ, ⓓ 　　④ ⓐ, ⓑ, ⓒ – ⓓ

⑤ ⓒ – ⓐ, ⓑ, ⓓ

🖉 출제율 95%

18 밑줄 친 (A)에 관한 설명으로 바르지 <u>않은</u> 것은?

① 해수면에서 약 14미터 아래에 지어졌다.

② 해양 생물에게 도움이 되는 재료들로 만들어진 조각상이 있다.

③ 칸쿤 근처 바다를 보호하기 위하여 만들어졌다.

④ 많은 형태의 바다 생명체들이 조각상에서 자라게 될 것이다.

⑤ 현재 많은 관광객들로 인해 훼손되었다.

[19~21] 다음 글을 읽고 물음에 답하시오.

Singapore is hot throughout the year. Most buildings need air conditioning, which uses a lot of energy and ①contributes to climate change. That's why architects in Singapore have begun to design eco-friendly buildings that use less air conditioning but are still cool ②inside. ____(A)____, many buildings in Singapore are designed to have an open structure. This structure makes it possible for ③outside air to move throughout a building. This natural air flow is how these buildings stay cool. In addition to making open structures, architects add large gardens. This greenery provides shade and ④protects parts of the building from direct sunlight, which keeps the building ⑤warmer.

Eco-friendly buildings like these not only help protect the environment, but also provide people with a good quality of life. Those are the goals of this new style of architecture. Hopefully, architects will keep coming up with new eco-friendly ideas.

🖉 출제율 95%

19 빈칸 (A)에 들어갈 말로 가장 적절한 것은?

① In addition 　　② For example

③ However 　　④ Still

⑤ In other words

🖉 출제율 100%

20 ①~⑤ 중 글의 흐름상 <u>어색한</u> 것은?

① 　　② 　　③ 　　④ 　　⑤

🖉 출제율 90%

21 Besides making open structures, what do architects add? Answer in English.

➡ _____

[01~03] 다음 글을 읽고 물음에 답하시오.

> B: Today, I'd like to make a suggestion about the trash problem at our school. I've found that many students just throw things away instead of recycling them. As you know, however, recycling is very important because it saves resources and helps protect the environment. So, in my opinion, we need to reduce the number of trash cans at school to encourage recycling. Why don't we place four different colored recycling bins on every floor instead? This will remind students to separate the paper, glass, plastic, and cans properly.

01 According to the boy, what's the matter with many students at school?

➡ _____

_____

02 What does the boy suggest to encourage recycling?

➡ _____

_____

03 What does the boy want to place on every floor?

➡ _____

_____

04 관계부사를 사용하여 주어진 두 문장을 한 문장으로 바꾸어 쓰시오.

(1) • He was born in the year.
  • The war ended then.

➡ _____

_____

(2) • Jane didn't come here yet.
  • I know the reason for that.

➡ _____

_____

(3) • This is the city.
  • I lived there 10 years ago.

➡ _____

_____

(4) • This is the way.
  • He caught the big fish in the way.

➡ _____

_____

05 괄호 안에 주어진 단어를 활용하여 빈칸을 채우시오.

(1) It is very dangerous _____ in the country which has corona virus all over. (they, live)

(2) It was a great honor _____ Korea. (I, visit)

(3) Was it smart _____ it a secret? (she, keep)

06 다음 두 문장의 의미가 같도록 문장의 빈칸을 완성하시오.

(1) It is natural that a baby should cry.
  = It is natural _____.

(2) Jane was considerate to let us know it.
  = It was _____ us know it.

(3) He kindly showed me the way to the station.
  = It was kind _____ me the way to the station.

Eat Your Cup and Save the Earth!

Here's an innovative, environmentally friendly item! It is a cookie cup. It's a cookie that is made in the shape of a cup. After you use the cup, you can just eat it. By doing this, you can save paper or plastic.

The cookie cup can change the world.

Be a part of the change!

07 What can you save by using the cup? Answer in English.

➡ _____

08 What does the cookie cup look like? Answer in English.

➡ _____

[09~11] 다음 글을 읽고 물음에 답하시오.

Singapore is hot throughout the year. Most buildings need air conditioning, which uses a lot of energy and contributes to climate change. That's why architects in Singapore have begun to design eco-friendly buildings that use less air conditioning but are still cool inside. For example, many buildings in Singapore are designed to have an open structure. This structure makes it possible for outside air to move throughout a building. This natural air flow is how these buildings stay cool. In addition to making open structures, architects add large gardens. This greenery provides shade and protects parts of the building from direct sunlight, which keeps the building cooler.

Eco-friendly buildings like these not only help protect the environment, but also provide people with a good quality of life. Those are the goals of this new style of architecture. Hopefully, architects will keep coming up with new eco-friendly ideas.

09 Write the reason why most buildings in Singapore need air conditioning. Use the phrase 'It's because.'

➡ _____
_____

10 What is the goal of eco-friendly buildings? Answer in English and use the phrase 'as well as.'

➡ _____
_____

11 위 글의 내용과 일치하도록 빈칸에 알맞은 말을 쓰시오.

Environmental problem

In Singapore, most buildings need (1)_____, which uses (2)_____ and contributes to (3)_____.

Ideas to solve the problem

Thanks to (4)_____, outside air moves throughout a building, so the building can be kept (5)_____.
Large (6)_____ provide shade and protect parts of the building (7)_____, which keeps the building cooler.

01 다음 대화의 내용과 일치하도록 수진이의 일기를 완성하시오.

Sujin: Jiho, hurry up! The elevator is going up soon.

Jiho: The science room is just on the third floor. Why don't we take the stairs?

Sujin: I don't want to walk all the way up there.

Jiho: Come on. Elevators use lots of energy. We need to save energy to protect the environment.

Sujin: But one elevator ride doesn't use that much energy.

Jiho: That's true, but the energy from all the elevator rides adds up over time. In my opinion, taking care of the environment starts with the little things.

Sujin: You have a point. Let's take the stairs.

I reflected on myself today. I used to ride an elevator when I went up to the science room on (A)_____. When I tried to go up there, Jiho suggested (B)_____. Actually, I didn't want to (C)_____. But, Jiho persuaded me to take the stairs. I thought that one elevator ride didn't use (D)_____, but Jiho reminded me of the importance of starting with little things to (E)_____. To protect the environment, I decided to save the energy with the little things.

02 A와 B에 주어진 것 중 각각 하나씩과 가주어를 이용하여 어법에 맞게 3 문장 이상 쓰시오.

A	she/dangerous	she/difficult	he/necessary	he/rude
B	talk loudly like that	learn German	take care of the children	ride a bike

(1) _____

(2) _____

(3) _____

(4) _____

단원별 모의고사

01 다음 영영풀이가 가리키는 것을 고르시오.

> a new or better idea, method, or device

① company   ② chemical
③ resource   ④ shade
⑤ innovation

02 다음 우리말에 맞게 빈칸을 완성하시오.

(1) 그늘에서부터 열매까지, 나무는 우리에게 많은 좋은 것들을 줍니다!
➡ From _____ to fruits, trees give us many good things!

(2) 기후 변화 때문에 전 세계적으로 온도가 상승하고 있다.
➡ Because of _____ change, _____ are rising around the world.

03 다음 문장의 빈칸에 들어갈 말을 〈보기〉에서 골라 알맞은 형태로 쓰시오.

> ┤ 보기 ├
> contribute to / a variety of / break down / take the stairs / would like to

(1) This furniture was made of _____ different woods.
(2) When did this elevator _____?
(3) Online classes _____ a better education.
(4) I _____ take the picture with my cousin.

(5) It is good for your health to _____ instead of using the elevator.

[04~05] 다음 대화를 읽고 물음에 답하시오.

> Emily: I read a ⓐ<u>cool</u> article today.
> Brian: What was it about?
> Emily: It was about a new bag. It just looks like a plastic bag, but it's made mostly of corn.
> Brian: That sounds really ⓑ<u>amazing</u>.
> Emily: Yes, but there's more. The bag ⓒ<u>breaks down</u> in soil in only three months and disappears in about three minutes in warm water!
> Brian: Wow! That will help us ⓓ<u>increase</u> plastic waste by a lot!
> Emily: I know! The company will start selling the bag sometime this year. I ⓔ<u>can't</u> wait to use it!

04 위 대화의 ⓐ~ⓔ 중 흐름상 어색한 것을 고르시오.

① ⓐ cool   ② ⓑ amazing
③ ⓒ breaks down   ④ ⓓ increase
⑤ ⓔ can't

05 위 대화를 읽고 대답할 수 없는 것은?

① What is the article Emily read about?
② What is the new bag made of?
③ How long does the new bag take to break down in soil?
④ When is the company going to sell the new bag?
⑤ What is Brian looking forward to?

[06~07] 다음 글을 읽고 물음에 답하시오.

B: Today, I'd like to make a suggestion about the trash problem at our school. (A) I've found that many students just throw things away instead of recycling them. (B) As you know, however, recycling is very important because it saves resources and helps protect the environment. (C) So, in my opinion, we need to reduce the number of trash cans at school to encourage recycling. (D) This will remind students to separate the paper, glass, plastic, and cans properly. (E)

06 위 글의 (A)~(E) 중 주어진 문장이 들어가기에 적절한 곳은?

Why don't we place four different colored recycling bins on every floor instead?

① (A) ② (B) ③ (C) ④ (D) ⑤ (E)

07 위 글의 내용과 일치하도록 빈칸을 완성하시오.

<A New Recycling System in Our School>
a. Reduce (A)_____.
b. Place four different colored recycling bins on (B)_____.
c. (C)_____ items into different bins to recycle.

08 다음 대화가 자연스럽게 이어지도록 순서대로 배열하시오.

(A) But I'm bored with my old bags.
(B) Oh, that sounds interesting! I can't wait to make my own bag.
(C) I want to buy a new bag.

(D) You already have too many bags. In my opinion, you don't need any more.
(E) Then how about using old clothes to make a new bag? You can find out how to do it online.

➡ _____

09 다음 대화의 내용과 일치하도록 빈칸을 완성하시오.

Tom: I think we're using too many plastic bags.
Jane: I agree. It's not good for the environment. How can we reduce our use of plastic bags?
Tom: In my opinion, we should bring reusable bags when we go shopping.

To protect the environment, we need to _____. For example, it can be one of the ways to _____ when we go shopping.

10 다음 우리말을 주어진 단어를 이용하여 영작하시오.

(1) 우리는 미래 세대를 위해 환경을 보호해야 한다. (generations, should)
➡ _____
_____

(2) 창의적인 사람은 새로운 아이디어들을 떠올리는 것을 잘한다. (good, up)
➡ _____

(3) 중국의 수중 도시는 전 세계의 잠수부들을 매료시킨다. (attract, over)
➡ _____

11 다음 중 어법상 어색한 것을 고르시오.

① It is not easy for him to find out the answer.

② Wasn't it clever for him to solve the puzzle?

③ It is difficult for me to take care of the baby.

④ It was impossible for me to cross the river by swimming.

⑤ It is easy for Jeongmin to study math.

12 다음 중 어법상 어색한 것은?

① I've left my wallet in the restaurant where we had lunch.

② Describe the way how you did it.

③ This is the house where I used to live.

④ I still remember the day when I went to Paris.

⑤ I want to know the reason why Eden hasn't come home yet.

13 다음 빈칸에 들어갈 말을 순서대로 묶은 것은?

• It is fun _____ Jihun to ride a roller coaster.

• This natural air flow is _____ these buildings stay cool.

① of – how   ② of – when

③ for – how   ④ for – when

⑤ with – why

14 다음 문장에서 어법상 어색한 것을 바르게 고치시오.

(1) He regrets the way how he lived his life.

➡ _____

(2) Do you remember that restaurant which we met for the first time?

➡ _____

(3) It is exciting of Jia to ride a roller coaster.

➡ _____

(4) It is kind for you to invite me.

➡ _____

15 〈보기〉와 같이 문장을 바꿔 쓰시오.

┌─ 보기 ├─
You should choose good friends.
→ It is important for you to choose good friends.
└─────────────

(1) She should study English diligently every day.

➡ It is important _____

_____.

(2) She kindly explained the process of making a newspaper.

➡ It was nice _____

_____.

16 다음 중 밑줄 친 부분의 쓰임이 〈보기〉와 같은 것은?

┌─ 보기 ├─
Sunday is the day <u>when</u> I can relax.
└─────────────

① It was a time <u>when</u> fountain pens were rare.

② Until <u>when</u> can you stay here?

③ I loved history <u>when</u> I was at school.

④ <u>When</u> did you see him last?

⑤ He works <u>when</u> he might rest.

17 다음 우리말을 주어진 어휘를 이용하여 영작하시오.

(1) 그녀는 때때로 자기가 건강했던 때를 생각한다.
(about, healthy)

➡ _____

_____

(2) 우리가 지난주에 피자를 먹었던 식당의 이름이 무엇인가요? (what, the name, had)

➡ _____

_____

(3) 어떤 사람들은 스마트폰 없이 사는 것이 불가능해 보인다. (seems, some people, their smartphones)

➡ _____

_____

(4) 우리는 내일 그 경기에서 이기기가 쉽지 않을 것이다. (won't, the game, win)

➡ _____

_____

[18~21] 다음 글을 읽고 물음에 답하시오.

Cancun is a city where 4.8 million tourists travel every year. One of the most popular activities to do there is looking at the area's beautiful sea life underwater. ① However, tourist activities are seriously damaging parts of the sea near Cancun. ② To prevent this, artists did something interesting. They thought if they attracted tourists to a different part of the sea, the dying areas could have time to get better. ③ They made an underwater museum away from the places where sea life was dying. ④ The statues are made from materials that support sea life. They provide additional places for plants and animals to live on.

⑤ Over time, many types of sea life will grow on the statues, which will make the artwork unique. The artists want people to see a variety of sea life on the statues. If people realize how rich sea life is, they will understand (A)바다를 지키는 것이 얼마나 중요한지.

18 ①~⑤ 중 주어진 문장이 들어가기에 가장 적절한 곳은?

It's about 14 meters below the surface and contains 500 statues.

①　　②　　③　　④　　⑤

19 주어진 단어를 활용하여 밑줄 친 우리말 (A)를 영어로 쓰시오.

(important / it / save)

➡ _____

20 What did artists do in order for the dying areas to have time to get better? Answer in English.

➡ _____

_____

21 위 글의 제목으로 가장 적절한 것은?

① Cancun: the Most Famous Tourist Attraction in Mexico
② A Creative Way to Save the Earth: An Underwater Museum in Cancun
③ What Makes People Attracted to Cancun: Various Activities on Land

④ Various Ways to Protect the Environment All Around the World

⑤ Warning of Animals: Signals Toward Protecting the Environment

[22~25] 다음 글을 읽고 물음에 답하시오.

Singapore is hot throughout the year. Most buildings need air conditioning, which ① uses a lot of energy and contributes to climate change.

(A) This natural air flow is how these buildings stay cool. In addition to ②making open structures, architects add large gardens. This greenery provides shade and protects parts of the building from direct sunlight, ③that keeps the building cooler.

(B) For example, many buildings in Singapore are designed to have an open structure. This structure makes it possible ④for outside air to move throughout a building.

(C) That's why architects in Singapore have begun to design eco-friendly buildings that use less air conditioning but are still cool inside.

Eco-friendly buildings like these not only help protect the environment, but also provide people with a good quality of life. Those are the goals of this new style of architecture. Hopefully, architects will keep coming up with new eco-friendly ideas.

Every field ⑤has different ways of protecting the environment. With more innovation, humans and nature will be able to live together in harmony far into the future.

22 자연스러운 글이 되도록 (A)~(C)를 바르게 나열하시오.

➡ _____

23 ①~⑤ 중 어법상 바르지 않은 것은?

①　　②　　③　　④　　⑤

24 다음 중 위 글에 나오는 단어의 풀이가 <u>아닌</u> 것은?

① a new thing or a new method of doing something

② less harmful to the environment than other similar products or services

③ the general atmosphere or situation somewhere

④ a person who designs buildings

⑤ a person visiting a place for pleasure and interest, especially when they are on holiday

25 다음은 싱가포르 건물의 특징을 소개하는 Tim의 말이다. 틀린 부분을 한 군데 찾아 바르게 고쳐 쓰시오.

Many buildings in Singapore have an open structure. It keeps the people moving throughout a building.

_____ ➡ _____

MEMO

INSIGHT
on the textbook

교과서 파헤치기

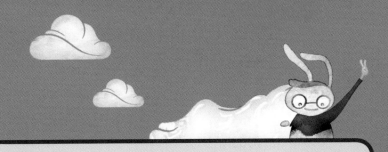

※ 다음 영어를 우리말로 쓰시오.

01 recently _____

02 aware _____

03 cause _____

04 panic _____

05 collapse _____

06 smash _____

07 damage _____

08 exit _____

09 avoid _____

10 serious _____

11 wildfire _____

12 worse _____

13 properly _____

14 common _____

15 affect _____

16 nervously _____

17 missing _____

18 earthquake _____

19 exactly _____

20 destroy _____

21 heavy rain _____

22 whole _____

23 crawl _____

24 flood _____

25 immediately _____

26 include _____

27 natural disaster _____

28 mention _____

29 tap _____

30 confusion _____

31 urgently _____

32 occur _____

33 reaction _____

34 violently _____

35 based on~ _____

36 as well _____

37 get a discount _____

38 a variety of _____

39 in case of ~ _____

40 a large number of _____

41 tip over _____

42 pull over _____

43 break into pieces _____

※ 다음 우리말을 영어로 쓰시오.

01 격렬하게 _____

02 초래하다 _____

03 반응 _____

04 혼란, 혼동 _____

05 더 나쁜 _____

06 제대로, 적절하게 _____

07 최근에 _____

08 파괴하다 _____

09 흔한 _____

10 손상 _____

11 실종된 _____

12 가슴 _____

13 붕괴되다, 무너지다 _____

14 불안하게 _____

15 재난 _____

16 홍수 _____

17 지진 _____

18 (일·사건 등이) 발생하다 _____

19 기어가다 _____

20 세게 부딪치다 _____

21 폭염 _____

22 극심한 공포 _____

23 정확하게 _____

24 포함하다 _____

25 특수 효과 _____

26 갑자기 _____

27 나가다, 퇴장하다 _____

28 영향을 주다 _____

29 두들기다 _____

30 긴급하게 _____

31 즉시 _____

32 실제로 _____

33 폭우 _____

34 심각한 _____

35 길 한쪽으로 차를 대다 _____

36 ～의 한 가운데 _____

37 다양한 _____

38 넘어지다, 기울어지다 _____

39 ～의 경우에 _____

40 ～에 바탕을 둔 _____

41 매우 많은 _____

42 집어넣다 _____

43 굴러 떨어지다 _____

※ 다음 영영풀이에 알맞은 단어를 <보기>에서 골라 쓴 후, 우리말 뜻을 쓰시오.

1 _____ : to leave a place: _____

2 _____ : wanting to know about something: _____

3 _____ : correctly, or in a way that is considered right: _____

4 _____ : happening often and to many people or in many places: _____

5 _____ : to hit something violently and very hard: _____

6 _____ : to break apart and fall down suddenly: _____

7 _____ : a fire that moves quickly and cannot be controlled: _____

8 _____ : to make something happen, especially something bad: _____

9 _____ : a very large amount of water that covers an area that is usually dry:
   _____

10 _____ : to make someone or something part of a larger group: _____

11 _____ : a sudden shaking of the Earth's surface that often causes a lot of damage:
   _____

12 _____ : to move along on your hands and knees with your body close to the
   ground: _____

13 _____ : to move backward or forward or from side to side while hanging from a
   fixed point: _____

14 _____ : to do an action or activity that usually requires training or skill: _____

15 _____ : to damage something so badly that it no longer exists or cannot be used
   or repaired: _____

16 _____ : a sudden event such as a flood, storm, or accident which causes great
   damage or suffering: _____

보기			
smash	earthquake	properly	exit
cause	include	collapse	wildfire
destroy	common	crawl	disaster
perform	curious	flood	swing

※ 다음 우리말과 일치하도록 빈칸에 알맞은 말을 쓰시오.

Listen & Talk 1 A

B: There _____ a big _____ in Europe. Did you _____ _____ it?

G: No, I didn't. But _____ aren't that _____ in winter, _____ they? I'm _____ about _____ that _____.

B: Me too. _____ do some online _____.

Listen & Talk 1 B

G: There _____ _____ _____ many _____ _____ in Korea _____ _____.

B: I agree. There was an _____ in the _____ last week. Also a _____ is coming this week.

G: I'm _____ about _____ _____ _____ _____ causes the _____ _____ in Korea.

B: Actually I read a _____ yesterday about the _____ from _____ _____ of _____ _____. Number one is _____.

G: I see. I _____ earthquakes are _____.

B: No, second is _____ rain, and third is _____ _____.

G: _____ about earthquakes?

B: _____ _____ the report, _____ are fourth. But the _____ from earthquakes has _____ _____ recently _____ they have _____ _____ more often in Korea.

G: I see. It _____ _____ we have to be _____ for a _____ of _____ _____ in Korea.

Listen & Talk 1 C

B: Hey, did you _____ _____ the big _____ in California?

G: No, I didn't. _____ _____ are they?

B: They've _____ a large _____ _____ _____ and _____ _____.

G: _____ the fires still _____ _____?

B: Yes, _____ the wind has made the fires _____. I hope all the people _____ _____ are okay.

G: _____ _____ I. I'm _____ how many people had to _____ their homes.

B: _____ _____ _____ 20,000 people had to _____ their _____, and about 400 people are _____ in that area.

G: That's _____. I hope they're _____ _____.

B: 유럽에 큰 홍수가 있었어. 그것에 대해 들었니?

G: 아니. 하지만 겨울에는 홍수가 그렇게 흔하지 않아, 그렇지 않니? 나는 어떻게 그런 일이 일어났는지 궁금해.

B: 나도 그래. 온라인 검색을 해보자.

G: 요즈음 한국에서 많은 자연 재해가 있는 것 같아.

B: 동의해. 지난주에 남부에서 지진이 있었어. 또한 이번 주에는 태풍이 올 거야.

G: 나는 어떤 종류의 자연 재해가 한국에서 가장 큰 피해를 주는지 궁금해.

B: 사실 나는 어제 각 유형의 자연 재해로 인한 피해에 관한 보고서를 읽었어. 첫 번째가 폭풍이야.

G: 그렇구나. 지진이 두 번째인 것 같아.

B: 아니야. 두 번째는 폭우이고 세 번째는 폭설이야.

G: 지진은?

B: 보고서에 따르면, 지진은 네 번째야. 하지만 최근 한국에서 지진이 더 자주 일어나기 때문에 지진으로 인한 피해가 증가하고 있어.

G: 그렇구나. 한국에서는 다양한 자연 재해에 대비를 해야 할 것 같아.

B: 안녕. 너 캘리포니아에서 일어난 큰 화재에 대해 들었니?

G: 아니. 얼마나 심각하니?

B: 많은 집들과 다른 건물들을 파괴했어.

G: 아직도 화재가 진행되고 있니?

B: 그래. 사실 바람이 화재를 더 악화시켰어. 나는 거기 사는 모든 사람들이 괜찮기를 바라.

G: 나도 그래. 얼마나 많은 사람들이 집을 떠나야 했는지 궁금해.

B: 사실 2만 명 이상이 집을 떠나야 했고, 약 400명이 실종되었어.

G: 끔찍하구나. 나는 그들이 안전한 곳에 있기를 바라.

Listen & Talk 2 A

B: Mom, _____ _____ do we _____ _____ _____ the _____ _____ _____ _____?

W: Well, we need _____, some food, and _____.

B: _____ _____, Mom?

W: Oh, _____ _____ that you _____ _____ for the _____.

Listen & Talk 2 B

W: _____ CPR _____ can _____ someone's life. _____ are the _____ for _____ CPR. First, check that the person _____ help. _____ the person and shout, "_____ you okay?" If there's no _____, call 119 for help. Second, _____, look, and _____ _____ _____. If the person's not _____, begin CPR. Make _____ you _____ your _____ _____ the middle of the person's _____. Use your body _____ to press _____ on the chest. After 30 presses, give the person two _____. _____ _____ CPR _____ _____ _____.

Listen & Talk 2 D

A: _____ _____ _____ a fire, _____ should I _____?

B: _____ _____ that you _____ your mouth with a _____ _____.

A: Anything _____?

B: _____ _____ _____ you _____ the building _____.

Do It Yourself A

G: Did you _____ that earthquakes are _____ more _____ in Korea than _____?

B: Oh, _____? I've _____ _____ an earthquake in Korea.

G: They _____ _____ in the _____ part of Korca, but now they are occurring in _____ _____ _____ _____.

B: I didn't know that. I'm _____ about _____ earthquakes have _____ so often in Korea _____.

G: _____ _____ we do some _____ to find out?

B: Sounds good, but where _____ we look first?

G: _____ _____ _____ our science teacher first? I think she can _____ us.

B: Okay. _____ go and _____ her.

B: 엄마, 자연 재해 생존 장비에 무엇을 더 넣어야 할까요?

W: 글쎄. 우리는 물, 약간의 식량 그리고 라디오가 필요해.

B: 다른 것은요, 엄마?

W: 오, 라디오 건전지를 반드시 포함하도록 해.

W: 제대로 심폐소생술을 수행하는 것은 누군가의 생명을 구할 수 있습니다. 여기 적절한 심폐소생술을 위한 단계가 있습니다. 첫째, 그 사람이 도움을 필요로 하는지 확인하십시오. 그 사람을 두드리며 "괜찮으세요?' 라고 큰소리로 외치세요. 반응이 없으면 119에 전화를 걸어 도움을 요청하세요. 둘째, 호흡을 하는지 듣고, 보고, 느끼세요. 그 사람이 숨을 쉬지 않으면 심폐소생술을 시작하세요. 손을 반드시 그 사람의 가슴 가운데에 놓도록 하세요. 가슴을 더 세게 누르기 위해 체중을 이용하세요. 30번 누른 후, 그 사람에게 두 번 바람을 불어 넣으시오. 도움이 올 때까지 심폐소생술을 계속하세요.

A: 화재가 발생하면 어떻게 해야 하나요?

B: 반드시 젖은 천으로 입을 가리도록 해.

A: 다른 것은 뭐가 있을까요?

B: 즉시 건물 밖으로 나가도록 해야 해.

G: 한국에서 지진이 전보다 자주 일어나고 있다는 말을 들었니?

B: 오, 정말? 나는 한국에서 지진을 느껴본 적이 없어.

G: 보통 지진이 한국의 남부에서 발생하지만, 이제는 다른 지역에서도 발생하고 있어.

B: 그건 몰랐어. 나는 왜 최근에 한국에서 지진이 그렇게 자주 발생하는지 궁금해.

G: 알아내기 위해 조사를 해보는 게 어떨까?

B: 좋은 것 같아. 하지만 먼저 어디에서 찾아야 하지?

G: 먼저 과학 선생님께 여쭤보면 어떨까? 나는 선생님께서 우리를 도울 수 있을 거라고 생각해.

B: 알았어. 가서 선생님을 찾아보자.

※ 다음 우리말에 맞도록 대화를 영어로 쓰시오.

 해석

Listen & Talk 1 A

B: _____

G: _____

　 _____

B: _____

B: 유럽에 큰 홍수가 있었어. 그것에 대해 들었니?
G: 아니. 하지만 겨울에는 홍수가 그렇게 흔하지 않아, 그렇지 않니? 나는 어떻게 그런 일이 일어났는지 궁금해.
B: 나도 그래. 온라인 검색을 해보자.

Listen & Talk 1 B

G: _____

B: _____

　 _____

G: _____

　 _____

B: _____

　 _____

G: _____

B: _____

G: _____

B: _____

　 _____

G: _____

　 _____

G: 요즈음 한국에서 많은 자연 재해가 있는 것 같아.
B: 동의해. 지난주에 남부에서 지진이 있었어. 또한 이번 주에는 태풍이 올 거야.
G: 나는 어떤 종류의 자연 재해가 한국에서 가장 큰 피해를 주는지 궁금해.
B: 사실 나는 어제 각 유형의 자연 재해로 인한 피해에 관한 보고서를 읽었어. 첫 번째가 폭풍이야.
G: 그렇구나. 지진이 두 번째인 것 같아.
B: 아니야. 두 번째는 폭우이고 세 번째는 폭설이야.
G: 지진은?
B: 보고서에 따르면, 지진은 네 번째야. 하지만 최근 한국에서 지진이 더 자주 일어나기 때문에 지진으로 인한 피해가 증가하고 있어.
G: 그렇구나. 한국에서는 다양한 자연 재해에 대비를 해야 할 것 같아.

Listen & Talk 1 C

B: _____

G: _____

B: _____

G: _____

B: _____

　 _____

G: _____

B: _____

　 _____

G: _____

B: 안녕. 너 캘리포니아에서 일어난 큰 화재에 대해 들었니?
G: 아니. 얼마나 심각하니?
B: 많은 집들과 다른 건물들을 파괴했어.
G: 아직도 화재가 진행되고 있니?
B: 그래. 사실 바람이 화재를 더 악화시켰어. 나는 거기 사는 모든 사람들이 괜찮기를 바라.
G: 나도 그래. 얼마나 많은 사람들이 집을 떠나야 했는지 궁금해.
B: 사실 2만 명 이상이 집을 떠나야 했고, 약 400명이 실종되었어.
G: 끔찍하구나. 나는 그들이 안전한 곳에 있기를 바라.

Listen & Talk 2 A

B: _____

W: _____

B: _____

W: _____

Listen & Talk 2 B

W: _____

_____

_____

_____

_____

_____

_____

Listen & Talk 2 D

A: _____

B: _____

A: _____

B: _____

Do It Yourself A

G: _____

B: _____

G: _____

_____

B: _____

_____

G: _____

B: _____

G: _____

B: _____

B: 엄마, 자연 재해 생존 장비에 무엇을 더 넣어야 할까요?

W: 글쎄. 우리는 물, 약간의 식량 그리고 라디오가 필요해.

B: 다른 것은요, 엄마?

W: 오, 라디오 건전지를 반드시 포함하도록 해.

W: 제대로 심폐소생술을 수행하는 것은 누군가의 생명을 구할 수 있습니다. 여기 적절한 심폐소생술을 위한 단계가 있습니다. 첫째, 그 사람이 도움을 필요로 하는지 확인하십시오. 그 사람을 두드리며 "괜찮으세요?'라고 큰소리로 외치세요. 반응이 없으면 119에 전화를 걸어 도움을 요청하세요. 둘째, 호흡을 하는지 듣고, 보고, 느끼세요. 그 사람이 숨을 쉬지 않으면 심폐소생술을 시작하세요. 손을 반드시 그 사람의 가슴 가운데에 놓도록 하세요. 가슴을 더 세게 누르기 위해 체중을 이용하세요. 30번 누른 후, 그 사람에게 두 번 바람을 불어 넣으시오. 도움이 올 때까지 심폐소생술을 계속하세요.

A: 화재가 발생하면 어떻게 해야 하나요?

B: 반드시 젖은 천으로 입을 가리도록 해.

A: 다른 것은 뭐가 있을까요?

B: 즉시 건물 밖으로 나가도록 해야 해.

G: 한국에서 지진이 전보다 자주 일어나고 있다는 말을 들었니?

B: 오, 정말? 나는 한국에서 지진을 느껴본 적이 없어.

G: 보통 지진이 한국의 남부에서 발생하지만, 이제는 다른 지역에서도 발생하고 있어.

B: 그건 몰랐어. 나는 왜 최근에 한국에서 지진이 그렇게 자주 발생하는지 궁금해.

G: 알아내기 위해 조사를 해보는 게 어떨까?

B: 좋은 것 같아. 하지만 먼저 어디에서 찾아야 하지?

G: 먼저 과학 선생님께 여쭤보면 어떨까? 나는 선생님께서 우리를 도울 수 있을 거라고 생각해.

B: 알았어. 가서 선생님을 찾아보자.

※ 다음 우리말과 일치하도록 빈칸에 알맞은 것을 골라 쓰시오.

1 _____ _____ to an _____
   A. Up   B. Waking   C. Earthquake

2 One night _____ February, after I _____ _____ to bed, an earthquake _____.
   A. hit   B. gone   C. in   D. had

3 I _____ _____ suddenly _____ my bed was _____.
   A. because   B. up   C. shaking   D. woke

4 I _____ my brother was _____ my bed _____ a _____.
   A. as   B. joke   C. shaking   D. thought

5 But then I _____ the mirror on my desk _____ to the floor and _____ into _____.
   A. break   B. fall   C. pieces   D. heard

6 I knew it wasn't my brother then, but I still didn't know _____ _____ _____ _____.
   A. exactly   B. what   C. happening   D. was

7 Soon the _____ room began to shake _____, and my confusion _____ to _____.
   A. violently   B. whole   C. panic   D. turned

8 My mom _____ that it was an _____ and _____ _____ my room.
   A. into   B. shouted   C. ran   D. earthquake

9 _____ it was my first time _____ an earthquake, I didn't know _____ to _____.
   A. how   B. since   C. react   D. experiencing

10 I _____ _____ _____, "What should I do?"
   A. saying   B. kept   C. just

11 My mom _____ me and my brother _____ _____ _____.
   A. out   B. pulled   C. of   D. bed

12 We _____ to the kitchen and _____ _____ the table.
   A. crawled   B. ran   C. under

13 I could see the light _____ violently and books _____ to the _____.
   A. falling   B. swinging   C. floor

1 지진에 눈을 뜨는 것

2 2월 어느 날 밤, 내가 잠자리에 든 후에 지진이 일어났다.

3 침대가 흔들렸기 때문에 나는 갑자기 잠에서 깼다.

4 나는 남동생이 장난으로 침대를 흔들고 있다고 생각했다.

5 하지만 그때 나는 내 책상 위에 있던 거울이 바닥으로 떨어져 산산조각이 나는 소리를 들었다.

6 그때 나는 남동생이 그런 것이 아니라는 것을 알았지만, 정확히 무슨 일이 일어나고 있었는지를 여전히 알지 못했다.

7 머지않아 방 전체가 심하게 흔들리기 시작했고 혼란스러움은 공포로 변했다.

8 엄마가 지진이라고 소리를 지르며 내 방으로 뛰어 들어왔다.

9 지진을 경험한 것이 처음이었기 때문에, 나는 어떻게 반응해야 할지 몰랐다.

10 나는 그저 "어떻게 해야 하지?" 라는 말을 반복했다.

11 엄마는 나와 남동생을 침대 밖으로 잡아끌었다.

12 우리는 주방으로 달려가서 식탁 아래로 기어들어 갔다.

13 나는 전등이 심하게 흔들리는 것과 책이 바닥으로 떨어지는 것을 볼 수 있었다.

14 Our family picture _____ from the wall and the glass _____ it _____.

A. covering   B. dropped   C. broke

15 A cup _____ _____ and _____ _____ the kitchen table.

A. off   B. tipped   C. rolled   D. over

16 _____ _____, I could hear _____ _____ in the apartment break.

A. second   B. else   C. every   D. something

17 I started _____ _____ that the building would _____.

A. to   B. collapse   C. worry

18 Then the shaking _____ _____ _____.

A. to   B. seemed   C. stop

19 We started _____ _____ the _____.

A. door   B. toward   C. crawling

20 _____ that _____, my mom's cell phone _____.

A. moment   B. rang   C. at

21 It was my dad, who was _____ _____ _____ _____.

A. home   B. work   C. coming   D. from

22 He _____, "It _____!

A. stopped   B. shouted

23 _____ _____ _____ the building!

A. out   B. get   C. of

24 _____ the _____!

A. stairs   B. take

25 _____ _____ the elevator!

A. take   B. don't

26 Hurry!"

27 "_____ _____ you?

A. are   B. where

28 Are you _____?" my mom _____ _____.

A. urgently   B. okay   C. asked

29 My dad _____, "_____ _____.

A. worry   B. answered   C. don't

30 _____ _____.

A. okay   B. I'm

14 우리 가족 사진이 벽에서 떨어졌고 사진을 덮고 있던 유리가 깨졌다.

15 컵이 넘어지고 식탁에서 굴러 떨어졌다.

16 매 순간, 나는 아파트에 있는 다른 어떤 것들이 부서지는 소리를 들을 수 있었다.

17 나는 건물이 무너지지는 않을까 하는 걱정이 들기 시작했다.

18 그때 흔들림이 멈추는 것 같았다.

19 우리는 문으로 기어가기 시작했다.

20 그 순간, 엄마의 휴대 전화가 울렸다.

21 전화를 한 사람은 바로 아빠였는데, 직장에서 퇴근하던 중이었다.

22 아빠는 소리쳤다. "지진이 멈췄어요!

23 건물 밖으로 나와요!

24 계단을 이용해요!

25 엘리베이터를 타면 안 돼요!

26 서둘러요!"

27 "어디예요?

28 괜찮아요?"라고 엄마가 다급하게 물었다.

29 아빠가 대답했다. "걱정 말아요.

30 나는 괜찮아요.

31 I was _____ _____ when the _____ started.

    A. home   B. shaking   C. driving

32 But I _____ _____ _____ .

    A. over   B. pulled   C. immediately

33 I'm listening to the radio _____ _____ to find out what's _____ _____ ."

    A. now   B. on   C. right   D. going

34 We nervously _____ our _____ _____ the stairs and _____ .

    A. way   B. outside   C. made   D. down

35 I _____ _____ .

    A. around   B. looked

36 _____ of buildings had _____ and _____ _____ several cars.

    A. smashed   B. fallen   C. parts   D. had

37 We went to an _____ space to _____ more _____ .

    A. falling   B. open   C. avoid   D. pieces

38 How _____ all this _____ _____ in a _____ minutes?

    A. few   B. have   C. happened   D. could

39 _____ I had done many earthquake _____ in school, I had never _____ I'd experience a _____ earthquake.

    A. real   B. drills   C. thought   D. although

40 I still _____ _____ when I _____ that night.

    A. scared   B. remember   C. get

41 I can't _____ the _____ I _____ when the furniture was shaking and things were _____ to the floor.

    A. falling   B. felt   C. panic   D. forget

42 After that night, I began to _____ earthquake _____ .

    A. drills   B. take   C. seriously

43 I _____ that I should be _____ for the next earthquake, which can _____ at any _____ .

    A. occur   B. prepared   C. realized   D. time

31 진동이 시작할 때 운전해서 집으로 가던 중이었어요.

32 하지만 즉시 차를 길 한쪽에 댔어요.

33 무슨 일이 일어나는지 알기 위해 지금 라디오를 듣고 있어요."

34 우리는 초조한 마음으로 계단을 내려가서 밖으로 나갔다.

35 나는 주변을 둘러보았다.

36 건물의 일부분이 떨어져 나갔고 몇몇 차들은 박살이 났다.

37 우리는 추가적인 낙하물을 피하기 위해 공터로 갔다.

38 어떻게 이런 일이 몇 분 만에 일어날 수 있단 말인가?

39 비록 학교에서 많은 지진 대피 훈련을 해 왔지만, 내가 실제 지진을 겪으리라고는 전혀 생각해 보지 않았었다.

40 그날 밤을 기억하면 나는 여전히 두려워진다.

41 가구가 흔들리고 물건들이 바닥으로 떨어졌을 때 내가 느꼈던 공포심을 나는 잊을 수가 없다.

42 그날 밤 이후, 나는 지진 대피 훈련에 진지하게 임하기 시작했다.

43 나는 언제든 발생할 수 있는 다음 지진을 대비해야 한다는 것을 깨달았다.

※ 다음 우리말과 일치하도록 빈칸에 알맞은 말을 쓰시오.

1 _____ _____ to an _____

2 One night _____ February, after I _____ _____ _____ _____, an earthquake _____.

3 I woke up suddenly because my bed _____ _____.

4 I thought my brother _____ _____ my bed _____ _____ _____.

5 But then I _____ the mirror on my desk _____ _____ _____ _____ and _____ _____ _____.

6 I knew it wasn't my brother _____, but I _____ _____ know _____ _____ _____ _____.

7 Soon the whole room began _____ _____ _____, and my _____ _____ _____.

8 My mom _____ _____ it was an earthquake and _____ _____ my room.

9 Since it was _____ _____ _____ _____ an earthquake, I didn't know _____ _____ _____.

10 I just _____ _____, "What should I do?"

11 My mom _____ me and my brother _____ _____ _____.

12 We _____ _____ the kitchen and _____ _____ the table.

13 I could _____ the light _____ _____ and books _____ _____ the floor.

1 지진에 눈을 뜨는 것

2 2월 어느 날 밤, 내가 잠자리에 든 후에 지진이 일어났다.

3 침대가 흔들렸기 때문에 나는 갑자기 잠에서 깼다.

4 나는 남동생이 장난으로 침대를 흔들고 있다고 생각했다.

5 하지만 그때 나는 내 책상 위에 있던 거울이 바닥으로 떨어져 산산조각이 나는 소리를 들었다.

6 그때 나는 남동생이 그런 것이 아니라는 것을 알았지만, 정확히 무슨 일이 일어나고 있었는지를 여전히 알지 못했다.

7 머지않아 방 전체가 심하게 흔들리기 시작했고 혼란스러움은 공포로 변했다.

8 엄마가 지진이라고 소리를 지르며 내 방으로 뛰어 들어왔다.

9 지진을 경험한 것이 처음이었기 때문에, 나는 어떻게 반응해야 할지 몰랐다.

10 나는 그저 "어떻게 해야 하지?"라는 말을 반복했다.

11 엄마는 나와 남동생을 침대 밖으로 잡아끌었다.

12 우리는 주방으로 달려가서 식탁 아래로 기어들어 갔다.

13 나는 전등이 심하게 흔들리는 것과 책이 바닥으로 떨어지는 것을 볼 수 있었다.

14 Our family picture _____ from the wall and the glass _____ _____ _____.

15 A cup _____ _____ and _____ _____ the kitchen table.

16 _____ _____, I could _____ something else in the apartment _____.

17 I started _____ _____ that the building would _____.

18 Then the _____ _____ _____ _____.

19 We started _____ _____ the door.

20 _____ _____ _____, my mom's cell phone _____.

21 It was my dad, who was _____ _____ _____ _____.

22 He _____, "_____ _____!

23 _____ _____ _____ the building!

24 _____ the _____!

25 _____ _____ the elevator!

26 _____!"

27 "_____ are you?

28 Are you _____?" my mom _____ _____.

29 My dad _____, "_____ _____.

30 I'm _____.

---

14 우리 가족 사진이 벽에서 떨어졌고 사진을 덮고 있던 유리가 깨졌다.

15 컵이 넘어지고 식탁에서 굴러 떨어졌다.

16 매 순간, 나는 아파트에 있는 다른 어떤 것들이 부서지는 소리를 들을 수 있었다.

17 나는 건물이 무너지지는 않을까 하는 걱정이 들기 시작했다.

18 그때 흔들림이 멈추는 것 같았다.

19 우리는 문으로 기어가기 시작했다.

20 그 순간, 엄마의 휴대 전화가 울렸다.

21 전화를 한 사람은 바로 아빠였는데, 직장에서 퇴근하던 중이었다.

22 아빠는 소리쳤다. "지진이 멈췄어요!

23 건물 밖으로 나와요!

24 계단을 이용해요!

25 엘리베이터를 타면 안 돼요!

26 서둘러요!"

27 "어디예요?

28 괜찮아요?"라고 엄마가 다급하게 물었다.

29 아빠가 대답했다. "걱정 말아요.

30 나는 괜찮아요.

31 I _____ _____ _____ when the _____ started.

32 But I _____ _____ _____.

33 I'm listening to the radio _____ _____ to _____ what's _____ _____."

34 We _____ _____ _____ _____ down the stairs and _____.

35 I _____ _____.

36 _____ _____ buildings _____ _____ and _____ _____ several cars.

37 We went to an open space _____ _____ more _____ _____.

38 How _____ all this _____ _____ in _____ _____ minutes?

39 _____ I had done many _____ _____ in school, I had never thought I'd _____ _____ _____ _____.

40 I still _____ _____ when I _____ that night.

41 I _____ _____ _____ _____ _____ _____ when the furniture was shaking and things _____ _____ _____ the floor.

42 _____ that night, I began to _____ earthquake _____ _____.

43 I _____ that I should _____ _____ _____ the next earthquake, which can _____ _____ _____ _____.

31 진동이 시작할 때 운전해서 집으로 가던 중이었어요.

32 하지만 즉시 차를 길 한쪽에 댔어요.

33 무슨 일이 일어나는지 알기 위해 지금 라디오를 듣고 있어요."

34 우리는 초조한 마음으로 계단을 내려가서 밖으로 나갔다.

35 나는 주변을 둘러보았다.

36 건물의 일부분이 떨어져 나갔고 몇몇 차들은 박살이 났다.

37 우리는 추가적인 낙하물을 피하기 위해 공터로 갔다.

38 어떻게 이런 일이 몇 분 만에 일어날 수 있단 말인가?

39 비록 학교에서 많은 지진 대피 훈련을 해 왔지만, 내가 실제 지진을 겪으리라고는 전혀 생각해 보지 않았었다.

40 그날 밤을 기억하면 나는 여전히 두려워진다.

41 가구가 흔들리고 물건들이 바닥으로 떨어졌을 때 내가 느꼈던 공포심을 나는 잊을 수가 없다.

42 그날 밤 이후, 나는 지진 대피 훈련에 진지하게 임하기 시작했다.

43 나는 언제든 발생할 수 있는 다음 지진을 대비해야 한다는 것을 깨달았다.

※ 다음 문장을 우리말로 쓰시오.

1 ▶ Waking Up to an Earthquake

➡ _____

2 ▶ One night in February, after I had gone to bed, an earthquake hit.

➡ _____

3 ▶ I woke up suddenly because my bed was shaking.

➡ _____

4 ▶ I thought my brother was shaking my bed as a joke.

➡ _____

5 ▶ But then I heard the mirror on my desk fall to the floor and break into pieces.

➡ _____

6 ▶ I knew it wasn't my brother then, but I still didn't know what exactly was happening.

➡ _____

7 ▶ Soon the whole room began to shake violently, and my confusion turned to panic.

➡ _____

8 ▶ My mom shouted that it was an earthquake and ran into my room.

➡ _____

9 ▶ Since it was my first time experiencing an earthquake, I didn't know how to react.

➡ _____

10 ▶ I just kept saying, "What should I do?"

➡ _____

11 ▶ My mom pulled me and my brother out of bed.

➡ _____

12 ▶ We ran to the kitchen and crawled under the table.

➡ _____

13 ▶ I could see the light swinging violently and books falling to the floor.

➡ _____

14 Our family picture dropped from the wall and the glass covering it broke.

➡ _____

15 A cup tipped over and rolled off the kitchen table.

➡ _____

16 Every second, I could hear something else in the apartment break.

➡ _____

17 I started to worry that the building would collapse.

➡ _____

18 Then the shaking seemed to stop.

➡ _____

19 We started crawling toward the door.

➡ _____

20 At that moment, my mom's cell phone rang.

➡ _____

21 It was my dad, who was coming home from work.

➡ _____

22 He shouted, "It stopped!

➡ _____

23 Get out of the building!

➡ _____

24 Take the stairs!

➡ _____

25 Don't take the elevator!

➡ _____

26 Hurry!"

➡ _____

27 "Where are you?

➡ _____

28 Are you okay?" my mom asked urgently.

➡ _____

29 My dad answered, "Don't worry.

➡ _____

30 I'm okay.

➡ _____

31 I was driving home when the shaking started.

➡ _____

32 But I pulled over immediately.

➡ _____

33 I'm listening to the radio right now to find out what's going on."

➡ _____

34 We nervously made our way down the stairs and outside.

➡ _____

35 I looked around.

➡ _____

36 Parts of buildings had fallen and had smashed several cars.

➡ _____

37 We went to an open space to avoid more falling pieces.

➡ _____

38 How could all this have happened in a few minutes?

➡ _____

39 Although I had done many earthquake drills in school, I had never thought I'd experience a real earthquake.

➡ _____

40 I still get scared when I remember that night.

➡ _____

41 I can't forget the panic I felt when the furniture was shaking and things were falling to the floor.

➡ _____

42 After that night, I began to take earthquake drills seriously.

➡ _____

43 I realized that I should be prepared for the next earthquake, which can occur at any time.

➡ _____

※ 다음 괄호 안의 단어들을 우리말에 맞도록 바르게 배열하시오.

1 (Up / Walking / to / Earthquake / an)
➡ _____

2 (night / one / February, / in / I / after / gone / had / bed, / to / an / hit. / earthquake)
➡ _____

3 (woke / I / up / because / suddenly / bed / my / shaking. / was)
➡ _____

4 (thought / I / brother / my / shaking / was / bed / my / a / as / joke.)
➡ _____

5 (then / but / heard / I / mirror / the / my / on / desk / to / fall / floor / the / and / into / pieces. / break)
➡ _____
_____

6 (knew / I / wasn't / it / brother / my / then, / I / but / still / know / didn't / exactly / what / happening. / was)
➡ _____
_____

7 (the / soon / whole / began / room / shake / to / violently, / and / confusion / my / to / turned / panic.)
➡ _____
_____

8 (mom / my / that / shouted / was / it / earthquake / an / and / into / ran / room. / my)
➡ _____

9 (it / since / was / first / my / time / an / experiencing / earthquake, / didn't / I / how / know / react. / to)
➡ _____
_____

10 (just / I / saying, / kept / should / "what / do?" / I)
➡ _____

11 (mom / my / me / pulled / and / brother / my / of / out / bed.)
➡ _____

12 (ran / we / the / to / kitchen / and / under / crawled / table. / the)
➡ _____

13 (could / I / the / see / swinging / light / and / violently / books / to / falling / floor. / the)
➡ _____

1 지진에 눈을 뜨는 것

2 2월 어느 날 밤, 내가 잠자리에 든 후에 지진이 일어났다.

3 침대가 흔들렸기 때문에 나는 갑자기 잠에서 깼다.

4 나는 남동생이 장난으로 침대를 흔들고 있다고 생각했다.

5 하지만 그때 나는 내 책상 위에 있던 거울이 바닥으로 떨어져 산산조각이 나는 소리를 들었다.

6 그때 나는 남동생이 그런 것이 아니라는 것을 알았지만, 정확히 무슨 일이 일어나고 있었는지를 여전히 알지 못했다.

7 머지않아 방 전체가 심하게 흔들리기 시작했고 혼란스러움은 공포로 변했다.

8 엄마가 지진이라고 소리를 지르며 내 방으로 뛰어 들어왔다.

9 지진을 경험한 것이 처음이었기 때문에, 나는 어떻게 반응해야 할지 몰랐다.

10 나는 그저 "어떻게 해야 하지?" 라는 말을 반복했다.

11 엄마는 나와 남동생을 침대 밖으로 잡아끌었다.

12 우리는 주방으로 달려가서 식탁 아래로 기어들어 갔다.

13 나는 전등이 심하게 흔들리는 것과 책이 바닥으로 떨어지는 것을 볼 수 있었다.

14 (family / our / dropped / picture / the / from / wall / and / glass / the / covering / broke. / it)

➡ _____

15 (cup / a / over / tipped / and / off / rolled / kitchen / the / table.)

➡ _____

16 (second, / every / could / I / something / hear / else / the / in / break. / apartment)

➡ _____

17 (started / I / worry / to / the / that / building / collapse. / would)

➡ _____

18 (the / then / seemed / shaking / stop. / to)

➡ _____

19 (started / we / toward / crawling / door. / the)

➡ _____

20 (that / at / moment, / mom's / my / phone / cell / rang.)

➡ _____

21 (was / it / dad, / my / was / who / home / coming / work. / from)

➡ _____

22 (shouted, / he / stopped! / "it)

➡ _____

23 (out / get / the / of / building!)

➡ _____

24 (the / take / stairs!)

➡ _____

25 (take / don't / elevator! / the)

➡ _____

26 (hurry!")

➡ _____

27 (are / "where / you?)

➡ _____

28 (you / are / okay?" / mom / my / urgently. / asked)

➡ _____

29 (dad / my / "don't / answered, / worry)

➡ _____

30 (okay. / I'm)

➡ _____

14 우리 가족 사진이 벽에서 떨어졌고 사진을 덮고 있던 유리가 깨졌다.

15 컵이 넘어지고 식탁에서 굴러 떨어졌다.

16 매 순간, 나는 아파트에 있는 다른 어떤 것들이 부서지는 소리를 들을 수 있었다.

17 나는 건물이 무너지지는 않을까 하는 걱정이 들기 시작했다.

18 그때 흔들림이 멈추는 것 같았다.

19 우리는 문으로 기어가기 시작했다.

20 그 순간, 엄마의 휴대 전화가 울렸다.

21 전화를 한 사람은 바로 아빠였는데, 직장에서 퇴근하던 중이었다.

22 아빠는 소리쳤다. "지진이 멈췄어요!

23 건물 밖으로 나와요!

24 계단을 이용해요!

25 엘리베이터를 타면 안 돼요!

26 서둘러요!"

27 "어디예요?

28 괜찮아요?"라고 엄마가 다급하게 물었다.

29 아빠가 대답했다. "걱정 말아요.

30 나는 괜찮아요.

31 (was / I / home / driving / when / shaking / the / started.)

➡ _____

32 (I / but / over / pulled / immediately.)

➡ _____

33 (listening / I'm / the / to / right / radio / now / find / to / out / going / what's / on.")

➡ _____

34 (nervously / we / our / made / down / way / stairs / the / outside. / and)

➡ _____

35 (looked / I / around.)

➡ _____

36 (of / parts / buildings / fallen / had / and / smashed / had / cars. / several)

➡ _____

37 (went / we / an / to / open / to / space / avoid / falling / more / pieces.)

➡ _____

38 (could / how / this / all / happened / have / a / in / few / minutes?)

➡ _____

39 (I / although / done / had / earthquake / many / in / drills, / school, / had / I / thought / never / experience. / I'd / real / a / earthquake.)

➡ _____

40 (still / I / scared / get / I / when / that / remember / night.)

➡ _____

41 (can't / I / the / forget / panic / felt / I / the / when / was / furniture / shaking / and / were / things / to / falling / floor. / the)

➡ _____

42 (that / after / night, / began / I / take / to / drills / earthquake / seriously.)

➡ _____

43 (realized / I / that / I / be / should / prepared / the / for / earthquake, / next / can / which / at / occur / time. / any)

➡ _____

_____

31 진동이 시작할 때 운전해서 집으로 가던 중이었어요.

32 하지만 즉시 차를 길 한쪽에 댔어요.

33 무슨 일이 일어나는지 알기 위해 지금 라디오를 듣고 있어요."

34 우리는 초조한 마음으로 계단을 내려가서 밖으로 나갔다.

35 나는 주변을 둘러보았다.

36 건물의 일부분이 떨어져 나갔고 몇몇 차들은 박살이 났다.

37 우리는 추가적인 낙하물을 피하기 위해 공터로 갔다.

38 어떻게 이런 일이 몇 분 만에 일어날 수 있단 말인가?

39 비록 학교에서 많은 지진 대피 훈련을 해 왔지만, 내가 실제 지진을 겪으리라고는 전혀 생각해 보지 않았었다.

40 그날 밤을 기억하면 나는 여전히 두려워진다.

41 가구가 흔들리고 물건들이 바닥으로 떨어졌을 때 내가 느꼈던 공포심을 나는 잊을 수가 없다.

42 그날 밤 이후, 나는 지진 대피 훈련에 진지하게 임하기 시작했다.

43 나는 언제든 발생할 수 있는 다음 지진을 대비해야 한다는 것을 깨달았다.

※ 다음 우리말을 영어로 쓰시오.

1 지진에 눈을 뜨는 것

➡ _____

2 2월 어느 날 밤, 내가 잠자리에 든 후에 지진이 일어났다.

➡ _____

3 침대가 흔들렸기 때문에 나는 갑자기 잠에서 깼다.

➡ _____

4 나는 남동생이 장난으로 침대를 흔들고 있다고 생각했다.

➡ _____

5 하지만 그때 나는 내 책상 위에 있던 거울이 바닥으로 떨어져 산산조각이 나는 소리를 들었다.

➡ _____

6 그때 나는 남동생이 그런 것이 아니라는 것을 알았지만, 정확히 무슨 일이 일어나고 있었는지를 여전히 알지 못했다.

➡ _____

7 머지않아 방 전체가 심하게 흔들리기 시작했고 혼란스러움은 공포로 변했다.

➡ _____

8 엄마가 지진이라고 소리를 지르며 내 방으로 뛰어 들어왔다.

➡ _____

9 지진을 경험한 것이 처음이었기 때문에, 나는 어떻게 반응해야 할지 몰랐다.

➡ _____

10 나는 그저 "어떻게 해야 하지?"라는 말을 반복했다.

➡ _____

11 엄마는 나와 남동생을 침대 밖으로 잡아끌었다.

➡ _____

12 우리는 주방으로 달려가서 식탁 아래로 기어들어 갔다.

➡ _____

13 나는 전등이 심하게 흔들리는 것과 책이 바닥으로 떨어지는 것을 볼 수 있었다.

➡ _____

14 우리 가족 사진이 벽에서 떨어졌고 사진을 덮고 있던 유리가 깨졌다.

➡ _____

15 컵이 넘어지고 식탁에서 굴러 떨어졌다.

➡ _____

16 매 순간, 나는 아파트에 있는 다른 어떤 것들이 부서지는 소리를 들을 수 있었다.

➡ _____

17 나는 건물이 무너지지는 않을까 하는 걱정이 들기 시작했다.

➡ _____

18 그때 흔들림이 멈추는 것 같았다.

➡ _____

19 우리는 문으로 기어가기 시작했다.

➡ _____

20 그 순간, 엄마의 휴대 전화가 울렸다.

➡ _____

21 전화를 한 사람은 바로 아빠였는데, 직장에서 퇴근하던 중이었다.

➡ _____

22 아빠는 소리쳤다, "지진이 멈췄어요!

➡ _____

23 건물 밖으로 나와요!

➡ _____

24 계단을 이용해요!

➡ _____

25 엘리베이터를 타면 안 돼요!

➡ _____

26 서둘러요!"

➡ _____

27 "어디예요?

➡ _____

28 괜찮아요?"라고 엄마가 다급하게 물었다.

➡ _____

29 아빠가 대답했다. "걱정 말아요.

➡ _____

30 나는 괜찮아요.

➡ _____

31 진동이 시작할 때 운전해서 집으로 가던 중이었어요.

➡ _____

32 하지만 즉시 차를 길 한쪽에 댔어요.

➡ _____

33 무슨 일이 일어나는지 알기 위해 지금 라디오를 듣고 있어요."

➡ _____

34 우리는 초조한 마음으로 계단을 내려가서 밖으로 나갔다.

➡ _____

35 나는 주변을 둘러보았다.

➡ _____

36 건물의 일부분이 떨어져 나갔고 몇몇 차들은 박살이 났다.

➡ _____

37 우리는 추가적인 낙하물을 피하기 위해 공터로 갔다.

➡ _____

38 어떻게 이런 일이 몇 분 만에 일어날 수 있단 말인가?

➡ _____

39 비록 학교에서 많은 지진 대피 훈련을 해 왔지만, 내가 실제 지진을 겪으리라고는 전혀 생각해 보지 않았었다.

➡ _____

_____

40 그날 밤을 기억하면 나는 여전히 두려워진다.

➡ _____

41 가구가 흔들리고 물건들이 바닥으로 떨어졌을 때 내가 느꼈던 공포심을 나는 잊을 수가 없다.

➡ _____

42 그날 밤 이후, 나는 지진 대피 훈련에 진지하게 임하기 시작했다.

➡ _____

43 나는 언제든 발생할 수 있는 다음 지진을 대비해야 한다는 것을 깨달았다.

➡ _____

※ 다음 우리말과 일치하도록 빈칸에 알맞은 말을 쓰시오.

After You Read B

1. R: How did you feel _____ the _____ _____?
2. W: I _____ _____ panic _____ the whole room _____ _____ _____.
3. R: _____ _____! What did you do next?
4. W: We _____ _____ under the table after my mom _____ _____ _____ _____ _____.
5. R: What was _____ _____ _____ _____?
6. W: _____ _____ things _____ _____ to the floor. I _____ many things in the apartment _____.
7. R: What _____ you _____ after that night?
8. W: I realized that I _____ _____ _____ _____ the next earthquake. It _____ _____ _____ _____ _____!

1. R: 지진이 일어났을 때 어떻게 느끼셨습니까?
2. W: 방 전체가 심하게 흔들렸기 때문에 공포에 사로잡히기 시작했어요.
3. R: 얼마나 무서웠을까! 그 다음에 무엇을 했나요?
4. W: 어머니가 우리를 침대에서 끌어내린 후, 우리는 식탁 아래로 기어갔어요.
5. R: 그 순간에 무슨 일이 일어나고 있었나요?
6. W: 많은 것들이 바닥으로 떨어지고 있었어요. 나는 아프트 안에 있는 많은 것들이 깨지는 소리를 들었어요.
7. R: 그날 밤 이후에 무엇을 깨달았나요?
8. W: 나는 내가 다음번 지진에 대비해야 한다는 것을 깨달았어요. 지진은 언제든지 일어날 수 있어요!

Think & Write Step 3

San Andreas

1. I _____ _____ _____ _____ you about the movie *San Andreas*.
2. This movie _____ _____ _____ Los Angeles and San Francisco _____ 2014.
3. The _____ _____, a search-and-rescue _____, must search for his _____ family _____ an earthquake.
4. The _____ _____ _____ in the _____ _____ are very good.
5. The movie is _____ _____ sad _____ _____, but the story is very interesting.
6. I give *San Andreas* four stars. _____ and _____ _____!

San Andreas
1. 저는 영화 San Andreas에 대해 말하고 싶습니다.
2. 이 영화의 배경은 2014년 Los Angeles와 San Francisco입니다.
3. 수색구조 조종사인 주인공은 지진이 일어난 동안 행방불명된 그의 가족을 찾아야 합니다.
4. 재난 장면에 사용된 특수효과는 매우 좋습니다.
5. 이 영화는 가끔 약간 슬프지만, 이야기는 매우 재미있습니다.
6. 저는 San Andreas에게 별 4개를 줍니다. 가서 보세요!

※ 다음 우리말을 영어로 쓰시오.

After You Read B

1. R: 지진이 일어났을 때 어떻게 느끼셨습니까?
   ➡ _____

2. W: 방 전체가 심하게 흔들렸기 때문에 공포에 사로잡히기 시작했어요.
   ➡ _____

3. R: 얼마나 무서웠을까! 그 다음에 무엇을 했나요?
   ➡ _____

4. W: 어머니가 우리를 침대에서 끌어내린 후, 우리는 식탁 아래로 기어갔어요.
   ➡ _____

5. R: 그 순간에 무슨 일이 일어나고 있었나요?
   ➡ _____

6. W: 많은 것들이 바닥으로 떨어지고 있었어요. 나는 아프트 안에 있는 많은 것들이 깨지는 소리를 들었어요.
   ➡ _____

7. 그날 밤 이후에 무엇을 깨달았나요?
   ➡ _____

8. W: 나는 내가 다음번 지진에 대비해야 한다는 것을 깨달았어요. 지진은 언제든지 일어날 수 있어요!
   ➡ _____

Think & Write Step 3

San Andreas

1. 저는 영화 *San Andreas*에 대해 말하고 싶습니다.
   ➡ _____

2. 이 영화의 배경은 2014년 Los Angeles와 San Francisco입니다.
   ➡ _____

3. 수색구조 조종사인 주인공은 지진이 일어난 동안 행방불명된 그의 가족을 찾아야 합니다.
   ➡ _____

4. 재난 장면에 사용된 특수효과는 매우 좋습니다.
   ➡ _____

5. 이 영화는 가끔 약간 슬프지만, 이야기는 매우 재미있습니다.
   ➡ _____

6. 저는 *San Andreas*에게 별 4개를 줍니다. 가서 보세요!
   ➡ _____

※ 다음 영어를 우리말로 쓰시오.

01 strict _____

02 achieve _____

03 ensure _____

04 supporter _____

05 reasoning _____

06 confident _____

07 analyze _____

08 logical _____

09 misunderstanding _____

10 deliver _____

11 positive _____

12 divide _____

13 edit _____

14 contact _____

15 ability _____

16 decorate _____

17 election _____

18 translate _____

19 valued _____

20 representative _____

21 effective _____

22 vision _____

23 determine _____

24 approach _____

25 hands-off _____

26 analyst _____

27 motivate _____

28 return _____

29 outgoing _____

30 presentation _____

31 realize _____

32 relieved _____

33 switch _____

34 research _____

35 be stuck in _____

36 lead by example _____

37 come up with _____

38 be in charge of _____

39 work out _____

40 get along _____

41 call for _____

42 deal with _____

43 hang out _____

※ 다음 우리말을 영어로 쓰시오.

01	분석가	22	준비하다
02	자신감 있는	23	성취하다, 이루다
03	긍정적인	24	발표
04	귀중한, 존중 받는	25	(선거에) 입후보하다
05	배달하다	26	선거
06	접근하다	27	결정하다, 결심하다
07	접촉	28	분석하다
08	오해	29	논리적인, 타당한
09	조사, 연구	30	목적, 목표
10	동기를 부여하다	31	대신에
11	외향적인, 사교적인	32	엄격한
12	지지자	33	적절히, 제대로
13	바꾸다, 전환하다	34	통찰력, 비전, 시력
14	해석하다	35	편들다
15	안심이 되는	36	~을 생각해 내다
16	나누다, 분리하다	37	사이좋게 지내다
17	추리, 추론	38	~을 실망시키다
18	편집하다	39	~에 속하다
19	효과적인	40	공들여 일하다
20	능력	41	~을 처리하다, ~을 돌보다
21	대표(자)	42	~을 담당하다, 책임지다
		43	다루다, 처리하다

※ 다음 영영풀이에 알맞은 단어를 <보기>에서 골라 쓴 후, 우리말 뜻을 쓰시오.

1 _____ : ability to lead: _____

2 _____ : to compete as a candidate in an election: _____

3 _____ : a piece of work that must be done: _____

4 _____ : the power or skill to do something: _____

5 _____ : making sense; being reasonable: _____

6 _____ : to make a change from one thing to another: _____

7 _____ : to come close to someone or something: _____

8 _____ : to prepare something written to be published or used: _____

9 _____ : a person who supports a political party, an idea, etc.: _____

10 _____ : to provide with a reason to do something: _____

11 _____ : to deeply study every piece of something to understand it: _____

12 _____ : sure that one has the ability to do things well: _____

13 _____ : successful, and working in the way that was intended: _____

14 _____ : letting people do what they want, without telling them what to do:

_____

15 _____ : somebody who has been chosen to speak, or make decisions on behalf of

a group: _____

16 _____ : the process of choosing a person or a group of people for a position,

especially a political position, by voting: _____

보기			
representative	analyze	switch	ability
supporter	run	election	edit
motivate	hands-off	approach	effective
logical	confident	task	leadership

※ 다음 우리말과 일치하도록 빈칸에 알맞은 말을 쓰시오.

Listen & Talk 1 A

G: Mom, we've got a _____.

W: What's the _____?

G: We're _____ _____ have dinner with Grandma this Saturday, _____? But I _____ _____ that Sujin's birthday party is _____ _____ _____. She's my best friend. _____ _____ _____ _____?

W: That sounds _____ a difficult _____. _____ talk about it _____ your dad.

G: Okay, Mom. I'd love to see Grandma, but I don't want to _____ my _____ _____ _____ party.

Listen & Talk 1 B

M: Junsu, are you okay? _____ _____ _____ _____?

B: Hello, Mr. Smith. I have a _____.

M: What _____?

B: You know Jaewoo, Yunho, and I are best friends, right? They _____ _____ _____, and now I'm _____ _____ the middle. I don't know _____ _____ _____.

M: That sounds hard. Do you know _____ they _____ _____?

B: Yes, but it doesn't sound like a _____ _____ to me. I guess they had _____ _____ _____ _____.

M: _____ _____ you all meet together and talk about it? I think they'll _____ _____ you.

B: That's a good idea. They're both good _____ _____ _____. I _____ _____ _____.

M: I understand. I hope everything _____ _____.

Listen & Talk 1 C

B: Hey, Mandy. _____ _____ _____ _____?

G: I don't know _____ _____ _____, Nick. My brother _____ _____ _____ _____ _____ _____ with his homework this Wednesday, but I told him I can't. I have so many _____ _____ _____ that day.

B: What do you _____ _____ do this Wednesday?

G: I need to go to the library to _____ _____ _____. Then I have to meet you to work on our _____. After that, I _____ _____ _____ _____ _____ an exam at night.

소녀: 엄마, 우리에게 문제가 생겼어요.
여성: 무슨 일이니?
소녀: 이번 주 토요일에 할머니와 저녁 식사를 하기로 했잖아요, 그렇죠? 그런데 수진이의 생일 파티가 토요일 저녁이라는 것을 방금 깨달았어요. 수진이는 저의 가장 친한 친구예요. 저 어떡하죠?
여성: 결정하기 힘든 문제인 것 같구나. 네 아빠와 함께 이야기해 보자.
소녀: 네, 엄마. 할머니를 정말 뵙고 싶지만, 가장 친한 친구의 생일 파티에 빠지고 싶지는 않아요.

남자: 준수야, 괜찮니? 무슨 일이야?
소년: 안녕하세요, Smith 선생님. 저에게 문제가 생겼어요.
남자: 무슨 일인데?
소년: 재우와 윤호, 그리고 제가 서로 가장 친한 사이라는 거 아시죠, 그렇죠? 그 둘이 싸웠고, 저는 이제 중간에 끼어버린 상태예요. 어떻게 해야 할지 모르겠어요.
남자: 힘들겠구나. 그 둘이 왜 싸웠는지는 아니?
소년: 네, 하지만 제가 보기에는 그다지 대단한 일도 아닌 것 같아요. 아무래도 그 둘 사이에 어떤 오해가 생긴 것 같아요.
남자: 너희 모두 다 같이 만나서 그것에 대해 이야기해 보는 게 어떠니? 그 둘이 네 말은 들을 것 같구나.
소년: 그거 좋은 생각이네요. 두 명 모두 저에게는 좋은 친구들이에요. 저는 누구의 편도 들 수 없어요.
남자: 이해한단다. 모두 잘 해결되기를 바란다.

남: 어이, Mandy. 무슨 일이야?
여: 어떻게 해야 할지 모르겠어, Nick. 내 동생이 이번 주 수요일에 숙제를 도와달라고 했는데, 도와줄 수 없다고 했어. 나는 그날 해야 할 일이 너무 많아.
남: 이번 주 수요일에 무엇을 해야 하는데?
여: 책을 반납하러 도서관에 가야 해. 그런 다음 우리의 발표 준비를 위해 너를 만나야 하고. 그다음에, 밤에는 시험 준비를 해야 해.

B: Oh, you _____ have _____ _____ to do.

G: Yes. But my brother _____ _____ _____, so I feel bad.

B: Well, then _____ _____ _____ on Thursday _____ for our presentation? Then you can do _____ and also _____ your brother on Wednesday.

G: That would _____ _____ _____ so much! Thanks for _____, Nick!

G: _____ _____ is coming. How do you want to _____ _____?

B: I want _____ _____ _____ for Sports Day.

G: That's great. You are really _____ _____ _____ _____. I _____ _____ _____ _____ you will take some wonderful pictures.

Listen & Talk 2 B

B: In the Send Our Stories project, we are going to make a picture book for children in other countries. We've _____ everyone _____ three groups. Each group will _____ _____ _____ a different task. Group A will _____ a Korean story _____ English. Group B will make drawings for the book and _____ it. After copies of the book _____ _____, Group C will be _____ _____ _____ sending them to the children. It won't be easy, but _____ _____ _____ _____ _____ the children _____ _____ these books will really enjoy them.

Listen & Talk 2 C

B: I'm so _____ about our museum _____ _____.

G1: Me too. _____ _____ our tasks. Yen, what are you _____ _____ _____?

G2: I'm in charge of _____ _____.

G1: Okay. Sejin, are you going to do _____ _____ on the museum?

B: Yes, I am. Are you going to _____ _____ _____ _____ _____, Emma?

G1: That's right. I think we're _____.

G2: Good. I _____ _____ _____ _____ our project will _____ _____ well.

남: 아, 너 정말로 할 일이 많구나.

여: 응. 하지만 내 동생이 실망한 것처럼 보여서, 기분이 좋지가 않아.

남: 음, 그럼 우리 발표를 위해 목요일에 대신 만나는 건 어때? 그러면 너는 수요일에 모든 일을 하고 네 동생도 도와줄 수 있어.

여: 그러면 정말 큰 도움이 될 거야! 이해해 줘서 고마워, Nick!

여: 곧 있으면 운동회야. 어떻게 돕고 싶니?

남: 나는 운동회 날 사진을 찍고 싶어.

여: 그거 좋다. 너는 정말 사진을 잘 찍잖아. 나는 네가 운동회 날에 멋진 사진들을 찍을 것이라는 것을 확신해.

남: Send Our Stories 프로젝트에서 우리는 외국의 아이들을 위한 그림책을 만들 예정입니다. 우리는 모두를 세 그룹으로 나누었습니다. 각 그룹은 서로 다른 작업을 담당할 것입니다. A 그룹은 한국어 이야기를 영어로 번역할 것입니다. B 그룹은 이 책의 그림을 그리고 편집을 할 것입니다. 책들이 인쇄되면, C 그룹은 이 책들을 아이들에게 보내는 일을 맡게 될 것입니다. 쉽지는 않겠지만, 저는 이 책을 받는 어린이들이 이 책을 정말로 좋아할 것이라고 확신합니다.

남: 우리의 박물관 견학이 정말 기대돼.

여1: 나도 그래. 각자 맡은 일을 확인해 보자. Yen, 너는 무엇을 담당하지?

여2: 나는 사진 촬영 담당이야.

여1: 그래. 세진아, 너는 박물관 조사를 할 거지?

남: 응, 맞아. 너는 견학 보고서를 작성할 거지, Emma?

여1: 맞아. 이제 우리는 준비가 된 것 같아.

여2: 좋아. 우리 프로젝트가 잘될 거라는 데 의심의 여지가 없어.

※ 다음 우리말에 맞도록 대화를 영어로 쓰시오.

Listen & Talk 1 A

G: _____

W: _____

G: _____

_____

_____

W: _____

G: _____

_____

소녀: 엄마, 우리에게 문제가 생겼어요.
여성: 무슨 일이니?
소녀: 이번 주 토요일에 할머니와 저녁 식사를 하기로 했잖아요, 그렇죠? 그런데 수진이의 생일 파티가 토요일 저녁이라는 것을 방금 깨달았어요. 수진이는 저의 가장 친한 친구예요. 저 어떡하죠?
여성: 결정하기 힘든 문제인 것 같구나. 네 아빠와 함께 이야기해 보자.
소녀: 네, 엄마. 할머니를 정말 뵙고 싶지만, 가장 친한 친구의 생일 파티에 빠지고 싶지는 않아요.

Listen & Talk 1 B

M: _____

B: _____

M: _____

B: _____

_____

M: _____

B: _____

_____

M: _____

B: _____

M: _____

남자: 준수야, 괜찮니? 무슨 일이야?
소년: 안녕하세요, Smith 선생님. 저에게 문제가 생겼어요.
남자: 무슨 일인데?
소년: 재우와 윤호, 그리고 제가 서로 가장 친한 사이라는 거 아시죠, 그렇죠? 그 둘이 싸웠고, 저는 이제 중간에 끼어버린 상태예요. 어떻게 해야 할지 모르겠어요.
남자: 힘들겠구나. 그 둘이 왜 싸웠는지는 아니?
소년: 네, 하지만 제가 보기에는 그다지 대단한 일도 아닌 것 같아요. 아무래도 그 둘 사이에 어떤 오해가 생긴 것 같아요.
남자: 너희 모두 다 같이 만나서 그것에 대해 이야기해 보는 게 어떠니? 그 둘이 네 말은 들을 것 같구나.
소년: 그거 좋은 생각이네요. 두 명 모두 저에게는 좋은 친구들이에요. 저는 누구의 편도 들 수 없어요.
남자: 이해한단다. 모두 잘 해결되기를 바란다.

Listen & Talk 1 C

B: _____

G: _____

_____

_____

B: _____

G: _____

남: 어이, Mandy. 무슨 일이야?
여: 어떻게 해야 할지 모르겠어, Nick. 내 동생이 이번 주 수요일에 숙제를 도와달라고 했는데, 도와줄 수 없다고 했어. 나는 그날 해야 할 일이 너무 많아.
남: 이번 주 수요일에 무엇을 해야 하는데?
여: 책을 반납하러 도서관에 가야 해. 그런 다음 우리의 발표 준비를 위해 너를 만나야 하고. 그다음에, 밤에는 시험 준비를 해야 해.

B: _____

G: _____

B: _____

_____

G: _____

남: 아, 너 정말로 할 일이 많구나.

여: 응. 하지만 내 동생이 실망한 것처럼 보여서, 기분이 좋지가 않아.

남: 음, 그럼 우리 발표를 위해 목요일에 대신 만나는 건 어때? 그러면 너는 수요일에 모든 일을 하고 네 동생도 도와줄 수 있어.

여: 그러면 정말 큰 도움이 될 거야! 이해해 줘서 고마워, Nick!

Listen & Talk 2 A

G: _____

B: _____

G: _____

_____

여: 곧 있으면 운동회야. 어떻게 돕고 싶니?

남: 나는 운동회 날 사진을 찍고 싶어.

여: 그거 좋다. 너는 정말 사진을 잘 찍잖아. 나는 네가 운동회 날에 멋진 사진들을 찍을 것이라는 것을 확신해.

Listen & Talk 2 B

B: _____

_____

_____

_____

_____

_____

남: Send Our Stories 프로젝트에서 우리는 외국의 아이들을 위한 그림책을 만들 예정입니다. 우리는 모두를 세 그룹으로 나누었습니다. 각 그룹은 서로 다른 작업을 담당할 것입니다. A 그룹은 한국어 이야기를 영어로 번역할 것입니다. B 그룹은 이 책의 그림을 그리고 편집을 할 것입니다. 책들이 인쇄되면, C 그룹은 이 책들을 아이들에게 보내는 일을 맡게 될 것입니다. 쉽지는 않겠지만, 저는 이 책을 받는 어린이들이 이 책을 정말로 좋아할 것이라고 확신합니다.

Listen & Talk 2 C

B: _____

G1: _____

G2: _____

G1: _____

B: _____

G1: _____

G2: _____

남: 우리의 박물관 견학이 정말 기대돼.

여1: 나도 그래. 각자 맡은 일을 확인해 보자. Yen, 너는 무엇을 담당하지?

여2: 나는 사진 촬영 담당이야.

여1: 그래. 세진아, 너는 박물관 조사를 할 거지?

남: 응, 맞아. 너는 견학 보고서를 작성할 거지, Emma?

여1: 맞아. 이제 우리는 준비가 된 것 같아.

여2: 좋아. 우리 프로젝트가 잘될 거라는 데 의심의 여지가 없어.

※ 다음 우리말과 일치하도록 빈칸에 알맞은 것을 골라 쓰시오.

1 _____ Are _____ _____.
　A. All　　　　　B. We　　　　　C. Leaders

2 Brian: The _____ is _____ _____.
　A. coming　　　B. election　　　C. up

3 _____ _____ _____ for class representative, Yumi?
　A. don't　　　B. why　　　C. run　　　D. you

4 Yumi: _____ _____.
　A. way　　　　B. no

5 I'm not the _____ _____ for that _____.
　A. right　　　B. position　　　C. person

6 I've _____ _____ about _____.
　A. thought　　B. never　　　C. running

7 Brian: _____ _____?
　A. not　　　　B. why

8 Yumi: _____ _____, Brian.
　A. on　　　　B. come

9 Leaders have _____ _____.
　A. qualities　　B. special

10 I don't think a person _____ me _____ _____ _____ a leader.
　A. can　　　　B. called　　　C. like　　　D. be

11 Brian: _____ do you _____?
　A. mean　　　B. what

12 I think you have very _____ _____ _____.
　A. leadership　　B. good　　　C. qualities

13 You're _____ _____ and _____.
　A. outgoing　　B. friendly　　C. really

14 You _____ _____ people _____.
　A. get　　　　B. help　　　C. along　　　D. also

15 I have _____ _____ that you will _____ _____ if you run.
　A. be　　　　B. doubt　　　C. elected　　　D. no

16 Brian told me this afternoon _____ I have _____ _____ _____.
　A. good　　　B. that　　　C. qualities　　　D. leadership

17 _____ one _____ _____ _____ me that before.
　A. ever　　　B. no　　　C. told　　　D. has

18 _____ does he _____ _____?
　A. think　　　B. why　　　C. so

19 Maybe he was _____ _____ _____ _____ nice.
　A. to　　　　B. just　　　C. be　　　D. trying

20 _____ he said that to me, _____, I started to _____.
　A. however　　B. when　　　C. think

---

1 우리는 모두 리더들이다

2 Brian: "선거가 다가오고 있어.

3 유미야, 반 대표에 입후보하는 게 어때?"

4 유미: "아니.

5 나는 그 자리에 적절한 사람이 아니야.

6 나는 입후보하는 것에 대해 생각해 본 적이 없어."

7 Brian: "왜?"

8 유미: "이봐, Brian.

9 리더들은 특별한 자질을 갖추고 있어.

10 나 같은 사람이 리더로 불릴 수 있다고 생각하지 않아."

11 Brian: "무슨 말이야?

12 내 생각에 너는 매우 좋은 지도력 자질들을 갖추고 있어.

13 너는 정말 친절하고 외향적이잖아.

14 또 너는 사람들이 어울리도록 도와주기도 해.

15 만약 네가 입후보한다면 당선될 거라고 믿어 의심치 않아."

16 Brian은 오늘 오후에 내게 내가 좋은 지도력 자질들을 갖추고 있다고 말했다.

17 이전에는 아무도 내게 그런 말을 한 적이 없었다.

18 왜 그는 그렇게 생각했을까?

19 아마도 그는 그저 친절하려고 했을 것이다.

20 그러나 그가 내게 그렇게 말했을 때, 나는 생각하기 시작했다.

21 _____ I really _____ a _____ ?
A. become   B. can   C. leader

22 I _____ _____ .
A. know   B. don't

23 I think leaders should have a _____ , clear _____ , and the _____ to _____ others.
A. vision   B. motivate   C. goals   D. ability

24 I don't have _____ _____ _____ _____ .
A. those   B. any   C. things   D. of

25 Then I _____ started to _____ _____ these are the only _____ that make a good leader.
A. wonder   B. qualities   C. suddenly   D. if

26 _____ I'm _____ .
A. wrong   B. maybe

27 Maybe there are _____ _____ _____ .
A. leadership   B. other   C. qualities

28 So I _____ to _____ some _____ .
A. online   B. decided   C. research   D. do

29 Here's _____ I _____ !
A. found   B. what

30 **GREEN LEADERS: "_____ _____ "**
A. Builders   B. Team

31 _____ that the team _____ _____
A. valued   B. ensure   C. feels

32 _____ a _____ _____
A. environment   B. create   C. positive

33 Are _____ and easy to _____ _____
A. to   B. friendly   C. talk

34 **RED LEADERS: "_____ _____ "**
A. Analysts   B. Logical

35 _____ good _____ _____
A. skills   B. have   C. reasoning

36 _____ problems and _____
A. situations   B. analyze

37 Think of the most _____ ways to _____ the team's _____
A. achieve   B. effective   C. goals

38 **PURPLE LEADERS: "_____ _____ "**
A. Managers   B. Hands-Off

39 _____ others to work _____ their _____
A. own   B. allow   C. on

40 Do not _____ _____ _____ people
A. control   B. to   C. try

41 Give _____ only _____ it is _____
A. needed   B. advice   C. when

---

21 내가 정말 리더가 될 수 있을까?

22 나는 모르겠다.

23 나는 리더가 비전, 명확한 목표, 그리고 다른 사람들에게 동기를 부여할 능력을 가지고 있어야 한다고 생각한다.

24 나는 그러한 것들 중 어느 것도 가지고 있지 않다.

25 그때 나는 갑자기 이것들이 좋은 리더를 만드는 유일한 자질들인지 궁금해하기 시작했다.

26 아마도 내가 틀린지도 모른다.

27 어쩌면 다른 지도력 자질들이 있는지도 모른다.

28 그래서 나는 온라인으로 조사해 보기로 결심했다.

29 여기에 내가 찾은 것이 있다!

30 〈녹색 리더〉 '팀 조직자'

31 팀이 반드시 가치 있다고 느끼게 한다

32 긍정적인 환경을 조성한다

33 친절하고 말을 걸기 쉽다

34 〈빨간색 리더〉 '논리적 분석가'

35 좋은 추론 기술을 갖고 있다

36 문제와 상황들을 분석한다

37 팀의 목표를 성취하는 가장 효과적인 방법들을 생각한다

38 〈보라색 리더〉 '방임적 관리자'

39 다른 사람들이 스스로 일하도록 해 준다

40 사람들을 통제하려고 하지 않는다

41 필요할 때만 조언한다

42 **ORANGE LEADERS:** " _____ _____ "
    A. Directors   B. Strict

43 _____ everyone's _____
    A. clear   B. make   C. role

44 _____ _____ everything is finished _____ _____
    A. time   B. sure   C. on   D. make

45 _____ each _____ is done _____
    A. properly   B. step   C. ensure

46 **YELLOW LEADERS:** " _____ _____ "
    A. Supporters   B. Quiet

47 Lead _____ _____
    A. example   B. by

48 _____ the team members _____
    A. instead   B. let   C. shine

49 _____ the team _____
    A. needs   B. meet   C. members'

50 **BLUE LEADERS:** " _____ _____ "
    A. Thinkers   B. Creative

51 _____ problems _____ new _____
    A. in   B. approach   C. ways

52 _____ _____ fresh ideas
    A. up   B. come   C. with

53 _____ _____ tasks _____ _____ others
    A. from   B. deal   C. differently   D. with

54 I was _____ that there are actually many _____ leadership styles, but soon I _____ the _____ .
    A. realized   B. different   C. reason   D. surprised

55 We _____ _____ many different groups, and many different situations can _____ _____ in our lives.
    A. up   B. belong   C. to   D. come

56 They all _____ _____ different leadership _____ .
    A. for   B. styles   C. call

57 _____ group's _____ _____ _____ the best leadership style.
    A. situation   B. each   C. determines   D. unique

58 "I am a _____ of many different groups, and I have _____ _____ in each _____ ."
    A. responsibilities B. part   C. different   D. group

59 _____ _____ everything, I became _____ _____ .
    A. more   B. reading   C. confident   D. after

60 I _____ that I have _____ _____ the _____ of a "green leader."
    A. some   B. discovered   C. qualities   D. of

61 If my classmates think a green leader would _____ our class _____ , they might _____ me to be class _____ !
    A. better   B. pick   C. make   D. representative

62 Okay, _____ _____ it!
    A. try   B. let's

---

42 〈주황색 리더〉 '엄격한 감독관'

43 모두의 역할을 분명하게 해 준다

44 모든 일을 제때 끝날 것을 확실히 한다

45 각 단계가 적절히 이행되도록 한다

46 〈노란색 리더〉 '조용한 지지자'

47 솔선수범한다

48 팀원들이 대신 빛나도록 해 준다

49 팀원들의 요구 사항을 충족한다

50 〈파란색 리더〉 '창조적 사상가'

51 새로운 방식으로 문제들에 접근한다

52 신선한 아이디어를 떠올린다

53 다른 사람들과 다르게 일을 처리한다

54 나는 실제로 서로 다른 많은 지도력 유형들이 있어서 놀랐지만, 곧 그 이유를 깨달았다.

55 우리는 서로 다른 여러 집단에 속하고, 우리 인생에서 서로 다른 많은 상황들이 발생할 수 있다.

56 그것들은 모두 서로 다른 지도력 유형들을 요구한다.

57 각 집단의 독특한 상황이 최고의 지도력 유형을 결정한다.

58 "나는 서로 다른 많은 집단의 일부이고, 각 집단에서 각각 다른 책임을 갖고 있어."

59 모든 것을 읽고 나서, 나는 더 자신감이 생겼다.

60 나는 '녹색 리더'의 자질들 중 일부분을 가지고 있다는 것을 알게 되었다.

61 만약 나의 반 친구들이 녹색 리더가 우리 학급을 더 좋게 만들 거라고 생각한다면, 그들은 학급 대표로 나를 뽑을지도 모른다!

62 좋아, 시도해 보자!

※ 다음 우리말과 일치하도록 빈칸에 알맞은 말을 쓰시오.

1 _____ _____ _____ Leaders

2 Brian: The _____ is _____ _____ .

3 _____ _____ _____ run for class _____ , Yumi?

4 Yumi: _____ _____ .

5 I'm not the _____ _____ for that _____ .

6 I've never _____ _____ _____ .

7 Brian: _____ _____ ?

8 Yumi: _____ _____ , Brian.

9 Leaders have _____ _____ .

10 I don't think a person _____ me _____ _____ _____ a leader.

11 Brian: _____ do you _____ ?

12 I think you have very _____ _____ _____ .

13 You're really _____ and _____ .

14 You _____ _____ people _____ _____ .

15 I have _____ _____ that you _____ _____ _____ if you run.

16 Brian told me this afternoon that I have _____ _____ _____ .

17 No one _____ _____ _____ me that before.

18 _____ does he _____ _____ ?

19 Maybe he was just _____ _____ _____ nice.

20 When he said that to me, _____ , I started _____ _____ .

1	우리는 모두 리더들이다
2	Brian: "선거가 다가오고 있어.
3	유미야, 반 대표에 입후보하는 게 어때?"
4	유미: "아니.
5	나는 그 자리에 적절한 사람이 아니야.
6	나는 입후보하는 것에 대해 생각해 본 적이 없어."
7	Brian: "왜?"
8	유미: "이봐, Brian.
9	리더들은 특별한 자질을 갖추고 있어.
10	나 같은 사람이 리더로 불릴 수 있다고 생각하지 않아."
11	Brian: "무슨 말이야?
12	내 생각에 너는 매우 좋은 지도력 자질들을 갖추고 있어.
13	너는 정말 친절하고 외향적이잖아.
14	또 너는 사람들이 어울리도록 도와주기도 해.
15	만약 네가 입후보한다면 당선될 거라고 믿어 의심치 않아."
16	Brian은 오늘 오후에 내게 내가 좋은 지도력 자질들을 갖추고 있다고 말했다.
17	이전에는 아무도 내게 그런 말을 한 적이 없었다.
18	왜 그는 그렇게 생각했을까?
19	아마도 그는 그저 친절하려고 했을 것이다.
20	그러나 그가 내게 그렇게 말했을 때, 나는 생각하기 시작했다.

21 Can I really _____ _____ _____?

22 I _____ _____.

23 I think leaders should have _____ _____, clear _____, and the ability _____ _____ _____.

24 I don't have _____ _____ _____ _____.

25 Then I suddenly started to _____ _____ these are the only _____ that make a good leader.

26 Maybe I'm _____.

27 Maybe there are _____ _____ _____.

28 So I decided to _____ _____ _____ _____.

29 Here's _____ I _____!

30 **GREEN LEADERS: "Team _____"**

31 Ensure that the team _____ _____

32 Create a _____ _____

33 Are friendly and easy _____ _____ _____

34 **RED LEADERS: "_____ _____"**

35 Have good _____ _____

36 _____ problems and _____

37 Think of the most _____ to _____ _____ _____

38 **PURPLE LEADERS: "_____ _____"**

39 _____ others to work _____ _____ _____

40 Do not _____ _____ _____ people

41 Give _____ only when _____ _____ _____

21 내가 정말 리더가 될 수 있을까?

22 나는 모르겠다.

23 나는 리더가 비전, 명확한 목표, 그리고 다른 사람들에게 동기를 부여할 능력을 가지고 있어야 한다고 생각한다.

24 나는 그러한 것들 중 어느 것도 가지고 있지 않다.

25 그때 나는 갑자기 이것들이 좋은 리더를 만드는 유일한 자질들인지 궁금해하기 시작했다.

26 아마도 내가 틀린지도 모른다.

27 어쩌면 다른 지도력 자질들이 있는지도 모른다.

28 그래서 나는 온라인으로 조사해 보기로 결심했다.

29 여기에 내가 찾은 것이 있다!

30 〈녹색 리더〉 '팀 조직자'

31 팀이 반드시 가치 있다고 느끼게 한다

32 긍정적인 환경을 조성한다

33 친절하고 말을 걸기 쉽다

34 〈빨간색 리더〉 '논리적 분석가'

35 좋은 추론 기술을 갖고 있다

36 문제와 상황들을 분석한다

37 팀의 목표를 성취하는 가장 효과적인 방법들을 생각한다

38 〈보라색 리더〉 '방임적 관리자'

39 다른 사람들이 스스로 일하도록 해 준다

40 사람들을 통제하려고 하지 않는다

41 필요할 때만 조언한다

42 ORANGE LEADERS: "_____ _____"

43 Make _____ _____ _____

44 _____ _____ everything is finished _____ _____

45 Ensure _____ _____ is done _____

46 YELLOW LEADERS: "_____ _____"

47 Lead _____ _____

48 Let the team members _____ _____

49 _____ the team members' _____

50 BLUE LEADERS: "_____ _____"

51 _____ problems _____ _____ _____

52 _____ _____ _____ fresh ideas

53 _____ _____ tasks _____ _____ others

54 I was surprised that there are actually many different leadership styles, but soon I _____ _____ _____.

55 We _____ _____ many different groups, and many different situations can _____ _____ in our lives.

56 They all _____ _____ different leadership styles.

57 Each group's _____ _____ _____ the best leadership style.

58 "I am _____ _____ _____ many different groups, and I have _____ _____ in each group."

59 After reading everything, I became _____ _____.

60 I discovered that I have _____ _____ _____ _____ of a "green leader."

61 If my classmates think a green leader would make our class better, they might _____ _____ to be _____ _____!

62 Okay, _____ _____ it!

42 〈주황색 리더〉 '엄격한 감독관'

43 모두의 역할을 분명하게 해 준다

44 모든 일을 제때 끝날 것을 확실히 한다

45 각 단계가 적절히 이행되도록 한다

46 〈노란색 리더〉 '조용한 지지자'

47 솔선수범한다

48 팀원들이 대신 빛나도록 해 준다

49 팀원들의 요구 사항을 충족한다

50 〈파란색 리더〉 '창조적 사상가'

51 새로운 방식으로 문제들에 접근한다

52 신선한 아이디어를 떠올린다

53 다른 사람들과 다르게 일을 처리한다

54 나는 실제로 서로 다른 많은 지도력 유형들이 있어서 놀랐지만, 곧 그 이유를 깨달았다.

55 우리는 서로 다른 여러 집단에 속하고, 우리 인생에서 서로 다른 많은 상황들이 발생할 수 있다.

56 그것들은 모두 서로 다른 지도력 유형들을 요구한다.

57 각 집단의 독특한 상황이 최고의 지도력 유형을 결정한다.

58 "나는 서로 다른 많은 집단의 일부이고, 각 집단에서 각각 다른 책임을 갖고 있어."

59 모든 것을 읽고 나서, 나는 더 자신감이 생겼다.

60 나는 '녹색 리더'의 자질들 중 일부분을 가지고 있다는 것을 알게 되었다.

61 만약 나의 반 친구들이 녹색 리더가 우리 학급을 더 좋게 만들 거라고 생각한다면, 그들은 학급 대표로 나를 뽑을지도 모른다!

62 좋아, 시도해 보자!

※ 다음 문장을 우리말로 쓰시오.

1 We Are All Leaders
➡ _____

2 Brian: The election is coming up.
➡ _____

3 Why don't you run for class representative, Yumi?
➡ _____

4 Yumi: No way.
➡ _____

5 I'm not the right person for that position.
➡ _____

6 I've never thought about running.
➡ _____

7 Brian: Why not?
➡ _____

8 Yumi: Come on, Brian.
➡ _____

9 Leaders have special qualities.
➡ _____

10 I don't think a person like me can be called a leader.
➡ _____

11 Brian: What do you mean?
➡ _____

12 I think you have very good leadership qualities.
➡ _____

13 You're really friendly and outgoing.
➡ _____

14 You also help people get along.
➡ _____

15 I have no doubt that you will be elected if you run.
➡ _____

16 Brian told me this afternoon that I have good leadership qualities.
➡ _____

17 No one has ever told me that before.
➡ _____

18 Why does he think so?
➡ _____

19 Maybe he was just trying to be nice.
➡ _____

20 When he said that to me, however, I started to think.
➡ _____

21 Can I really become a leader?

➡ _____

22 I don't know.

➡ _____

23 I think leaders should have a vision, clear goals, and the ability to motivate others.

➡ _____

24 I don't have any of those things.

➡ _____

25 Then I suddenly started to wonder if these are the only qualities that make a good leader.

➡ _____

26 Maybe I'm wrong.

➡ _____

27 Maybe there are other leadership qualities.

➡ _____

28 So I decided to do some research online.

➡ _____

29 Here's what I found!

➡ _____

30 GREEN LEADERS: "Team Builders"

➡ _____

31 Ensure that the team feels valued

➡ _____

32 Create a positive environment

➡ _____

33 Are friendly and easy to talk to

➡ _____

34 RED LEADERS: "Logical Analysts"

➡ _____

35 Have good reasoning skills

➡ _____

36 Analyze problems and situations

➡ _____

37 Think of the most effective ways to achieve the team's goals

➡ _____

38 PURPLE LEADERS: "Hands-Off Managers"

➡ _____

39 Allow others to work on their own

➡ _____

40 Do not try to control people

➡ _____

41 Give advice only when it is needed

➡ _____

42 ORANGE LEADERS: "Strict Directors"
➡ _____

43 Make everyone's role clear
➡ _____

44 Make sure everything is finished on time
➡ _____

45 Ensure each step is done properly
➡ _____

46 YELLOW LEADERS: "Quiet Supporters"
➡ _____

47 Lead by example
➡ _____

48 Let the team members shine instead
➡ _____

49 Meet the team members' needs
➡ _____

50 BLUE LEADERS: "Creative Thinkers"
➡ _____

51 Approach problems in new ways
➡ _____

52 Come up with fresh ideas
➡ _____

53 Deal with tasks differently from others
➡ _____

54 I was surprised that there are actually many different leadership styles, but soon I realized the reason.
➡ _____

55 We belong to many different groups, and many different situations can come up in our lives.
➡ _____

56 They all call for different leadership styles.
➡ _____

57 Each group's unique situation determines the best leadership style.
➡ _____

58 "I am a part of many different groups, and I have different responsibilities in each group."
➡ _____

59 After reading everything, I became more confident.
➡ _____

60 I discovered that I have some of the qualities of a "green leader."
➡ _____

61 If my classmates think a green leader would make our class better, they might pick me to be class representative!
➡ _____

62 Okay, let's try it!
➡ _____

※ 다음 괄호 안의 단어들을 우리말에 맞도록 바르게 배열하시오.

1 (Are / We / Leaders / All)
➡ _____

2 (Brian: / election / the / coming / is / up.)
➡ _____

3 (don't / why / run / you / class / for / Yumi? / representative,)
➡ _____

4 (Yumi: / way. / no)
➡ _____

5 (not / I'm / right / the / for / person / position. / that)
➡ _____

6 (never / I've / thought / running. / about)
➡ _____

7 (Brain: / not? / why)
➡ _____

8 (Yumi: / on, / come / Brian.)
➡ _____

9 (have / leaders / qualities. / special)
➡ _____

10 (don't / I / a / think / like / person / me / be / can / called / leader. / a)
➡ _____

11 (Brian: / do / what / mean? / you)
➡ _____

12 (think / I / have / you / very / leadership / good / qualities.)
➡ _____

13 (really / you're / outgoing. / and / friendly)
➡ _____

14 (also / you / people / help / along. / get)
➡ _____

15 (have / I / doubt / no / you / that / be / will / elected / if / run. / you)
➡ _____

16 (told / Brian / this / me / afternoon / I / that / have / leadership / good / qualities.)
➡ _____

17 (one / no / ever / has / me / told / before. / that)
➡ _____

18 (does / why / think / he / so?)
➡ _____

19 (he / maybe / just / was / to / trying / nice. / be)
➡ _____

20 (he / when / that / said / me, / to / however, / started / I / think. / to)
➡ _____

1 우리는 모두 리더들이다

2 Brian: "선거가 다가오고 있어.

3 유미야, 반 대표에 입후보하는 게 어때?"

4 유미: "아니.

5 나는 그 자리에 적절한 사람이 아니야.

6 나는 입후보하는 것에 대해 생각해 본 적이 없어."

7 Brian: "왜?"

8 유미: "이봐, Brian.

9 리더들은 특별한 자질을 갖추고 있어.

10 나 같은 사람이 리더로 불릴 수 있다고 생각하지 않아."

11 Brian: "무슨 말이야?

12 내 생각에 너는 매우 좋은 지도력 자질들을 갖추고 있어.

13 너는 정말 친절하고 외향적이잖아.

14 또 너는 사람들이 어울리도록 도와주기도 해.

15 만약 네가 입후보한다면 당선될 거라고 믿어 의심치 않아."

16 Brian은 오늘 오후에 내게 내가 좋은 지도력 자질들을 갖추고 있다고 말했다.

17 이전에는 아무도 내게 그런 말을 한 적이 없었다.

18 왜 그는 그렇게 생각했을까?

19 아마도 그는 그저 친절하려고 했을 것이다.

20 그러나 그가 내게 그렇게 말했을 때, 나는 생각하기 시작했다.

21 (I / can / really / become / leader? / a)
➡ _____

22 (know. / don't / I)
➡ _____

23 (think / I / should / leaders / a / have / vision, / goals, / clear / and / ability / the / motivate / to / others.)
➡ _____
_____

24 (don't / I / any / have / those / of / things.)
➡ _____

25 (I / then / started / suddenly / wonder / to / these / if / the / are / qualities / only / make / that / a / leader. / good)
➡ _____
_____

26 (I'm / maybe / wrong.)
➡ _____

27 (there / maybe / other / are / qualities. / leadership)
➡ _____

28 (I so / to / decided / some / do / online. / research)
➡ _____

29 (what / here's / found! / I)
➡ _____

30 (LEADERS: / GREEN / Builders" / "Team)
➡ _____

31 (that / ensure / the / feels / team / valued)
➡ _____

32 (a / creative / environment / positive)
➡ _____

33 (friendly / are / easy / and / talk / to / to)
➡ _____

34 (LEADERS: / RED / Analysts" / "Logical)
➡ _____

35 (good / have / skills / reasoning)
➡ _____

36 (problems / analyze / situations / and)
➡ _____

37 (of / think / most / the / effective / to / ways / the / achieve / goals / team's)
➡ _____

38 (LEADERS: / PURPLE / Managers" / "Hands-Off)
➡ _____

39 (others / allow / work / to / their / on / own)
➡ _____

40 (not / do / to / try / people / control)
➡ _____

41 (advice / give / when / only / is / it / needed.)
➡ _____

21 내가 정말 리더가 될 수 있을까?

22 나는 모르겠다.

23 나는 리더가 비전, 명확한 목표, 그리고 다른 사람들에게 동기를 부여할 능력을 가지고 있어야 한다고 생각한다.

24 나는 그러한 것들 중 어느 것도 가지고 있지 않다.

25 그때 나는 갑자기 이것들이 좋은 리더를 만드는 유일한 자질들인지 궁금해하기 시작했다.

26 아마도 내가 틀린지도 모른다.

27 어쩌면 다른 지도력 자질들이 있는지도 모른다.

28 그래서 나는 온라인으로 조사해 보기로 결심했다.

29 여기에 내가 찾은 것이 있다!

30 〈녹색 리더〉 '팀 조직자'

31 팀이 반드시 가치 있다고 느끼게 한다

32 긍정적인 환경을 조성한다

33 친절하고 말을 걸기 쉽다

34 〈빨간색 리더〉 '논리적 분석가'

35 좋은 추론 기술을 갖고 있다

36 문제와 상황들을 분석한다

37 팀의 목표를 성취하는 가장 효과적인 방법들을 생각한다

38 〈보라색 리더〉 '방임적 관리자'

39 다른 사람들이 스스로 일하도록 해 준다

40 사람들을 통제하려고 하지 않는다

41 필요할 때만 조언한다

Step4

42 (LEADERS: / ORANGE / Directors" / "Strict)
➡ _____

43 (everyone's / make / clear / role)
➡ _____

44 (sure / make / is / everything / on / finished / time)
➡ _____

45 (each / ensure / is / step / properly / done)
➡ _____

46 (LEADERS: / YELLOW / Supporters" / "Quiet)
➡ _____

47 (by / lead / example)
➡ _____

48 (the / let / members / team / instead / shine)
➡ _____

49 (the / meet / members's / team / needs)
➡ _____

50 (LEADERS: / BLUE / Thinkers" / "Creative)
➡ _____

51 (problems / approach / new / in / ways)
➡ _____

52 (up / come / fresh / with / ideas)
➡ _____

53 (with / deal / differently / tasks / others / from)
➡ _____

54 (was / I / surprised / there / that / actually / are / different / many / styles, / leadership / soon / but / realized / I / reason. / the)
➡ _____

55 (belong / we / many / to / groups, / different / many / and / situations / different / come / can / in / up / lives. / our)
➡ _____

56 (all / they / for / call / leadership / different / styles.)
➡ _____

57 (group's / each / situation / unique / the / determines / best / style. / leadership)
➡ _____

58 (am / "I / part / a / of / different / many / groups, / I / and / have / responsibilities / different / in / group." / each)
➡ _____

59 (reading / after / everything, / became / I / confident. / more)
➡ _____

60 (discovered / I / that / have / I / of / some / qualities / the / a / of / leader." / "green)
➡ _____

61 (my / if / think / classmates / green / a / would / leader / our / make / better, / class / might / they / me / pick / be / to / representative! / class)
➡ _____

62 (let's / okay, / it! / try)
➡ _____

---

42 〈주황색 리더〉 '엄격한 감독관'

43 모두의 역할을 분명하게 해 준다

44 모든 일을 제때 끝날 것을 확실히 한다

45 각 단계가 적절히 이행되도록 한다

46 〈노란색 리더〉 '조용한 지지자'

47 솔선수범한다

48 팀원들이 대신 빛나도록 해 준다

49 팀원들의 요구 사항을 충족한다

50 〈파란색 리더〉 '창조적 사상가'

51 새로운 방식으로 문제들에 접근한다

52 신선한 아이디어를 떠올린다

53 다른 사람들과 다르게 일을 처리한다

54 나는 실제로 서로 다른 많은 지도력 유형들이 있어서 놀랐지만, 곧 그 이유를 깨달았다.

55 우리는 서로 다른 여러 집단에 속하고, 우리 인생에서 서로 다른 많은 상황들이 발생할 수 있다.

56 그것들은 모두 서로 다른 지도력 유형들을 요구한다.

57 각 집단의 독특한 상황이 최고의 지도력 유형을 결정한다.

58 "나는 서로 다른 많은 집단의 일부이고, 각 집단에서 각각 다른 책임을 갖고 있어."

59 모든 것을 읽고 나서, 나는 더 자신감이 생겼다.

60 나는 '녹색 리더'의 자질들 중 일부분을 가지고 있다는 것을 알게 되었다.

61 만약 나의 반 친구들이 녹색 리더가 우리 학급을 더 좋게 만들 거라고 생각한다면, 그들은 학급 대표로 나를 뽑을지도 모른다!

62 좋아, 시도해 보자!

44 Lesson 4. My Roles in Society

※ **다음 우리말을 영어로 쓰시오.**

1 우리는 모두 리더들이다
➡ _____

2 Brian: "선거가 다가오고 있어.
➡ _____

3 유미야, 반 대표에 입후보하는 게 어때?"
➡ _____

4 유미: "아니.
➡ _____

5 나는 그 자리에 적절한 사람이 아니야.
➡ _____

6 나는 입후보하는 것에 대해 생각해 본 적이 없어."
➡ _____

7 Brian: "왜?"
➡ _____

8 유미: "이봐, Brian.
➡ _____

9 리더들은 특별한 자질을 갖추고 있어.
➡ _____

10 나 같은 사람이 리더로 불릴 수 있다고 생각하지 않아."
➡ _____

11 Brian: "무슨 말이야?
➡ _____

12 내 생각에 너는 매우 좋은 지도력 자질들을 갖추고 있어.
➡ _____

13 너는 정말 친절하고 외향적이잖아.
➡ _____

14 또 너는 사람들이 어울리도록 도와주기도 해.
➡ _____

15 만약 네가 입후보한다면 당선될 거라고 믿어 의심치 않아."
➡ _____

16 Brian은 오늘 오후에 내게 내가 좋은 지도력 자질들을 갖추고 있다고 말했다.
➡ _____

17 이전에는 아무도 내게 그런 말을 한 적이 없었다.
➡ _____

18 왜 그는 그렇게 생각했을까?
➡ _____

19 아마도 그는 그저 친절하려고 했을 것이다.
➡ _____

20 그러나 그가 내게 그렇게 말했을 때, 나는 생각하기 시작했다.
➡ _____

21 내가 정말 리더가 될 수 있을까?

➡ _____

22 나는 모르겠다.

➡ _____

23 나는 리더가 비전, 명확한 목표, 그리고 다른 사람들에게 동기를 부여할 능력을 가지고 있어야 한다고 생각한다.

➡ _____

24 나는 그러한 것들 중 어느 것도 가지고 있지 않다.

➡ _____

25 그때 나는 갑자기 이것들이 좋은 리더를 만드는 유일한 자질들인지 궁금해하기 시작했다.

➡ _____

26 아마도 내가 틀린지도 모른다.

➡ _____

27 어쩌면 다른 지도력 자질들이 있는지도 모른다.

➡ _____

28 그래서 나는 온라인으로 조사해 보기로 결심했다.

➡ _____

29 여기에 내가 찾은 것이 있다!

➡ _____

30 〈녹색 리더〉 '팀 조직자'

➡ _____

31 팀이 반드시 가치 있다고 느끼게 한다

➡ _____

32 긍정적인 환경을 조성한다

➡ _____

33 친절하고 말을 걸기 쉽다

➡ _____

34 〈빨간색 리더〉 '논리적 분석가'

➡ _____

35 좋은 추론 기술을 갖고 있다

➡ _____

36 문제와 상황들을 분석한다

➡ _____

37 팀의 목표를 성취하는 가장 효과적인 방법들을 생각한다

➡ _____

38 〈보라색 리더〉 '방임적 관리자'

➡ _____

39 다른 사람들이 스스로 일하도록 해 준다

➡ _____

40 사람들을 통제하려고 하지 않는다

➡ _____

41 필요할 때만 조언한다

➡ _____

42 〈주황색 리더〉 '엄격한 감독관'
➡ _____

43 모두의 역할을 분명하게 해 준다
➡ _____

44 모든 일을 제때 끝날 것을 확실히 한다
➡ _____

45 단계가 적절히 이행되도록 한다
➡ _____

46 〈노란색 리더〉 '조용한 지지자'
➡ _____

47 솔선수범한다
➡ _____

48 팀원들이 대신 빛나도록 해 준다
➡ _____

49 팀원들의 요구 사항을 충족한다
➡ _____

50 〈파란색 리더〉 '창조적 사상가'
➡ _____

51 새로운 방식으로 문제들에 접근한다
➡ _____

52 신선한 아이디어를 떠올린다
➡ _____

53 다른 사람들과 다르게 일을 처리한다
➡ _____

54 나는 실제로 서로 다른 많은 지도력 유형들이 있어서 놀랐지만, 곧 그 이유를 깨달았다.
➡ _____

55 우리는 서로 다른 여러 집단에 속하고, 우리 인생에서 서로 다른 많은 상황들이 발생할 수 있다.
➡ _____

56 그것들은 모두 서로 다른 지도력 유형들을 요구한다.
➡ _____

57 각 집단의 독특한 상황이 최고의 지도력 유형을 결정한다.
➡ _____

58 "나는 서로 다른 많은 집단의 일부이고, 각 집단에서 각각 다른 책임을 갖고 있어."
➡ _____

59 모든 것을 읽고 나서, 나는 더 자신감이 생겼다.
➡ _____

60 나는 '녹색 리더'의 자질들 중 일부분을 가지고 있다는 것을 알게 되었다.
➡ _____

61 만약 나의 반 친구들이 녹색 리더가 우리 학급을 더 좋게 만들 거라고 생각한다면, 그들은 학급 대표로 나를 뽑을지도 모른다!
➡ _____
_____

62 좋아, 시도해 보자!
➡ _____

※ 다음 우리말과 일치하도록 빈칸에 알맞은 말을 쓰시오.

Presentation Time Step 3

1. Our group _____ _____ _____ _____ _____ our class birthday party.

2. I _____ _____ a cake.

3. Woojin and Taeho _____ _____ _____ _____.

4. Yeji _____ _____ birthday _____ _____.

5. I have _____ _____ _____ our birthday party _____ _____ _____ _____ _____ fun!

After You Read B

1. Hi, I'm Jennifer. I try _____ _____ _____ _____ _____ and _____ _____ _____ _____ _____.

2. The _____ _____ is _____ the members of my team _____.

3. Hello, I'm Heejin. I _____ _____ problems _____ _____ _____.

4. I _____ _____ _____ to _____ _____ _____ _____ new ideas.

5. Hi, I'm Chris. I _____ my team's problems and _____, and then I _____ _____ the most _____ _____ _____ _____ _____ _____.

Do It Yourself B

1. Brian: _____ _____ _____ _____ _____ _____ for class representative, Yumi?

2. Yumi: No way. I've _____ _____ _____ _____ _____.

3. Brian: _____ _____?

4. Yumi: Leaders _____ _____ _____ _____.

5. I don't think _____ _____ _____ me _____ _____ _____ a leader.

6. Brian: _____ _____ you _____?

7. You're _____ _____ and _____.

8. You also _____ _____ _____ _____.

9. I have _____ _____ that you _____ _____ _____ _____ if you _____.

1. 우리 모둠은 우리 학급 생일 파티를 준비하기 위한 과제를 선정했다.
2. 나는 케이크를 살 것이다.
3. 우진이와 태호는 교실을 장식할 것이다.
4. 예지는 생일 파티 노래를 연주할 것이다.
5. 나는 우리의 생일 파티가 아주 재미있을 것을 확신한다.

1. 안녕, 나는 Jennifer야. 나는 솔선수범하며 다른 사람들의 요구를 해결하려고 노력해.
2. 중요한 것은 우리 팀 구성원들이 빛나는 거야.
3. 안녕, 나는 희진이야. 나는 문제에 새로운 방법으로 접근하는 것이 즐거워.
4. 나는 최선을 다해서 새로운 아이디어를 제시해.
5. 안녕, 나는 Chris야. 나는 우리 팀의 문제점과 상황을 분석해. 그런 다음 우리의 목표를 달성하기 위한 가장 효과적인 방법들을 찾아.

1. Brian: 유미야, 반 대표에 입후보하는 게 어때?
2. Yumi: 아니. 나는 입후보하는 것에 대해 생각해 본 적이 없어.
3. Brian: 왜?
4. Yumi: 리더들은 특별한 자질을 갖추고 있어.
5. 나 같은 사람이 리더로 불릴 수 있다고 생각하지 않아.
6. Brian: 무슨 말이야?
7. 너는 정말 친절하고 외향적이잖아.
8. 또 너는 사람들이 어울리도록 도와주기도 해.
9. 만약 네가 입후보한다면 당선될 거라고 믿어 의심치 않아.

※ 다음 우리말을 영어로 쓰시오.

Presentation Time Step 3

1. 우리 모둠은 우리 학급 생일 파티를 준비하기 위한 과제를 선정했다.
➡ _____

2. 나는 케이크를 살 것이다.
➡ _____

3. 우진이와 태호는 교실을 장식할 것이다.
➡ _____

4. 예지는 생일 파티 노래를 연주할 것이다.
➡ _____

5. 나는 우리의 생일 파티가 아주 재미있을 것을 확신한다.
➡ _____

After You Read B

1. 안녕, 나는 Jennifer야. 나는 솔선수범하며 다른 사람들의 요구를 해결하려고 노력해.
➡ _____

2. 중요한 것은 우리 팀 구성원들이 빛나는 거야.
➡ _____

3. 안녕, 나는 희진이야. 나는 문제에 새로운 방법으로 접근하는 것이 즐거워.
➡ _____

4. 나는 최선을 다해서 새로운 아이디어를 제시해.
➡ _____

5. 안녕, 나는 Chris야. 나는 우리 팀의 문제점과 상황을 분석해. 그런 다음 우리의 목표를 달성하기 위한 가장 효과적인 방법들을 찾아.
➡ _____
_____

Do It Yourself B

1. Brian: 유미야, 반 대표에 입후보하는 게 어때?
➡ _____

2. Yumi: 아니. 나는 입후보하는 것에 대해 생각해 본 적이 없어.
➡ _____

3. Brian: 왜?
➡ _____

4. Yumi: 리더들은 특별한 자질을 갖추고 있어.
➡ _____

5. 나 같은 사람이 리더로 불릴 수 있다고 생각하지 않아.
➡ _____

6. Brian: 무슨 말이야?
➡ _____

7. 너는 정말 친절하고 외향적이잖아.
➡ _____

8. 또 너는 사람들이 어울리도록 도와주기도 해.
➡ _____

9. 만약 네가 입후보한다면 당선될 거라고 믿어 의심치 않아.
➡ _____

※ 다음 영어를 우리말로 쓰시오.

01 artwork _____

02 bright _____

03 architect _____

04 contain _____

05 architecture _____

06 explanation _____

07 statue _____

08 attract _____

09 grain _____

10 greenery _____

11 hopefully _____

12 climate _____

13 innovation _____

14 additional _____

15 material _____

16 damage _____

17 pollution _____

18 awareness _____

19 unwanted _____

20 prevent _____

21 incredible _____

22 protect _____

23 eco-friendly _____

24 provide _____

25 surface _____

26 theme _____

27 reduce _____

28 reusable _____

29 structure _____

30 separate _____

31 disappear _____

32 encourage _____

33 remind _____

34 resource _____

35 in addition to _____

36 break down _____

37 throw ~ away _____

38 be bored with _____

39 in harmony with _____

40 contribute to _____

41 a variety of _____

42 take care of _____

43 come up with _____

※ 다음 우리말을 영어로 쓰시오.

01 오염 _____

02 추가적인 _____

03 인식, 의식 _____

04 혁신 _____

05 건축가 _____

06 포함하다 _____

07 주제 _____

08 예방하다, 막다, 방지하다 _____

09 내내, 줄곧, 가로질러 _____

10 손상시키다 _____

11 보호하다, 지키다 _____

12 친환경적인 _____

13 자원 _____

14 격려하다, 장려하다 _____

15 끌다, 매혹시키다 _____

16 줄이다 _____

17 사라지다 _____

18 곡물, 알곡 _____

19 수중, 해저 _____

20 유일무이한, 독특한 _____

21 원치 않는, 불필요한 _____

22 재사용할 수 있는 _____

23 믿기 힘든, 굉장한 _____

24 제안 _____

25 (예술적) 작품 _____

26 자연적인 _____

27 의견 _____

28 설명 _____

29 심각하게, 진지하게 _____

30 적절하게 _____

31 깨닫다 _____

32 조각상 _____

33 구조(물) _____

34 분리하다 _____

35 무너지다, 고장 나다 _____

36 회복하다, 좋아지다 _____

37 ~을 돌보다 _____

38 ~을 생각해 내다 _____

39 다양한 _____

40 일리가 있다 _____

41 ~와 조화하여 _____

42 ~에 지루해하다 _____

43 ~ 이외에도 _____

※ 다음 영영풀이에 알맞은 단어를 <보기>에서 골라 쓴 후, 우리말 뜻을 쓰시오.

1 _____ : to harm something: _____

2 _____ : to no longer be seen: _____

3 _____ : the top layer of something: _____

4 _____ : below the water: _____

5 _____ : a person who designs buildings: _____

6 _____ : something that you are trying to do or achieve: _____

7 _____ : plants or vegetation: _____

8 _____ : the general weather of a region: _____

9 _____ : an object made from stone or metal: _____

10 _____ : the introduction of new things, ideas, or ways of doing something:

_____

11 _____ : the small hard seeds of food plants such as wheat, rice, etc.: _____

12 _____ : something created to be beautiful by a painter, sculptor, etc.: _____

13 _____ : information to help people understand something: _____

14 _____ : one's beliefs, ideas, thoughts, and assumptions about a matter: _____

15 _____ : capable of being used more than once: _____

16 _____ : an area of slight darkness that is produced when something blocks the

light of the sun: _____

보기			
innovation	grain	surface	disappear
shade	opinion	climate	goal
statue	artwork	damage	underwater
reusable	explanation	greenery	architect

※ 다음 우리말과 일치하도록 빈칸에 알맞은 말을 쓰시오.

해석

Listen & Talk 1 A

B: I think we're using too many _____ _____.

G: I agree. It's _____ _____ _____ the _____. How can we _____ our use of _____ _____?

B: _____ _____ _____, we _____ _____ _____ when we go shopping.

남: 내 생각엔 우리는 비닐봉지를 너무 많이 쓰는 것 같아.

여: 내 생각도 그래. 그건 환경에 좋지 않아. 우리 비닐봉지 사용을 어떻게 줄일 수 있을까?

남: 내 생각에는 물건을 사러 갈 때 재사용할 수 있는 가방을 가져 가야 해.

Listen & Talk 1 B

G: Jiho, hurry _____! The elevator is _____ _____ soon.

B: The science room is just on the _____ _____. _____ _____ _____ we _____ _____ _____?

G: I don't want to walk _____ _____ _____ up there.

B: Come on. Elevators use _____ _____ energy. We need to _____ energy to _____ _____.

G: But _____ _____ _____ doesn't use that _____ _____.

B: That's true, but the energy from all the elevator rides _____ _____ over time. _____ _____, _____ _____ _____ the environment starts with the _____ _____.

G: You _____ _____ _____ _____. _____ _____ the stairs.

여: 지호야, 서둘러! 엘리베이터가 곧 올라간다.

남: 과학실은 겨우 3층에 있잖아. 우리 계단을 오르는 건 어때?

여: 그 모든 계단을 올라서 가고 싶진 않아.

남: 잘 생각해 봐. 엘리베이터는 전기를 많이 쓰잖아. 우리는 환경을 보호하려면 에너지를 아껴야 해.

여: 하지만 엘리베이터를 한 번 탄다고 그렇게 많은 에너지를 사용하진 않잖아.

남: 그렇지, 하지만 엘리베이터를 타면서 사용하는 에너지는 시간이 흐르면서 누적될 거야. 내 생각에는, 환경을 보호하는 것은 작은 것부터 시작한다고 생각해.

여: 네 말이 일리가 있네. 계단을 이용하자.

Listen & Talk 1 C

B: Today, I'd _____ _____ _____ _____ _____ _____ _____ about the trash problem at our school. I've found that many students just _____ things _____ instead _____ _____ _____ them. _____ you know, however, recycling is very important _____ it saves _____ and helps _____ the environment. So, _____ _____ _____, we need to reduce the number of _____ _____ at school _____ _____ _____. Why don't we _____ four different _____ _____ _____ on every floor instead? This will _____ students to _____ the paper, glass, plastic, and cans _____.

남: 오늘 저는 우리 학교의 쓰레기 문제에 대해 제안을 하나 하고자 합니다. 저는 많은 학생들이 쓰레기를 재활용하는 대신에 그냥 버리는 것을 발견했습니다. 하지만, 여러분도 알다시피, 재활용은 자원을 아낄 수 있고 환경을 보호하는 것을 돕기 때문에 재활용하는 것은 정말 중요합니다. 그래서 제 생각에는 재활용을 권장하기 위해 학교에 있는 쓰레기통의 수를 줄이는 것이 필요하다고 생각합니다. 대신에 모든 층에 각기 색이 다른 4개의 재활용 통을 두는 것이 어떨까요? 이는 학생들이 종이, 유리, 플라스틱, 캔을 적절하게 구분할 수 있도록 상기시킬 것입니다.

Listen & Talk 2 A

B: Our club is _____ a photo contest next week.

G: _____ _____ _____ photos will be in it?

B: The _____ is pollution around the world. We _____ _____ this contest to _____ _____ _____ of environmental problems.

G: That sounds nice. I can't _____ _____ _____ _____!

Listen & Talk 2 B

G: I read a cool _____ today.

B: _____ was it _____?

G: It was about a new bag. It just _____ _____ a _____ _____, but it's _____ mostly _____ corn.

B: That sounds really _____.

G: Yes, but there's more. The bag _____ _____ in _____ in only three months and _____ in about _____ _____ in warm water!

B: Wow! That will help us _____ _____ _____ by a lot!

G: I know! The _____ will start _____ the bag sometime _____ _____. I can't _____ _____ _____ it!

Listen & Talk 2 C

B: What _____ we _____ _____ do this weekend, Mihee?

G: Why don't we go to the _____ _____ near my house?

B: A sheep park? How _____! Are there really sheep in the park?

G: Yes. They are there to _____ _____ _____.

B: _____ _____ they help the environment?

G: You know, people usually use _____ to kill _____ _____. The sheep in the park eat those plants, so the _____ are _____ _____.

B: What a _____ idea! I _____ _____ _____ visit the park!

Do It Yourself

G: I want _____ _____ a new bag.

B: You already have too many bags. _____ _____ _____, you don't need _____ _____.

G: But I'm _____ _____ my old bags.

B: Then how _____ _____ old clothes to make a new bag? You can _____ _____ _____ _____ _____ _____ _____ online.

G: Oh, that sounds _____! I can't wait _____ _____ my own bag.

남: 다음 주에 우리 동아리에서 사진 대회를 개최할 거야.

여: 어떤 종류의 사진들이 출품되니?

남: 주제는 세계의 환경오염이야. 우리는 학생들이 환경 문제에 대해 인식을 높일 수 있도록 이 대회를 개최하는 거야.

여: 그거 참 멋지네. 나도 어서 대회를 보고 싶다!

여: 오늘 굉장한 기사를 읽었어.

남: 무엇에 대한 기사였니?

여: 새로운 봉지에 관한 기사였어. 그것은 비닐봉지처럼 생겼지만, 대부분 옥수수로 만든 거야.

남: 그것 참 놀랍구나.

여: 응, 하지만 놀라운 게 더 있어. 그 봉지는 흙 속에서 3달 만에 분해되고 따뜻한 물속에서는 3분 만에 사라져!

남: 와! 그건 우리가 플라스틱 쓰레기를 줄이는 데 많이 도움이 되겠구나!

여: 내 말이 그 말이야! 그 회사는 올해 중으로 그 봉지를 팔기 시작할 거야. 어서 사용하고 싶어!

남: 이번 주말에 무엇을 할 계획이니, 미희야?

여: 우리 집 근처에 있는 양 공원에 가는 것은 어때?

남: 양 공원? 그것 참 흥미로운데! 공원에 정말로 양이 있는 거야?

여: 응. 그들은 환경을 보호하기 위해 거기에 있어.

남: 그들이 어떻게 환경에 도움을 줄 수 있지?

여: 있지, 사람들은 잡초를 없애기 위해 화학 물질을 사용하잖아. 그 공원에 있는 양들이 그런 잡초들을 먹어서, 화학물질이 필요하지 않게 돼.

남: 그것 참 놀라운 생각이구나! 어서 그 공원에 가보고 싶다!

여: 나 새로운 가방을 사고 싶어.

남: 넌 이미 너무 많은 가방을 가지고 있어. 내 생각에 넌 가방이 더 필요하지 않아.

여: 하지만 난 나의 오래된 가방들에 질렸는걸.

남: 그럼 새로운 가방을 만들기 위해 오래된 옷들을 사용하는 것은 어때? 만드는 방법은 온라인상에서 찾아볼 수 있어.

여: 오, 그것 참 흥미로운데! 어서 나만의 가방을 만들고 싶어!

※ 다음 우리말에 맞도록 대화를 영어로 쓰시오.

Listen & Talk 1 A

B: _____

G: _____

_____

B: _____

남: 내 생각엔 우리는 비닐봉지를 너무 많이 쓰는 것 같아.

여: 내 생각도 그래. 그건 환경에 좋지 않아. 우리 비닐봉지 사용을 어떻게 줄일 수 있을까?

남: 내 생각에는 물건을 사러 갈 때 재사용할 수 있는 가방을 가져 가야 해.

Listen & Talk 1 B

G: _____

B: _____

G: _____

B: _____

_____

G: _____

B: _____

_____

G: _____

여: 지호야, 서둘러! 엘리베이터가 곧 올라간다.

남: 과학실은 겨우 3층에 있잖아. 우리 계단을 오르는 건 어때?

여: 그 모든 계단을 올라서 가고 싶진 않아.

남: 잘 생각해 봐. 엘리베이터는 전기를 많이 쓰잖아. 우리는 환경을 보호하려면 에너지를 아껴야 해.

여: 하지만 엘리베이터를 한 번 탄다고 그렇게 많은 에너지를 사용하진 않잖아.

남: 그렇지, 하지만 엘리베이터를 타면서 사용하는 에너지는 시간이 흐르면서 누적될 거야. 내 생각에는, 환경을 보호하는 것은 작은 것부터 시작한다고 생각해.

여: 네 말이 일리가 있네. 계단을 이용하자.

Listen & Talk 1 C

B: _____

_____

_____

_____

_____

_____

_____

남: 오늘 저는 우리 학교의 쓰레기 문제에 대해 제안을 하나 하고자 합니다. 저는 많은 학생들이 쓰레기를 재활용하는 대신에 그냥 버리는 것을 발견했습니다. 하지만, 여러분도 알다시피, 재활용은 자원을 아낄 수 있고 환경을 보호하는 것을 돕기 때문에 재활용하는 것은 정말 중요합니다. 그래서 제 생각에는 재활용을 권장하기 위해 학교에 있는 쓰레기통의 수를 줄이는 것이 필요하다고 생각합니다. 대신에 모든 층에 각기 색이 다른 4개의 재활용 통을 두는 것이 어떨까요? 이는 학생들이 종이, 유리, 플라스틱, 캔을 적절하게 구분할 수 있도록 상기시킬 것입니다.

Listen & Talk 2 A

B: _____

G: _____

B: _____

_____

G: _____

Listen & Talk 2 B

G: _____

B: _____

G: _____

_____

B: _____

G: _____

_____

B: _____

G: _____

_____

Listen & Talk 2 C

B: _____

G: _____

B: _____

G: _____

B: _____

G: _____

_____

B: _____

Do It Yourself

G: _____

B: _____

G: _____

B: _____

_____

G: _____

남: 다음 주에 우리 동아리에서 사진 대회를 개최할 거야.

여: 어떤 종류의 사진들이 출품되니?

남: 주제는 세계의 환경오염이야. 우리는 학생들이 환경 문제에 대해 인식을 높일 수 있도록 이 대회를 개최하는 거야.

여: 그거 참 멋지네. 나도 어서 대회를 보고 싶다!

여: 오늘 굉장한 기사를 읽었어.

남: 무엇에 대한 기사였니?

여: 새로운 봉지에 관한 기사였어. 그것은 비닐봉지처럼 생겼지만, 대부분 옥수수로 만든 거야.

남: 그것 참 놀랍구나.

여: 응, 하지만 놀라운 게 더 있어. 그 봉지는 흙 속에서 3달 만에 분해되고 따뜻한 물속에서는 3분 만에 사라져!

남: 와! 그건 우리가 플라스틱 쓰레기를 줄이는 데 많이 도움이 되겠구나!

여: 내 말이 그 말이야! 그 회사는 올해 중으로 그 봉지를 팔기 시작할 거야. 어서 사용하고 싶어!

남: 이번 주말에 무엇을 할 계획이니, 미희야?

여: 우리 집 근처에 있는 양 공원에 가는 것은 어때?

남: 양 공원? 그것 참 흥미로운데! 공원에 정말로 양이 있는 거야?

여: 응. 양들은 환경을 보호하기 위해 거기에 있어.

남: 그들이 어떻게 환경에 도움을 줄 수 있지?

여: 있지, 사람들은 잡초를 없애기 위해 화학 물질을 사용하잖아. 그 공원에 있는 양들이 그런 잡초들을 먹어서, 화학물질이 필요하지 않게 돼.

남: 그것 참 놀라운 생각이구나! 어서 그 공원에 가보고 싶다!

여: 나 새로운 가방을 사고 싶어.

남: 넌 이미 너무 많은 가방을 가지고 있어. 내 생각에 넌 가방이 더 필요하지 않아.

여: 하지만 난 나의 오래된 가방들에 질렸는걸.

남: 그럼 새로운 가방을 만들기 위해 오래된 옷들을 사용하는 것은 어때? 만드는 방법은 온라인상에서 찾아볼 수 있어.

여: 오, 그것 참 흥미로운데! 어서 나만의 가방을 만들고 싶어!

※ 다음 우리말과 일치하도록 빈칸에 알맞은 것을 골라 쓰시오.

Join Hands, Save the Earth

1 It is important _____ _____ _____ _____ ways to protect the environment.

    A. to   B. for   C. us   D. find

2 Some people have found _____ _____ to _____ the _____.

    A. save   B. earth   C. ways   D. creative

3 One _____ is an _____ _____ in Cancun, Mexico.

    A. underwater   B. example   C. museum

4 Let's _____ Dr. Rosa Allison, an art _____, and listen to her _____ about the _____ museum.

    A. explanation   B. meet   C. professor   D. special

5 Rosa: Cancun is a city _____ 4.8 million _____ _____ every year.

    A. tourists   B. where   C. travel

6 One of the _____ _____ activities to do there is looking _____ the _____ beautiful sea life underwater.

    A. at   B. popular   C. area's   D. most

7 _____, tourist activities are seriously _____ _____ of the sea _____ Cancun.

    A. near   B. damaging   C. however   D. parts

8 _____ this, artists did _____ _____.

    A. prevent   B. interesting   C. to   D. something

9 They thought if they _____ tourists to a different _____ of the sea, the _____ areas could have time to get _____.

    A. dying   B. attracted   C. better   D. part

10 They made an _____ museum _____ from the places _____ sea life was _____.

    A. underwater   B. dying   C. where   D. away

11 It's _____ 14 meters _____ the surface and _____ 500 _____.

    A. contains   B. about   C. statues   D. below

12 The statues are _____ _____ _____ that _____ sea life.

    A. materials   B. made   C. support   D. from

13 They _____ additional places _____ plants and animals to _____ _____.

    A. on   B. for   C. provide   D. live

14 Over time, many _____ of sea life will grow on the _____, which will make the _____ _____.

    A. unique   B. statues   C. artwork   D. types

15 The artists want _____ to see a _____ of sea _____ on the _____.

    A. variety   B. life   C. statues   D. people

함께 손잡고, 지구를 구합시다

1 우리가 환경을 보호할 수 있는 방법을 찾는 것은 중요하다.

2 몇몇 사람들은 지구를 구하기 위한 창의적인 방법을 찾았다.

3 한 예로 멕시코 칸쿤에 있는 수중 박물관이 있다.

4 미술학 교수인 Rosa Allison 박사를 만나서 이 특별한 박물관에 대한 설명을 들어보자.

5 Rosa: 칸쿤은 매년 480만 명의 관광객이 여행하는 도시이다.

6 그곳에서 할 수 있는 가장 인기 있는 활동 중 하나는 그 지역의 바닷속의 아름다운 해양 생물을 관찰하는 것이다.

7 하지만, 관광 활동들이 칸쿤 근처의 바다 일부를 심각하게 훼손시키고 있다.

8 이러한 일을 방지하기 위해서, 예술가들이 흥미로운 생각을 해냈다.

9 그들은 만약 관광객들을 바다의 다른 쪽으로 유인한다면, 그 죽어가는 지역이 호전될 시간을 가질 수 있을 것이라 생각했다.

10 그들은 해양 생물이 죽어가는 지역으로부터 떨어진 해저에 수중 박물관을 만들었다.

11 그 박물관은 해수면에서 14미터 아래에 있으며 500개의 조각상이 있다.

12 그 조각상들은 해양 생물에게 도움이 되는 재료들로 만들어졌다.

13 그것들은 식물과 동물들이 살 수 있는 추가적인 장소를 제공한다.

14 시간이 흐르면, 많은 형태의 바다 생명체들이 그 조각상에서 자라게 될 것이며, 이것이 그 예술 작품을 독특하게 만들 것이다.

15 예술가들은 사람들이 그 조각상들에서 (살고 있는) 다양한 해양 생명체들을 보길 원한다.

16 If people _____ how _____ sea life is, they will understand how _____ it is to _____ the sea.

    A. save   B. rich   C. important   D. realize

17 In Singapore, people are _____ architecture to _____ the _____ on _____.

    A. protect   B. using   C. land   D. environment

18 Let's hear _____ Rajesh Khan, an _____, _____ about _____ buildings.

    A. eco-friendly   B. what   C. architect   D. says

19 Rajesh: Singapore is _____ _____ the _____.

    A. throughout   B. hot   C. year

20 Most buildings _____ air conditioning, _____ _____ a lot of energy and _____ to climate change.

    A. which   B. need   C. contributes   D. uses

21 That's _____ architects in Singapore have _____ to design eco-friendly buildings that use _____ air conditioning but are _____ cool inside.

    A. why   B. less   C. still   D. begun

22 For _____, many buildings in Singapore are _____ to have an _____ _____.

    A. structure   B. example   C. designed   D. open

23 This structure makes it possible for _____ _____ to _____ _____ a building.

    A. air   B. throughout   C. outside   D. move

24 This _____ air flow is _____ these buildings _____ _____.

    A. stay   B. natural   C. how   D. cool

25 In _____ to _____ open _____, architects _____ large gardens.

    A. add   B. making   C. addition   D. structures

26 This greenery _____ shade and _____ parts of the building from _____ sunlight, which _____ the building cooler.

    A. keeps   B. provides   C. direct   D. protects

27 Eco-friendly buildings like these not _____ help protect the environment, but _____ _____ people _____ a good quality of life.

    A. also   B. with   C. only   D. provide

28 Those are the _____ of this _____ _____ of _____.

    A. style   B. goals   C. architecture   D. new

29 Hopefully, architects will _____ _____ _____ _____ new eco-friendly ideas.

    A. up   B. keep   C. with   D. coming

30 Every _____ has different _____ of _____ the _____.

    A. ways   B. field   C. environment   D. protecting

31 _____ more innovation, humans and nature will be _____ to live together in harmony _____ _____ the future.

    A. able   B. far   C. with   D. into

16 만약 사람들이 해양 생물이 얼마나 풍부한지 깨닫는다면, 그들은 바다를 지키는 것이 얼마나 중요한지 이해할 것이다.

17 싱가포르에서는 사람들이 육지의 환경을 보호하기 위해 건축을 이용하고 있다.

18 건축가인 Rajesh Khan이 친환경 건물에 대해 말하는 것을 들어보자.

19 Rajesh: 싱가포르는 연중 더운 곳이다.

20 대부분의 건물들은 에어컨 가동이 필요한데, 이로 인해 많은 에너지가 사용되고 있으며 기후 변화의 원인이 되고 있다.

21 그것이 싱가포르의 건축가들이 에어컨을 덜 쓰면서도 실내에서 여전히 시원한 느낌이 들 수 있는 친환경적인 건물들을 디자인하기 시작한 이유이다.

22 가령, 싱가포르의 많은 건물들은 개방형 구조를 포함하게 디자인되었다.

23 이러한 구조는 외부 공기가 건물을 관통하는 것을 가능케 한다.

24 이러한 자연적인 공기의 흐름이 이 건물을 시원하게 유지해 주는 방법이다.

25 건축가들은 개방형 구조를 만드는 것 외에도 큰 정원을 더한다.

26 이러한 녹지 공간은 그늘을 제공하고 직사광선으로부터 건물의 부분들을 지켜주어 건물을 시원하게 유지한다.

27 이와 같은 친환경적인 건물들은 환경을 보호하는 것을 도울 뿐만 아니라 사람들에게 양질의 삶을 제공한다.

28 그것들이 바로 이러한 새로운 건축 방식의 목표이다.

29 바라건대, 건축가들은 새로운 친환경 아이디어를 계속해서 생각해 낼 것이다.

30 모든 분야에서 환경을 보호하는 다른 방식이 있다.

31 더 나은 혁신으로 인해 먼 미래에 인간과 자연은 함께 조화를 이루며 살아갈 수 있을 것이다.

※ 다음 우리말과 일치하도록 빈칸에 알맞은 것을 골라 쓰시오.

Join Hands, Save the Earth

1 _____ is important _____ _____ _____ _____ to protect the environment.

2 Some people have found _____ _____ _____ the earth.

3 One example is an _____ _____ in Cancun, Mexico.

4 Let's _____ Dr. Rosa Allison, an art _____, and _____ _____ her _____ about the special museum.

5 Rosa: Cancun is a city _____ 4.8 million _____ _____ _____.

6 One of _____ _____ activities _____ _____ there _____ _____ _____ the area's beautiful sea life underwater.

7 _____, tourist activities _____ _____ _____ _____ of the sea _____ Cancun.

8 _____ _____ _____, artists did _____ _____.

9 They thought _____ they _____ tourists _____ a different part of the sea, the _____ _____ could have time _____ _____ _____.

10 They _____ an _____ museum _____ _____ the places _____ sea life was _____.

11 It's _____ 14 _____ the _____ and _____ 500 _____.

12 The statues _____ _____ _____ materials _____ _____ _____ _____.

13 They _____ _____ _____ _____ _____ plants and animals _____ _____ _____.

14 Over time, many types of sea life _____ _____ the statues, _____ _____ _____ the artwork _____.

15 The artists _____ _____ _____ _____ _____ _____ sea life _____ the statues.

함께 손잡고, 지구를 구합시다

1 우리가 환경을 보호할 수 있는 방법을 찾는 것은 중요하다.

2 몇몇 사람들은 지구를 구하기 위한 창의적인 방법을 찾았다.

3 한 예로 멕시코 칸쿤에 있는 수중 박물관이 있다.

4 미술학 교수인 Rosa Allison 박사를 만나서 이 특별한 박물관에 대한 설명을 들어보자.

5 Rosa: 칸쿤은 매년 480만 명의 관광객이 여행하는 도시이다.

6 그곳에서 할 수 있는 가장 인기 있는 활동 중 하나는 그 지역의 바닷속의 아름다운 해양 생물을 관찰하는 것이다.

7 하지만, 관광 활동들이 칸쿤 근처의 바다 일부를 심각하게 훼손시키고 있다.

8 이러한 일을 방지하기 위해서, 예술가들이 흥미로운 생각을 해냈다.

9 그들은 만약 관광객들을 바다의 다른 쪽으로 유인한다면, 그 죽어가는 지역이 호전될 시간을 가질 수 있을 것이라 생각했다.

10 그들은 해양 생물이 죽어가는 지역으로부터 떨어진 해저에 수중 박물관을 만들었다.

11 그 박물관은 해수면에서 14미터 아래에 있으며 500개의 조각상이 있다.

12 그 조각상들은 해양 생물에게 도움이 되는 재료들로 만들어졌다.

13 그것들은 식물과 동물들이 살 수 있는 추가적인 장소를 제공한다.

14 시간이 흐르면, 많은 형태의 바다 생명체들이 그 조각상에서 자라게 될 것이며, 이것이 그 예술 작품을 독특하게 만들 것이다.

15 예술가들은 사람들이 그 조각상들에서 (살고 있는) 다양한 해양 생명체들을 보길 원한다.

16 If people realize _____ _____ _____ _____ _____,
they will understand _____ _____ _____ _____ to
save the sea.

17 In Singapore, people are _____ _____ _____
the environment _____ _____.

18 Let's hear _____ Rajesh Khan, an architect, _____ _____
_____ buildings.

19 Rajesh: Singapore is hot _____ _____ _____.

20 Most buildings _____ air conditioning, _____ _____ a lot
of energy and _____ _____ _____ _____.

21 _____ _____ architects in Singapore _____ _____
_____ _____ eco-friendly buildings _____ _____
_____ air conditioning but _____ _____ cool inside.

22 _____ _____, many buildings in Singapore _____
_____ _____ _____ an _____ _____.

23 This structure makes _____ possible _____
_____ _____ _____ _____ a building.

24 This _____ air flow is _____ _____ _____ _____
_____.

25 _____ _____ _____ _____ open structures, architects
add _____ _____.

26 This greenery _____ shade and _____ parts of the building
_____ _____ _____, which _____ the building cooler.

27 Eco-friendly buildings like these _____ _____ _____
protect the environment, _____ _____ _____ people
_____ a good _____ _____ _____.

28 Those are the _____ of this _____ _____ of _____.

29 Hopefully, architects _____ _____ _____ _____
_____ new _____ _____.

30 _____ _____ _____ different ways of _____ the
environment.

31 _____ more _____, humans and nature _____ _____
_____ _____ _____ _____ in harmony _____
_____ the future.

16 만약 사람들이 해양 생물이 얼
마나 풍부한지 깨닫는다면, 그
들은 바다를 지키는 것이 얼마
나 중요한지 이해할 것이다.

17 싱가포르에서는 사람들이 육지
의 환경을 보호하기 위해 건축
을 이용하고 있다.

18 건축가인 Rajesh Khan이 친환
경 건물에 대해 말하는 것을 들
어보자.

19 Rajesh: 싱가포르는 연중 더운
곳이다.

20 대부분의 건물들은 에어컨 가동
이 필요한데, 이로 인해 많은 에
너지가 사용되고 있으며 기후
변화의 원인이 되고 있다.

21 그것이 싱가포르의 건축가들이
에어컨을 덜 쓰면서도 실내에서
여전히 시원한 느낌이 들 수 있
는 친환경적인 건물들을 디자인
하기 시작한 이유이다.

22 가령, 싱가포르의 많은 건물들
은 개방형 구조를 포함하게 디
자인되었다.

23 이러한 구조는 외부 공기가 건물
을 관통하는 것을 가능케 한다.

24 이러한 자연적인 공기의 흐름이
이 건물을 시원하게 유지해 주
는 방법이다.

25 건축가들은 개방형 구조를 만드
는 것 외에도 큰 정원을 더한다.

26 이러한 녹지 공간은 그늘을 제
공하고 직사광선으로부터 건물
의 부분들을 지켜주어 건물을
시원하게 유지한다.

27 이와 같은 친환경적인 건물들은
환경을 보호하는 것을 도울 뿐
만 아니라 사람들에게 양질의
삶을 제공한다.

28 그것들이 바로 이리힌 새로운
건축 방식의 목표이다.

29 바라건대, 건축가들은 새로운
친환경 아이디어를 계속해서 생
각해 낼 것이다.

30 모든 분야에서 환경을 보호하는
다른 방식이 있다.

31 더 나은 혁신으로 인해 먼 미래
에 인간과 자연은 함께 조화를
이루며 살아갈 수 있을 것이다.

※ 다음 문장을 우리말로 쓰시오.

1 It is important for us to find ways to protect the environment.

➡ _____

2 Some people have found creative ways to save the earth.

➡ _____

3 One example is an underwater museum in Cancun, Mexico.

➡ _____

4 Let's meet Dr. Rosa Allison, an art professor, and listen to her explanation about the special museum.

➡ _____

5 Rosa: Cancun is a city where 4.8 million tourists travel every year.

➡ _____

6 One of the most popular activities to do there is looking at the area's beautiful sea life underwater.

➡ _____

7 However, tourist activities are seriously damaging parts of the sea near Cancun.

➡ _____

8 To prevent this, artists did something interesting.

➡ _____

9 They thought if they attracted tourists to a different part of the sea, the dying areas could have time to get better.

➡ _____

_____

10 They made an underwater museum away from the places where sea life was dying.

➡ _____

11 It's about 14 meters below the surface and contains 500 statues.

➡ _____

12 The statues are made from materials that support sea life.

➡ _____

13 They provide additional places for plants and animals to live on.

➡ _____

14 Over time, many types of sea life will grow on the statues, which will make the artwork unique.

➡ _____

15 The artists want people to see a variety of sea life on the statues.

➡ _____

16 ▷ If people realize how rich sea life is, they will understand how important it is to save the sea.
➡ _____

17 ▷ In Singapore, people are using architecture to protect the environment on land.
➡ _____

18 ▷ Let's hear what Rajesh Khan, an architect, says about eco-friendly buildings.
➡ _____

19 ▷ Rajesh: Singapore is hot throughout the year.
➡ _____

20 ▷ Most buildings need air conditioning, which uses a lot of energy and contributes to climate change.
➡ _____

21 ▷ That's why architects in Singapore have begun to design eco-friendly buildings that use less air conditioning but are still cool inside.
➡ _____
_____

22 ▷ For example, many buildings in Singapore are designed to have an open structure.
➡ _____

23 ▷ This structure makes it possible for outside air to move throughout a building.
➡ _____

24 ▷ This natural air flow is how these buildings stay cool.
➡ _____

25 ▷ In addition to making open structures, architects add large gardens.
➡ _____

26 ▷ This greenery provides shade and protects parts of the building from direct sunlight, which keeps the building cooler.
➡ _____

27 ▷ Eco-friendly buildings like these not only help protect the environment, but also provide people with a good quality of life.
➡ _____

28 ▷ Those are the goals of this new style of architecture.
➡ _____

29 ▷ Hopefully, architects will keep coming up with new eco-friendly ideas.
➡ _____

30 ▷ Every field has different ways of protecting the environment.
➡ _____

31 ▷ With more innovation, humans and nature will be able to live together in harmony far into the future.
➡ _____

※ 다음 괄호 안의 단어들을 우리말에 맞도록 바르게 배열하시오.

Join Hands, Save the Earth

1 (is / it / important / us / for / find / to / to / ways / protect / environment. / the)
➡ _____

2 (people / some / found / have / ways / creative / save / to / earth. / the)
➡ _____

3 (eample / one / an / is / museum / underwater / Cancun, / in / Mexico.)
➡ _____

4 (meet / let's / Rosa / Dr. / Allison, / art / an / professor, / listen / and / her / to / explanation / about / the / museum. / special)
➡ _____

5 (Rosa: / is / Cancun / city / a / where / million / 4.8 / travel / tourists / year. / every)
➡ _____

6 (of / one / most / the / activities / popular / do / to / is / there / at / looking / area's / the / life / beautiful / sea / underwater.)
➡ _____

7 (tourist / howerver, / are / activities / damaging / seriously / of / parts / sea / the / Cancun. / near)
➡ _____

8 (prevent / to / artists / this, / something / did / interesting.)
➡ _____

9 (thought / they / they / if / tourists / attracted / a / to / part / different / of / sea, / the / dying / the / could / areas / have / to / time / better. / get)
➡ _____

10 (made / they / underwater / an / away / museum / the / from / where / places / life / sea / dying. / was)
➡ _____

11 (about / it's / meters / 14 / the / below / and / surface / 500 / contains / statues.)
➡ _____

12 (statues / the / made / are / materials / from / support / that / life. / sea)
➡ _____

13 (provide / they / places / additional / plants / for / and / to / animals / live / on.)
➡ _____

14 (time, / over / types / many / sea / of / will / life / on / grow / statues, / the / will / which / make / the / unique. / artwork)
➡ _____

15 (artists / the / people / want / see / to / of / variety / a / sea / of / on / life / statues. / the)
➡ _____

함께 손잡고, 지구를 구합시다

1 우리가 환경을 보호할 수 있는 방법을 찾는 것은 중요하다.

2 몇몇 사람들은 지구를 구하기 위한 창의적인 방법을 찾았다.

3 한 예로 멕시코 칸쿤에 있는 수중 박물관이 있다.

4 미술학 교수인 Rosa Allison 박사를 만나서 이 특별한 박물관에 대한 설명을 들어보자.

5 Rosa: 칸쿤은 매년 480만 명의 관광객이 여행하는 도시이다.

6 그곳에서 할 수 있는 가장 인기 있는 활동 중 하나는 그 지역의 바닷속의 아름다운 해양 생물을 관찰하는 것이다.

7 하지만, 관광 활동들이 칸쿤 근처의 바다 일부를 심각하게 훼손시키고 있다.

8 이러한 일을 방지하기 위해서, 예술가들이 흥미로운 생각을 해냈다.

9 그들은 만약 관광객들을 바다의 다른 쪽으로 유인한다면, 그 죽어가는 지역이 호전될 시간을 가질 수 있을 것이라 생각했다.

10 그들은 해양 생물이 죽어가는 지역으로부터 떨어진 해저에 수중 박물관을 만들었다.

11 그 박물관은 해수면에서 14미터 아래에 있으며 500개의 조각상이 있다.

12 그 조각상들은 해양 생물에게 도움이 되는 재료들로 만들어졌다.

13 그것들은 식물과 동물들이 살 수 있는 추가적인 장소를 제공한다.

14 시간이 흐르면, 많은 형태의 바다 생명체들이 그 조각상에서 자라게 될 것이며, 이것이 그 예술 작품을 독특하게 만들 것이다.

15 예술가들은 사람들이 그 조각상들에서 (살고 있는) 다양한 해양 생명체들을 보길 원한다.

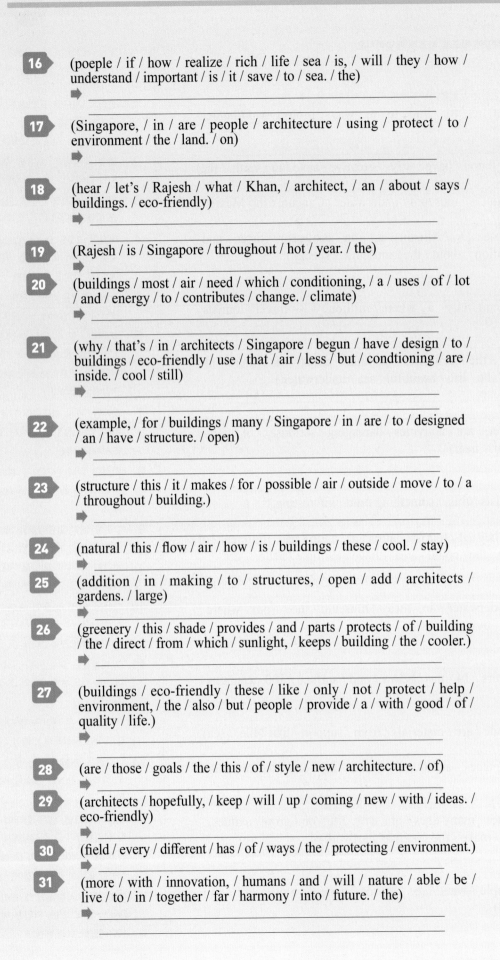

16 (poeple / if / how / realize / rich / life / sea / is, / will / they / how / understand / important / is / it / save / to / sea. / the)

➡ _____

17 (Singapore, / in / are / people / architecture / using / protect / to / environment / the / land. / on)

➡ _____

18 (hear / let's / Rajesh / what / Khan, / architect, / an / about / says / buildings. / eco-friendly)

➡ _____

19 (Rajesh / is / Singapore / throughout / hot / year. / the)

➡ _____

20 (buildings / most / air / need / which / conditioning, / a / uses / of / lot / and / energy / to / contributes / change. / climate)

➡ _____

21 (why / that's / in / architects / Singapore / begun / have / design / to / buildings / eco-friendly / use / that / air / less / but / condtioning / are / inside. / cool / still)

➡ _____

22 (example, / for / buildings / many / Singapore / in / are / to / designed / an / have / structure. / open)

➡ _____

23 (structure / this / it / makes / for / possible / air / outside / move / to / a / throughout / building.)

➡ _____

24 (natural / this / flow / air / how / is / buildings / these / cool. / stay)

➡ _____

25 (addition / in / making / to / structures, / open / add / architects / gardens. / large)

➡ _____

26 (greenery / this / shade / provides / and / parts / protects / of / building / the / direct / from / which / sunlight, / keeps / building / the / cooler.)

➡ _____

27 (buildings / eco-friendly / these / like / only / not / protect / help / environment, / the / also / but / people / provide / a / with / good / of / quality / life.)

➡ _____

28 (are / those / goals / the / this / of / style / new / architecture. / of)

➡ _____

29 (architects / hopefully, / keep / will / up / coming / new / with / ideas. / eco-friendly)

➡ _____

30 (field / every / different / has / of / ways / the / protecting / environment.)

➡ _____

31 (more / with / innovation, / humans / and / will / nature / able / be / live / to / in / together / far / harmony / into / future. / the)

➡ _____

16 만약 사람들이 해양 생물이 얼마나 풍부한지 깨닫는다면, 그들은 바다를 지키는 것이 얼마나 중요한지 이해할 것이다.

17 싱가포르에서는 사람들이 육지의 환경을 보호하기 위해 건축을 이용하고 있다.

18 건축가인 Rajesh Khan이 친환경 건물에 대해 말하는 것을 들어보자.

19 Rajesh: 싱가포르는 연중 더운 곳이다.

20 대부분의 건물들은 에어컨 가동이 필요한데, 이로 인해 많은 에너지가 사용되고 있으며 기후 변화의 원인이 되고 있다.

21 그것이 싱가포르의 건축가들이 에어컨을 덜 쓰면서도 실내에서 여전히 시원한 느낌이 들 수 있는 친환경적인 건물들을 디자인하기 시작한 이유이다.

22 가령, 싱가포르의 많은 건물들은 개방형 구조를 포함하게 디자인되었다.

23 이러한 구조는 외부 공기가 건물을 관통하는 것을 가능케 한다.

24 이러한 자연적인 공기의 흐름이 이 건물을 시원하게 유지해 주는 방법이다.

25 건축가들은 개방형 구조를 만드는 것 외에도 큰 정원을 더한다.

26 이러한 녹지 공간은 그늘을 제공하고 직사광선으로부터 건물의 부분들을 지켜주어 건물을 시원하게 유지한다.

27 이와 같은 친환경적인 건물들은 환경을 보호하는 것을 도울 뿐만 아니라 사람들에게 양질의 삶을 제공한다.

28 그것들이 바로 이러한 새로운 건축 방식의 목표이다.

29 바라건대, 건축가들은 새로운 친환경 아이디어를 계속해서 생각해 낼 것이다.

30 모든 분야에서 환경을 보호하는 다른 방식이 있다.

31 더 나은 혁신으로 인해 먼 미래에 인간과 자연은 함께 조화를 이루며 살아갈 수 있을 것이다.

※ 다음 우리말을 영어로 쓰시오.

1 우리가 환경을 보호할 수 있는 방법을 찾는 것은 중요하다.

➡ _____

2 몇몇 사람들은 지구를 구하기 위한 창의적인 방법을 찾았다.

➡ _____

3 한 예로 멕시코 칸쿤에 있는 수중 박물관이 있다.

➡ _____

4 미술학 교수인 Rosa Allison 박사를 만나서 이 특별한 박물관에 대한 설명을 들어보자.

➡ _____

5 Rosa: 칸쿤은 매년 480만 명의 관광객이 여행하는 도시이다.

➡ _____

6 그곳에서 할 수 있는 가장 인기 있는 활동 중 하나는 그 지역의 바닷속의 아름다운 해양 생물을 관찰하는 것이다.

➡ _____

7 하지만, 관광 활동들이 칸쿤 근처의 바다 일부를 심각하게 훼손시키고 있다.

➡ _____

8 이러한 일을 방지하기 위해서, 예술가들이 흥미로운 생각을 해냈다.

➡ _____

9 그들은 만약 관광객들을 바다의 다른 쪽으로 유인한다면, 그 죽어가는 지역이 호전될 시간을 가질 수 있을 것이라 생각했다.

➡ _____

_____

10 그들은 해양 생물이 죽어가는 지역으로부터 떨어진 해저에 수중 박물관을 만들었다.

➡ _____

11 그 박물관은 해수면에서 14미터 아래에 있으며 500개의 조각상이 있다.

➡ _____

12 그 조각상들은 해양 생물에게 도움이 되는 재료들로 만들어졌다.

➡ _____

13 그것들은 식물과 동물들이 살 수 있는 추가적인 장소를 제공한다.

➡ _____

14 시간이 흐르면, 많은 형태의 바다 생명체들이 그 조각상에서 자라게 될 것이며, 이것이 그 예술 작품을 독특하게 만들 것이다.

➡ _____

15 예술가들은 사람들이 그 조각상들에서 (살고 있는) 다양한 해양 생명체들을 보길 원한다.

➡ _____

16 ▶ 만약 사람들이 해양 생물이 얼마나 풍부한지 깨닫는다면, 그들은 바다를 지키는 것이 얼마나 중요한지 이해할 것이다.

➡ _____

17 ▶ 싱가포르에서는 사람들이 육지의 환경을 보호하기 위해 건축을 이용하고 있다.

➡ _____

18 ▶ 건축가인 Rajesh Khan이 친환경 건물에 대해 말하는 것을 들어보자.

➡ _____

19 ▶ Rajesh: 싱가포르는 연중 더운 곳이다.

➡ _____

20 ▶ 대부분의 건물들은 에어컨 가동이 필요한데, 이로 인해 많은 에너지가 사용되고 있으며 기후 변화의 원인이 되고 있다.

➡ _____

21 ▶ 그것이 싱가포르의 건축가들이 에어컨을 덜 쓰면서도 실내에서 여전히 시원한 느낌이 들 수 있는 친환경적인 건물들을 디자인하기 시작한 이유이다.

➡ _____
_____

22 ▶ 가령, 싱가포르의 많은 건물들은 개방형 구조를 포함하게 디자인되었다.

➡ _____

23 ▶ 이러한 구조는 외부 공기가 건물을 관통하는 것을 가능케 한다.

➡ _____

24 ▶ 이러한 자연적인 공기의 흐름이 이 건물을 시원하게 유지해 주는 방법이다.

➡ _____

25 ▶ 건축가들은 개방형 구조를 만드는 것 외에도 큰 정원을 더한다.

➡ _____

26 ▶ 이러한 녹지 공간은 그늘을 제공하고 직사광선으로부터 건물의 부분들을 지켜주어 건물을 시원하게 유지한다.

➡ _____
_____

27 ▶ 이와 같은 친환경적인 건물들은 환경을 보호하는 것을 도울 뿐만 아니라 사람들에게 양질의 삶을 제공한다.

➡ _____
_____

28 ▶ 그것들이 바로 이러한 새로운 건축 방식의 목표이다.

➡ _____

29 ▶ 바라건대, 건축가들은 새로운 친환경 아이디어를 계속해서 생각해 낼 것이다.

➡ _____

30 ▶ 모든 분야에서 환경을 보호하는 다른 방식이 있다.

➡ _____

31 ▶ 더 나은 혁신으로 인해 먼 미래에 인간과 자연은 함께 조화를 이루며 살아갈 수 있을 것이다.

➡ _____

※ 다음 우리말과 일치하도록 빈칸에 알맞은 말을 쓰시오.

Listen & Talk 2 D Talk Together

1. A: _____ you _____ of _____ _____? They're _____!
2. B: _____, I _____. _____ _____ about _____.
3. A: They _____ _____ _____ _____. They will _____ _____.
4. B: That _____ _____. I _____ _____ _____ _____ them.

1. A: 먹을 수 있는 수저에 대해 들어봤니? 정말 놀라워!
2. B: 아니, 들어 본 적이 없어. 그것에 대해 이야기해 봐.
3. A: 수저는 곡물로 만들어져. 그것들은 자원을 절약할 거야.
4. B: 정말 멋지다. 나는 그것들을 사용하는 게 정말 기다려져.

Presentation Time

1. _____ can we _____ _____ _____ _____ _____?
2. _____ _____ _____, we need a green wall.
3. _____ _____ _____ of our school is _____ _____ _____ for it.
4. A green wall _____ _____ _____ the building _____ _____ _____ _____.
5. This could _____ _____ _____ _____ _____ _____ _____ for air conditioning.

1. 우리는 어떻게 우리 학교를 친환경적으로 만들 수 있을까요?
2. 제 의견으로는, 우리는 식물로 덮인 벽이 필요합니다.
3. 우리 학교의 앞 벽은 그것을 위한 훌륭한 공간입니다.
4. 식물로 덮인 벽은 햇빛을 차단함으로써 건물을 시원하게 유지하는 것을 돕습니다.
5. 이것은 에어컨을 위해 사용되는 에너지의 양을 줄일 수 있습니다.

Think & Write Step 3

1. Eat Your Cup and _____ _____ _____!
2. Here' an _____, _____ _____ _____ _____!
3. It is _____ _____ _____.
4. It's a cookie that _____ _____ _____ _____ _____ _____ a cup.
5. _____ you use the cup, you _____ _____ _____ _____.
6. _____ _____ _____, you _____ _____ _____ or plastic.
7. The cookie cup _____ _____ _____ _____.
8. _____ _____ _____ _____ the change!

1. 컵을 먹고 지구를 구하세요!
2. 여기 혁신적이며 친환경적인 상품이 있습니다!
3. 이것은 과자컵입니다.
4. 이것은 컵 모양으로 만들어진 과자입니다.
5. 컵을 사용한 후에 그냥 그것을 먹을 수 있습니다.
6. 이렇게 함으로서 종이나 플라스틱을 절약할 수 있습니다.
7. 과자컵은 세상을 바꿀 수 있습니다.
8. 변화의 일부가 되십시오!

※ 다음 우리말을 영어로 쓰시오.

Listen & Talk 2 D Talk Together

1. A: 먹을 수 있는 수저에 대해 들어봤니? 정말 놀라워!

➡ _____

2. B: 아니, 들어 본 적이 없어. 그것에 대해 이야기해 봐.

➡ _____

3. A: 수저는 곡물로 만들어져. 그것들은 자원을 절약할 거야.

➡ _____

4. B: 정말 멋지다. 나는 그것들을 사용하는 게 정말 기다려져.

➡ _____

Presentation Time

1. 우리는 어떻게 우리 학교를 친환경적으로 만들 수 있을까요?

➡ _____

2. 제 의견으로는, 우리는 식물로 덮인 벽이 필요합니다.

➡ _____

3. 우리 학교의 앞 벽은 그것을 위한 훌륭한 공간입니다.

➡ _____

4. 식물로 덮인 벽은 햇빛을 차단함으로써 건물을 시원하게 유지하는 것을 돕습니다.

➡ _____

5. 이것은 에어컨을 위해 사용되는 에너지의 양을 줄일 수 있습니다.

➡ _____

Think & Write Step 3

1. 컵을 먹고 지구를 구하세요!

➡ _____

2. 여기 혁신적이며 친환경적인 상품이 있습니다!

➡ _____

3. 이것은 과자컵입니다.

➡ _____

4. 이것은 컵 모양으로 만들어진 과자입니다.

➡ _____

5. 컵을 사용한 후에 그냥 그것을 먹을 수 있습니다.

➡ _____

6. 이렇게 함으로서 종이나 플라스틱을 절약할 수 있습니다.

➡ _____

7. 과자컵은 세상을 바꿀 수 있습니다.

➡ _____

8. 변화의 일부가 되십시오!

➡ _____

영어 기출 문제집

적중100

1학기

정답 및 해설

능률 | 김성곤

중 3

적중100

영어 기출 문제집

1학기

정답 및 해설

능률 | 김성곤

중 3

적중 100

Always Aware,
Always Prepared

p.08

01 ①　　　　02 ⑤　　　　03 ②　　　　04 ④
05 ④　　　　06 (t)raining

01 주어진 단어는 동의어 관계이다. damage 손상(=harm)
　　exact 정확한 correct 정확한

02 내용상 자동차를 운전하던 사람이 방송을 듣기 위해서 차를 멈
　　춰 세운 상황으로 "길 한쪽으로 차를 대다"에 해당하는 'pull
　　over'가 적절하다.

03 ① 홍수 - 대개는 건조한 한 지역을 덮는 많은 양의 물 ② 지진
　　(earthquake) - 많은 손상을 가져오는 지표면의 갑작스러운 흔
　　들림 ③ 재난 - 큰 손상이나 고통을 초래하는 홍수, 폭풍 또는
　　사고와 같은 갑작스러운 사건 ④ 흔한 – 많은 장소나 많은 사람
　　에게 자주 일어나는 ⑤ 나가다, 퇴장하다 - 어떤 장소를 떠나다

04 ④ exit는 '출구; 나가다'라는 뜻이다. '들어가다'는 'enter'이다.

05 ① crawl 기어가다 ② based on ~에 바탕을 둔 ③ destroy
　　파괴되다 ④ shaking 흔들림 ⑤ ring 울리다

06 'drill 훈련'과 동의어 관계에 있는 것은 'training 훈련'이다.

p.09

01 properly　　02 out　　　03 (c)ollapse
04 (1) exactly　(2) pulled,out of　(3) In case of
05 include
06 (1) made our way　(2) scared　(3) seriously
07 (d)estroy　　08 (e)nter

01 perform을 수식하는 'proper 적절한'의 부사 'properly'가 올
　　바른 형태이다.

02 황사에서 마스크를 쓰는 것은 밖에 나갈 때이다. 밖에 나가다 =
　　go out 무슨 일 일어났는지 알아보기 위해 라디오를 듣고 있기
　　때문에 "알아내다 find out"이 적절하다.

03 collapse: 붕괴되다, 무너지다

04 (1) 정확하게 exactly (2) A를 끌어내다 pull A out of ~ (3)
　　~의 경우에 in case of ~

05 주어진 단어는 반의어 관계이다. destroy 파괴하다 construct
　　건설하다 include 포함하다 exclude 제외하다

06 (1) make one's way ~로 가다 (2) scared 겁먹은 (3)

seriously 진지하게

07 '어떤 것을 더 이상 존재하지 않거나 사용할 수 없거나 수리할
　　수 없도록 심하게 손상시키다'는 '파괴하다 destroy'에 해당한
　　다.

08 "exit 나가다"의 반대말은 "enter"이다.

p.10~11

1 ②　　　　2 ①

3 Make sure that you wear a mask when you go out.

01 (B) 한국의 산불에 대한 궁금증을 나타내자 그것에 대한 대답을
　　하고 (A) 다시 언제 일어났는지 질문을 하니까 (C) 2005년에
　　일어났다고 대답한다.

02 '반드시 ~해라.'의 의미로 'Make sure ~' 또는 'Be sure ~'를
　　쓴다.

03 '반드시 ~해라'의 의미로 'Make sure that ~'을 이용한다.

p.12

1 T　　2 F　　3 F　　4 T

p.14~15

Listen & Talk 1 A

was, flood, hear / floods, common, are, curious, how
/ research

Listen & Talk 1 B

seem, natural disasters, these / earthquake, south,
storm / curious, which, natural disaster, most
damage / report, damage, each type / guess, second
/ heavy, snow / What / Based, earthquakes, damage,
been increasing, because, been / seems like,
prepared, variety, natural disasters

Listen & Talk 1 C

hear about, fires / serious / destroyed, houses, other
/ Are, going on / actually, worse, living there / So do,
curious, leave / Actually, leave, missing / terrible,
somewhere

Listen & Talk 2 A

what else, put in, survival kit / water, radio / Anything / make, include, radio

Listen & Talk 2 B

Performing, save, Here, steps, proper, needs, Tap, Are, reaction, listen, feel, breathing, sure, place, in, chest, weight, harder, breaths, help

Listen & Talk 2 D

In case, what, do / Make, cover, wet / else / exit, immediately

Do It Yourself A

hear, occurring, often, before / really, felt / usually, southern, other places / curious, why, occurred / research / do / How about, help / Let's, find

시험대비 기본평가　　　p.16

01 ①　　　　02 ②

03 make sure that you include batteries for the radio

01 이어지는 문장에 화재의 상황에 대한 소개가 있으므로 화재 상황에 대한 질문이 빈칸에 들어가는 것이 적절하다.

02 화재가 난 경우의 주의사항에 추가하는 내용이므로 주의사항을 알려주는 표현인 'Make sure'가 적절하다.

03 '반드시 ~해라'는 'Make sure that 주어+동사'이다.

시험대비 실력평가　　　p.17~18

01 actually　　02 ③　　　03 ②

04 ②　　　05 It, that, are　06 prepared　07 ⑤

08 ①　　　09 ④　　　10 ④

01 문맥상 actual의 부사형이 와야 한다.

02 "~에 대하여 궁금하다"의 의미는 "I'm curious about ~" 또는 "I wonder ~"이다.

03 바람이 산불을 악화시키기는 했지만 바람 때문에 산불이 났다는 언급은 없다.

04 자연 재해가 가져오는 손상의 정도를 구체적으로 설명하는 것은 보고서를 읽었기 때문이므로 순서를 나열하기 전에 주어진 문장이 들어가야 한다.

05 There seem to ~는 It seems that ~ 구문으로 바꿔 쓸 수 있다.

06 be동사의 보어가 되는 형용사형으로 고쳐야 한다.

07 가장 많은 피해를 입히는 네 가지 재난은 나열되어 있지만 가장 적게 피해를 입히는 재난은 무엇인지 소개되지 않았다.

08 한국에서는 많은 산불이 일어난다는 말을 들었다고 말하자 (A) 양양에서 큰 산불이 있었다고 대답하고 (C) 그것이 언제 일어났

는지 궁금하다고 말하자. (B) 2005년에 일어났다고 대답한다.

09 'I think she can help us.'를 보면 과학 선생님께 질문하자는 'How about asking our science teacher first?'가 적절하다.

10 지진이 더 자주 일어나는 것에 대하여 조사를 해보자고 하는 것으로 보아 두 사람은 지진의 빈도가 늘어난 이유를 알지 못하고 있다고 해야 한다.

서술형 시험대비　　　p.19

01 I'm curious about　　02 What[How] about

03 It seems like we have to be prepared for a variety of natural disasters in Korea.

04 reaction

05 Make sure you place your hands in the middle of the person's chest.

06 We should start when the person is not breathing.

01 궁금하다는 의미로 curious를 써서 "I'm curious about"가 적절하다.

02 앞에 나온 폭우, 폭설 이외에 지진에 대한 궁금증을 나타내어 "지진은 어떻습니까?"의 의미로 'What about ~?'나 'How about ~?'가 적절하다.

03 '~인 것 같다'는 'It seems like ~'이다.

04 심폐소생술을 수행하기 전에 확인하는 단계에서 상대가 반응이 없을 때 119에 도움을 요청한다.

05 반드시 ~하도록 해라 = Make sure ~, 손을 ~의 가슴 가운데에 놓다 = put your hands in the middle of one's chest

06 그 사람이 숨을 쉬지 않을 때 심폐소생술을 시작해야 한다.

[교과서]
Grammar

핵심 Check　　　p.20~21

1 (1) had done　(2) had finished　(3) had

2 (1) Although　(2) since　(3) after

시험대비 기본평가　　　p.22

01 ⑤　　　　　02 (1) had already started

(2) had lied　(3) Although　(4) since　　03 ③

04 (1) Until last year, Linda had never visited Paris.

(2) Although he was rich, people thought he was poor.

(3) I couldn't sleep last night since I was so afraid.

01 주절의 동사가 recognized로 과거이고 그녀를 본 것은 그 이전의 사실이므로 과거완료를 써야 한다.

02 (1) 방문한 것보다 그가 출발한 것이 앞서는 것이므로 과거완료가 적절하다. (2) 거짓말을 한 것(앞선 사실)을 시인하는 것이므로 과거완료가 적절하다. (3) 앞과 뒤의 절의 내용이 상반되므로 Although가 적절하다. (4) 뒤의 절이 이유를 나타내고 있으므로 since가 적절하다.

03 첫 문장과 두 번째 문장이 원인과 결과를 언급하는 것으로 보아 원인이 되는 문장에 접속사 since를 쓰는 것이 적절하다.

04 (1) 경험을 나타내는 과거완료를 이용한다. (2) 서로 상반되는 내용이 나오므로 although를 이용한다. (3) 원인과 결과를 나타내는 since를 이용한다.

시험대비 실력평가   p.23~25

01 ②   02 ④   03 ①
04 (1) finished (2) had made (3) had prepared
   (4) Although (5) Since (6) Though
05 ③   06 ②   07 ⑤
08 (1) unless (2) after (3) though (4) when
   (5) since
09 ④   10 ②   11 ⑤
12 had learned   13 ③
14 (1) I missed the first bus though[although] I got up
      early in the morning.
   (2) Since[As, Because] I am a student, I will get a
      discount.
   (3) David was doing the dishes when[as] Monica
      called him.
   (4) All of them look tired after they worked hard.
   (5) I'll take the job unless the pay is much too low.
15 ③   16 ⑤   17 ①, ④

01 They talked about the accident that had happened there a few hours before.

02 We decided to leave though it started to rain.

03 첫 번째 빈칸에는 서로 상반되는 내용이 나오므로 양보절을 이끄는 Even though가 적절하다. 두 번째 빈칸에는 상상했던 것이 실제 보아서 아름다운 것보다 앞선 시제이므로 과거완료가 적절하다.

04 (1) 과거완료는 'had+과거분사'의 형태이므로 finished가 적절하다. (2) 깨달은 시점보다 실수한 시점이 앞서므로 had made가 적절하다. (3) since(~ 이래로)가 있으므로 had prepared가 적절하다. (4) 서로 상반되는 내용이 나오므로 Although가 적절하다. (5) 이끌리는 절이 뒤에 나오는 주절의 이유가 되므로 Since가 적절하다. (6) despite는 전치사이므로 뒤에 (대)명사나 동명사가 나온다. Though가 적절하다.

05 도착했을 때 이미 잠자러 간 것이므로 과거완료로 써야 하고 엄마는 깨어 있는 것이므로 같은 과거로 쓴다.

06 그녀가 죽은 것보다 앞서 일어난 일이므로 ⓑ의 has been은 had been으로 고쳐야 한다.

07 버스를 놓친 것이 이유이므로 since나 because가 적절하고 그것이 회의에 늦은 것보다 앞선 시제이므로 과거완료가 적절하다.

08 (1) 조건의 unless가 적절하다. (2) 시간의 전후 관계를 나타내는 after가 적절하다. (3) 서로 상반되는 내용이 나오므로 though가 적절하다. (4) 시간의 부사절을 이끄는 when이 적절하다. (5) 집에 있게 된 이유를 나타내는 since가 적절하다.

09 서로 상반되는 내용이 나오므로 양보절을 이끄는 Though가 적절하다.

10 서로 상반되는 내용이 나오므로 양보절을 이끄는 though가 적절하다.

11 내가 그녀를 만나기 전에 로마에서 살아온 것이므로 과거완료가 적절하다.

12 2015년에 배우기 시작했으므로 2015년 이래로 배워 왔다고 과거완료로 나타낼 수 있다.

13 <보기>는 계속 용법이다. ① 완료, ② 경험, ③ 계속, ④ 결과, ⑤ 대과거

14 (1) 앞 절과 뒤 이은 절의 내용이 원인과 결과가 아니라 상반되는 내용이므로 though 정도로 양보절을 이끌도록 하는 것이 적절하다. (2) 앞 절과 뒤 이은 절의 내용이 상반되는 내용이 아니라 원인과 결과로 볼 수 있으므로 Since 정도로 고치는 것이 적절하다. (3) 앞 절과 뒤 이은 절의 내용이 원인과 결과가 아니므로 when 정도로 고치는 것이 적절하다. (4) 시간의 순서상 일을 한 후에 피곤해 보였다고 하는 것이 적절하다. (5) 내용상 if가 아니라 unless(= if ~ not)가 적절하다.

15 양보의 접속사 though(비록 ~일지라도)를 이용한다.

16 '그때 이전'이므로 과거완료로 본 적이 있는지를 나타내는 것이 적절하다.

17 ① Although it's very hot outside, I will play soccer. ④ I remembered that I had met him at the party.

서술형 시험대비   p.26~27

01 (1) Mom had bought for me (2) he had bought
02 (1) had already left (2) he had gone back
03 (1) Even though the house was destroyed,
   (2) Don't waste things even if they are not yours.
   (3) He realized that he had discovered a whole
      new human species.
   (4) I wondered why he had done such a stupid
      thing.

04 (1) Because → Though[Although]

(2) As though → Even though

(3) Despite → Though[Although]

05 (1) had broken   (2) had already cleaned

06 (1) Horses sleep just like us though[although] they do so in a different way.

(2) Since[Because, As] the Earth is rotating, two tides occur each day.

(3) We had ice cream as dessert after we had lunch.

07 (1) Bella had already done the dishes when he came back home.

(2) Dave had never visited Paris until then.

(3) She told me why she had left him.

(4) The boy disappeared while walking home from school.

(5) He made his choice, although he regretted it later.

(6) Anne was fond of Tim, though[although] he often annoyed her.

08 Kay didn't recognize any of them, though[although] she had heard of their names.

01 각각 과거보다 앞선 시제에 행한 것을 나타내는 과거완료를 이용한다.

02 (1) 과거완료의 완료 용법을 이용한다. (2) 과거완료의 결과 용법을 이용한다.

03 (1) Even though가 양보절을 이끌도록 한다. (2) even if가 양보절을 이끌도록 한다. (3) 발견한 것이 깨달은 것보다 앞서므로 과거완료를 이용한다. (4) 어리석은 짓을 한 것이 의아해 하는 것보다 앞서므로 과거완료를 이용한다.

04 (1) 이유를 이끄는 것이 아니라 양보절을 이끄는 것으로 Though로 고치는 것이 적절하다. (2) even though: 비록 …일지라도, as though: 마치 …인 것처럼 (3) Despite는 전치사로 뒤에 (대)명사나 동명사가 나오므로 Though로 고친다.

05 과거의 어느 시점보다 먼저 일어난 일이나 상태를 나타내는 과거완료(대과거)를 이용한다.

06 내용에 맞게 (1)에는 양보를 나타내는 접속사, (2)에는 이유를 나타내는 접속사, (3)에는 시간의 순서를 나타내는 접속사를 이용한다.

07 (1) 그가 집에 돌아왔을 때보다 Bella가 설거지를 끝낸 시점이 앞서므로 과거완료가 적절하다. (2) until then으로 보아 그 때까지의 경험을 나타내는 과거완료가 적절하다. (3) 그를 떠난 후에 나에게 말하는 것이므로 떠난 것을 과거완료로 쓰는 것이 적절하다. (4) 접속사 while 뒤에 '주어+be동사'가 생략된 형태이다. 전치사 during이 아니라 while이 적절하다. (5) although는 접속사이므로 뒤에 '주어+동사'가 있는 절이 나와

야 한다. (6) despite는 전치사이므로 양보절을 이끄는 though 등으로 고친다.

08 서로 상반되는 내용이 이어지므로 양보절을 이끄는 접속사를 사용하고, 앞선 일에는 과거완료를 쓴다.

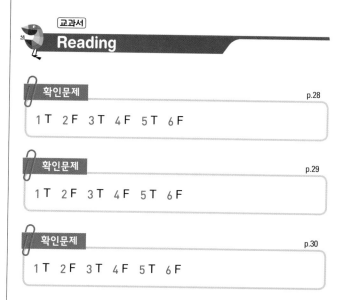

교과서
Reading

확인문제   p.28

1 T   2 F   3 T   4 F   5 T   6 F

확인문제   p.29

1 T   2 F   3 T   4 F   5 T   6 F

확인문제   p.30

1 T   2 F   3 T   4 F   5 T   6 F

교과서 확인학습 A   p.31~33

01 Waking Up   02 had gone to bed

03 was shaking   04 as a joke

05 fall to the floor, break into pieces

06 what exactly was happening

07 turned to panic   08 ran into

09 my first time experiencing 10 kept saying

11 out of bed   12 crawled under

13 swinging, falling   14 covering it broke

15 tipped over, rolled off   16 Every second

17 to worry, collapse   18 seemed to stop

19 crawling toward   20 At that moment

21 coming home from work   22 It stopped

23 out of   24 Take

25 Don't take   26 Hurry

27 Where   28 urgently

29 Don't worry   30 okay

31 was driving home   32 pulled over

33 right now, going on   34 made our way

35 around

36 had fallen, had smashed   37 to avoid

38 could, have happened

39 earthquake drills, a real earthquake

40 get scared   41 the panic I felt

42 take, drills seriously

43 be prepared for at any time

1 Waking Up to an Earthquake

2 One night in February, after I had gone to bed, an earthquake hit.

3 I woke up suddenly because my bed was shaking.

4 I thought my brother was shaking my bed as a joke.

5 But then I heard the mirror on my desk fall to the floor and break into pieces.

6 I knew it wasn't my brother then, but I still didn't know what exactly was happening.

7 Soon the whole room began to shake violently, and my confusion turned to panic.

8 My mom shouted that it was an earthquake and ran into my room.

9 Since it was my first time experiencing an earthquake, I didn't know how to react.

10 I just kept saying, "What should I do?"

11 My mom pulled me and my brother out of bed.

12 We ran to the kitchen and crawled under the table.

13 I could see the light swinging violently and books falling to the floor.

14 Our family picture dropped from the wall and the glass covering it broke.

15 A cup tipped over and rolled off the kitchen table.

16 Every second, I could hear something else in the apartment break.

17 I started to worry that the building would collapse.

18 Then the shaking seemed to stop.

19 We started crawling toward the door.

20 At that moment, my mom's cell phone rang.

21 It was my dad, who was coming home from work.

22 He shouted, "It stopped!

23 Get out of the building!

24 Take the stairs!

25 Don't take the elevator!

26 Hurry!"

27 "Where are you?

28 Are you okay?" my mom asked urgently.

29 My dad answered, "Don't worry.

30 I'm okay.

31 I was driving home when the shaking started.

32 But I pulled over immediately.

33 I'm listening to the radio right now to find out what's going on."

34 We nervously made our way down the stairs and outside.

35 I looked around.

36 Parts of buildings had fallen and had smashed several cars.

37 We went to an open space to avoid more falling pieces.

38 How could all this have happened in a few minutes?

39 Although I had done many earthquake drills in school, I had never thought I'd experience a real earthquake.

40 I still get scared when I remember that night.

41 I can't forget the panic I felt when the furniture was shaking and things were falling to the floor.

42 After that night, I began to take earthquake drills seriously.

43 I realized that I should be prepared for the next earthquake, which can occur at any time.

01 ⑤   02 ②   03 ③   04 ②

05 to swing → swing 또는 swinging,
to fall → fall 또는 falling

06 our family picture   07 ⑤   08 ②

09 ②   10 pulled over

11 fell → had fallen, smashed → had smashed

12 ④

13 I can't forget the panic I felt when the furniture was shaking and things were falling to the floor.

14 ②   15 ②   16 ③   17 ③

18 which[that] covered   19 collapse

20 ④   21 ③, ⑤

22 Since it was my first time experiencing an earthquake   23 ③

24 to fall → fall[falling], to break → break[breaking]

25 ③

26 Because it was her first time experiencing an earthquake.

27 ①, ③, ⑤   28 (A) scared   (B) seriously   (C) which

29 prepared for

01 ⓐ break into pieces: 산산조각이 나다, ⓑ turn to: (바람·조수·형세 등이) ~으로 변하다, 방향을 바꾸다

02 주어진 문장의 'my brother was shaking my bed'에 주목한다. ②번 앞 문장의 'my bed was shaking'의 원인을 설명하는 것이므로 ②번이 적절하다.

03 (A)와 ③: 대과거 용법(결과 용법으로 보는 것도 가능함), ①, ④: 경험 용법, ②: 완료 용법, ⑤: 계속 용법

04 글쓴이는 처음에는 남동생이 장난으로 침대를 흔들고 있다고 생각했지만, 곧 '남동생이 그런 것이 아니라는 것을 알았다'고 했다.

05 지각동사(see)+목적어+현재분사(원형부정사도 가능함.)

06 '우리 가족 사진'을 가리킨다.

07 '나는 건물이 무너지지는 않을까 하는 걱정이 들기 시작했다.'라고만 되어 있다.

08 ⓐ와 ③, ⑤: 부사적 용법, ①, ④: 명사적 용법, ②: 형용사적 용법

09 ② 긴급한, ① 신나는, 흥미진진한, ③ 감동적인, ④ 환상적인, ⑤ 지루한

10 pull over: (차량·운전자가) (정차하거나 다른 차가 지나가도록) 길 한쪽으로 빠지다[차를 대다]

11 건물의 일부분이 떨어져 나갔고 몇몇 차들이 박살이 난 것이 계단을 내려가서 밖으로 나간 것보다 먼저 일어난 일이므로 과거완료로 쓰는 것이 적절하다.

12 '어떻게 이런 일이 몇 분 만에 일어날 수 있단 말인가?'에서, 글쓴이의 혼란스럽고 어리둥절한 심경을 알 수 있다. puzzled: 어리둥절해하는, 얼떨떨한, ② 부끄러운, ③ 실망한, ⑤ 우울한

13 the panic과 I felt 사이에 목적격 관계대명사 that[which]이 생략되어 있다.

14 이 글은 글쓴이가 지진을 겪은 뒤에 언제든 발생할 수 있는 다음 지진을 대비해야 한다는 것을 깨달았다는 내용의 글이므로, 어울리는 속담으로는 ②번 '예방이 치료보다 낫다.'가 적절하다. ① 어려울 때 친구가 진정한 친구이다. ③ 모든 구름의 뒤편은 은빛으로 빛난다.(괴로움 뒤에는 기쁨이 있다.) ④ 잘 생각해 보고 행동하라(돌다리도 두들겨 보고 건너라). ⑤ 해가 비칠 때 건초를 말려라.(기회를 잘 이용하라.)

15 (A)의 'I knew it wasn't my brother then'은 (B)의 첫 문장에 대한 글쓴이의 생각을 바로잡는 것이므로 (B) 다음에 (A)가 이어지고 (C)에서 엄마의 지진이라는 소리에 글쓴이가 상황을 알게 되는 것이므로 (A) 다음에 (C)가 와야 한다. 그러므로 (B)-(A)-(C)의 순서가 적절하다.

16 ③은 글쓴이의 엄마를 가리키고, 나머지는 다 글쓴이의 아빠를 가리킨다.

17 필자의 아빠는 엘리베이터를 타면 안 된다고 말했다.

18 주격 관계대명사 which[that]를 사용하여 과거시제로 고치는 것이 적절하다.

19 지진이 얼마나 오래 계속되었는지는 알 수 없다. ① She pulled the writer and her brother out of bed. ② They took refuge under the kitchen table. take refuge 피난하다, 대피하다, ③ She could see the light swinging violently and books falling to the floor. ⑤ Because every second, she could hear something else in the apartment break.

21 지진이 일어나기 전에 잠자리에 든 것이 먼저 일어난 일이기 때

문에 과거완료로 쓰는 것이 적절하다. 또한, after처럼 시간의 전후 관계를 분명히 알 수 있는 접속사가 있는 경우에는 과거완료 대신 과거시제로 써도 무방하다.

22 be one's first time+-ing: ~하는 게 처음이다

23 위 글은 글쓴이가 처음 겪는 지진 때문에 잠에서 깨어 공포를 느끼는 내용이므로, 제목으로는 '지진에 눈을 뜨는 것'이 적절하다. ② play a joke on: ~에게 장난을 치다, ⑤ in panic: 당황하여

24 지각동사(heard)+목적어+원형부정사(현재분사도 가능함.)

25 ⓑ와 ②, ④, ⑤: [이유를 나타내어] …이므로, …이니까, ①, ③: …한 이래로

26 '지진을 경험한 것이 처음이었기' 때문이다.

27 ⓑ와 ①, ③, ⑤: 경험 용법, ② 계속 용법, ④ 완료 용법

28 (A) 감정을 나타내는 동사는 수식받는 명사가 감정을 느끼게 되는 경우에 과거분사를 써야 하므로 scared가 적절하다. (B) take를 수식하므로 부사 seriously가 적절하다. (C) 관계대명사 that은 계속적용법으로 쓸 수 없으므로 which가 적절하다.

29 글쓴이는 언제든 발생할 수 있는 다음 지진을 '대비해야 한다'는 것을 깨달았다.

🦉 서술형 시험대비　　p.42~43

01 Because her bed was shaking.

02 happened → happening　　03 I should

04 (A) pulled　(B) covering　(C) break

05 I could see the light swinging violently and books falling to the floor.

06 (A) the kitchen　(B) crawled　　07 it

08 the shaking　　　　　09 at once, right away

10 (A) driving home　(B) listening to the radio

11 had done

12 How could all this have happened in a few minutes?

13 be occurred → occur

14 (A) gets scared　(B) the panic

---

01 '침대가 흔들렸기 때문에' 갑자기 잠에서 깼다.

02 happen은 수동태로 쓸 수 없으므로 happening으로 고치는 것이 적절하다.

03 의문사+to부정사 = 의문사+'주어+should'+동사원형으로 바꿔 쓸 수 있다.

04 (A) 침대 밖으로 '잡아끌었다'고 해야 하므로 pulled가 적절하다. pull: 끌다, 당기다, push: 밀다, (B) 사진을 '덮고 있던' 유리라고 해야 하므로 covering이 적절하다. (C) '지각동사 (hear)+목적어+원형부정사'로 써야 하므로 break가 적절하다.

05 지각동사(see)+목적어+현재분사

06 글쓴이는 엄마와 남동생과 함께 '주방'으로 달려가서 식탁 아래

로 '기어들어 갔다.'

07 'seemed to부정사'를 'it seemed that 주어+동사'로 바꿔 쓸 수 있다.

08 '흔들림'을 가리킨다.

09 immediately = at once = right away: 즉시, 당장, 현재시제일 때는 right now도 가능함.

10 글쓴이의 아빠는 진동이 시작할 때 '운전해서 집으로 가던' 중이었지만, 즉시 차를 길 한쪽에 댔다. 그는 무슨 일이 일어나는지 알기 위해 바로 그 때 '라디오를 듣고 있었다.'

11 과거(지진이 일어났던 상황)보다 더 이전에 지진 훈련을 했었기 때문에 과거완료로 쓰는 것이 적절하다.

12 이런 일이 일어난 것이 공터로 간 것보다 먼저 일어난 일이므로 과거완료로 써야 하는데, 가능성을 나타내기 위해 쓰인 could 뒤에서 have happened로 바뀐 것이다.

13 occur는 수동태로 쓸 수 없으므로, be occurred를 occur로 고치는 것이 적절하다.

14 그녀는 여전히 '두려워지고', 가구가 흔들리고 물건들이 바닥으로 떨어졌을 때 그녀가 느꼈던 '공포심'을 잊을 수가 없다.

영역별 핵심문제
p.45~49

01 ②　　　　02 ①　　　　03 ⑤
04 (c)ollapse　　　　　　05 ④
06 I'm curious about how many people had to leave their homes
07 ①　　　08 ③　　　09 ③　　　10 ⑤
11 ③　　　　12 natural disaster
13 Anything else　　　14 ①　　　15 ③
16 Though[Although, Even though]　　　17 ③
18 (1) Although it's very hot outside, I will walk my dog.
(2) Since they had to paint quickly to capture the effect of light, they did not sketch their paintings in advance.
(3) Although most people recognize it as a jewel, the diamond most directly affects our daily lives as a tool.
19 ⓑ, ⓓ, ⓔ　20 ⑤　　　21 break into pieces
22 ③　　　　23 (A) to stop　(B) who　(C) home
24 happening　　　　　25 ①, ②, ④
26 ③　　　27 ①, to tell　28 ③　　　29 ④

01 a report about: ~에 관한 보고서 be curious about ~에 관하여 궁금하다

02 violently 격렬하게 properly 적절하게 recently 최근에 actually 실제로 exactly 정확히

03 aware 인식하는 missing 실종된 exact 정확한 proper 적절

한 common 흔한

04 '갑자기 부서지거나 무너지다'에 해당하는 것은 '붕괴하다 collapse'이다.

05 이어지는 대화로 보아 소녀는 산불에 대해 알고 있지 않아서 산불에 대해 질문을 하는 상황이 적절하다.

06 '나는 ~에 대해 궁금하다'는 'I'm curious about ~'이다. 얼마나 많은 사람이 집을 떠나야 했는지 = how many people had to leave their homes

07 ① 'a large number of houses'는 '매우 많은 주택'이라는 뜻으로 '하나의 큰 주택'은 아니다.

08 지진의 발생에 관한 글로 "발생하다"는 뜻의 occur를 현재진행의 시제에 맞게 "occurring"으로 써야 한다.

09 "I'm curious about why earthquakes have occurred so often in Korea recently."를 보면 소년은 한국에서 지진이 최근에 더 자주 발생하는 원인에 대하여 궁금증을 가지고 있다는 것을 알 수 있다.

10 ⑤ 지진이 두 번째라는 추측에 대하여 아니라고 대답했으므로 지진이 아닌 다른 것을 언급해야 한다.

11 "I guess earthquakes are second."를 통해서 소녀는 지진이 두 번째로 많은 피해를 야기시킨다고 추측하고 있다는 것을 알 수 있다.

12 비상 상황에 사용할 물품을 준비하는 것으로 보아 자연 재난 상황에 사용할 생존 장비를 꾸리는 것을 알 수 있다.

13 반드시 건전지를 포함하라는 것으로 보아 앞에 나온 것에 대하여 추가로 준비할 것에 대한 질문이 있었음을 알 수 있다.

14 although로 이끌리는 절은 주절과 상반되는 내용이 나온다.

15 When he arrived at home, they had already eaten dinner. 도착하기 전에 이미 먹은 것이므로 도착한 것은 과거로, 먹은 것은 과거완료로 써야 한다.

16 아침에 차로 갔다가 걸어서 집에 돌아온 그림이므로 양보절을 이끄는 접속사가 적절하다.

17 already로 보아 과거완료가 나와야 한다.

18 내용에 맞게 (1), (3)에는 서로 상반되는 내용이 나오므로 although를, (2)에는 이유를 나타내고 있으므로 since를 이용한다.

19 ⓐ have visited → visited ⓒ had got → got, was → had been ⓕ Since → Though

20 지진을 경험한 것이 처음이었기 '때문', 나는 어떻게 반응해야 할지 몰랐다고 하는 것이 적절하다. since는 이유를 나타내는 부사절을 이끄는 접속사로 '… 때문에'라는 의미이다. ③ …에도 불구하고, ④ 그런데, …한데, …에 반해서

21 break into pieces: 산산조각이 나다

22 후반부의 'my confusion turned to panic(혼란스러움은 공포로 변했다)'을 통해 'puzzled'와 'frightened'를 찾을 수 있다. puzzled: 어리둥절해하는, frightened: 겁먹은, 무서워

하는, ① scared: 겁먹은, ② nervous: 초조한, satisfied: 만족한, ④ pleased: 기쁜, 기뻐하는, upset: 속상한, ⑤ confused: 혼란스러워 하는

23 (A) seem to부정사: ~인 것 같다. (B) that은 계속적 용법으로 쓸 수 없으므로 who가 적절하다. (C) home은 부사이므로 to 없이 쓰는 것이 적절하다.

24 What's going on? = What's happening?: 무슨 일이야?

25 ⓐ와 ③, ⑤: 부사적 용법, ①, ④: 명사적 용법, ②: 형용사적 용법

26 글쓴이가 학교에서 지진 대피 훈련을 몇 번 했는지는 알 수 없다. ① She saw that parts of buildings had fallen and had smashed several cars. ② They went to an open space. ④ No. ⑤ She realized that she should be prepared for the next earthquake, which can occur at any time.

27 would like to부정사: ~하고 싶다

28 위 글은 '영화 비평문'이다. review (책·연극·영화 등에 대한) 논평[비평], 감상문, ① (신문·잡지의) 글, 기사, ② 수필, ④ 독후감, ⑤ 전기

29 '주인공의 나이'는 알 수 없다. ① San Andreas. ② Los Angeles and San Francisco in 2014. ③ A search-and-rescue pilot. ⑤ It's about the search for the missing family during an earthquake.

단원별 예상문제

p.50~53

01 ① 02 ② 03 ④
04 (1) (c)overing (2) made our way
05 ④ 06 ② 07 ④ 08 ③
09 ② 10 ④
11 (1) Since (2) Though (3) when
12 (1) had taken (2) had practiced
   (3) had happened 13 ②
14 I still didn't know what exactly was happening
   또는 I still didn't know exactly what was
   happening
15 comfort → panic 16 ③ 17 ③
18 ② 19 ④ 20 a tsunami
21 ④

01 주어진 단어는 동의어 관계이다. destroy 파괴하다 damage 손상을 입히다 recently 최근에 lately 최근에

02 침대가 흔들리는 것으로 보아 지진이 난 것을 알 수 있다.

03 컵이 넘어지고, 식탁에서 물건이 떨어지는 등의 상황에서 "굴러 떨어지다"는 "roll off"가 적절하다. 오늘 할 일을 내일로 미루지 마라 put off 미루다

04 (1) covering 덮고 있는 (2) make one's way 가다

05 'No, second is heavy rain'은 제시문의 추측이 잘못되었음을 알려주는 것이므로 주어진 문장은 ⓓ가 적절하다.

06 이어지는 설명에 피해를 입히는 자연재해의 종류가 나열되어 있는 것으로 보아 자연재해의 종류에 대하여 궁금해하는 것이 적절하다.

07 ④ 태풍이 가져온 손해가 얼마나 큰지는 소개되지 않았다.

08 지진이 났을 때는 탁자 밑으로 대피를 해야 하기 때문에 "over the table"을 "under the table"로 바꾸어야 한다.

09 대화 속의 "How scary!"는 놀라움에 공감하는 의미의 감탄문으로 질문의 내용은 아니다.

10 ① After she (had) finished her homework, she went to bed. ② I knew the story because I had read the book. ③ I couldn't get in the room because I had forgotten my key. ⑤ He carried out all the responsibilities I had given to him.

11 (1) 이유를 나타내고 있으므로 Since (2) 상반되는 내용이므로 Though (3) 시간의 부사절을 이끄는 when이 적절하다.

12 각각 한 시제 앞선 일에 대한 것이므로 과거완료 시제로 쓰는 것이 적절하다.

13 첫 번째 문장에서는 예상한 것이 성취한 것보다 앞선 시제이므로 과거완료 had expected가 적절하다. 두 번째 문장에서는 다음에 어지는 절의 이유에 해당하므로 Since가 적절하다.

14 부정문에서 still은 부정어 앞에 위치한다. exactly가 was happening을 수식하는 것이 아니라 의문사 what을 수식하고 있고, 이런 경우에는, 의문사 바로 앞이나 뒤에 위치하는 것이 정상적인 어순이다.

15 머지않아 방 전체가 심하게 흔들리기 시작했다고 했으므로, 혼란스러움은 '공포'로 변했다라고 하는 것이 적절하다. comfort: 안락, 편안

16 지진이 일어났을 때 필자의 동생이 무엇을 하고 있었는지는 대답할 수 없다. ① It occurred one night in February. ② No. ④ No. ⑤ No.

17 ⓐ in a few minutes: 몇 분 만에, ⓑ be prepared for: ~에 대비하고 있다

18 주어진 문장의 looked around에 주목한다. ②번 뒤에 주변을 둘러본 상황이 이어지고 있으므로 ②번이 적절하다.

19 이 글은 글쓴이가 지진을 겪은 뒤에 언제든 발생할 수 있는 다음 지진을 대비해야 한다는 것을 깨달았다는 내용의 글이므로, 주제로는 ④번이 적절하다. 예방은 치료약보다 낫다; 유비무환이다. (좋지 않은 일이 일어나기 전에 예방하는 편이 그 결과에 대처하는 것보다 쉽고 유효하다.)

20 '쓰나미'를 가리킨다.

21 near Haeundae Beach를 near Gwangalli Beach로 고쳐야 한다.

01 curious about   02 So am I.

03 (1) damage   (2) get   (3) hands   (4) cover

04 (1) David had lost his glasses, so he couldn't read anything.

(2) After he (had) moved to a new city, he joined the company baseball team.

(3) In summer, food is easily spoiled unless it is kept well.

(4) Our feet remain firmly on the earth though[although] our planet is spinning on its axis.

05 (1) had quit   (2) had been married

(3) you do not like

06 (1) A man notified the police that his store had been robbed.

(2) Even though she does not have hands, there is nothing she cannot do.

07 (A) woke up   (B) because   (C) how

08 experienced / I experienced

09 (A) her brother   (B)happening

10 Don't take the elevator!

11 in order to / so as to / in order that, may[can] / so that, may[can]

12 She started crawling toward the door.

01 함께 조사를 해보자는 제안을 하는 것으로 보아 궁금증을 나타내는 "I'm curious about ~"가 되는 것이 적절하다.

02 '~도 마찬가지이다'의 의미로 동의를 나타내는 표현은 'So +주어+동사.'이다.

03 (1) 손상, 손해 damage (2) 겁먹다 get scared (3) 두 손을 올려놓다 place one's hands (4) 씌우다[가리다] cover

04 (1) 안경을 잃어버린 것이 앞선 일이므로 과거완료로 나타낸다. (2) 앞선 일이므로 과거완료로 나타낸다. After가 있으므로 단순히 과거로 고쳐도 좋다. (3) 조건을 나타내는 내용이므로 unless로 고치는 것이 적절하다. (4) 상반되는 내용이 나오므로 since를 though로 고치는 것이 적절하다.

05 (1) 충격을 받기 전에 그가 그만 둔 것이므로 과거완료를 이용한다. (2) 결혼한 것을 말하는 것이므로 과거완료를 이용한다. to가 있으므로 수동태로 써야 하는 것에 주의한다. (3) though는 앞이나 뒤의 절의 내용과 상반되는 내용을 이끈다.

06 (1) 가게에 강도가 든 것이므로 수동태로 써야 하며, 강도가 든 것이 신고하는 시점보다 앞서므로 과거완료로 써야 한다. (2) even이 있으므로 양보절을 이끄는 even though를 이용한다.

07 (A) '잠에서 깼다'고 해야 하므로 woke up이 적절하다. fall asleep: 잠들다, (B) 뒤에 절이 이어지므로 because가 적절하

다. because of+명사구, (C) '어떻게' 반응해야 할지 몰랐다고 해야 하므로 how가 적절하다.

08 be one's first time+-ing = be the first time+that+주어+동사: ~하는 게 처음이다, for the first time: 처음으로

09 글쓴이가 책상 위에 있던 거울이 바닥으로 떨어져 산산조각이 나는 소리를 들었을 때, 침대가 흔들렸던 것이 '남동생' 때문이 아니라 어떤 다른 이유 때문이었다는 것은 알 수 있었지만, 무슨 일이 '일어나고' 있었는지를 확신하지 못했다.

10 take the elevator: 엘리베이터를 타다

11 부사적 용법의 목적을 나타내는 to부정사는 in order[so as] to부정사나 in order that[so that] ~ may[can]로 바꿔 쓸 수 있다.

12 그녀는 문으로 기어가기 시작했다.

|모범답안|

01 (1) often eat fast food though it is not good for the health

(2) likes English though he is not good at it

(3) studies hard though her grades are not good

(4) played soccer though it rained outside

02 (A) is set   (B) a tsunami

(C) in only ten minutes

(D) natural disaster movies   (E) special effects

01 ③	02 ②	03 ②	04 over
05 ②	06 ⑤	07 So do I.	08 ②
09 ⑤	10 ③	11 ⑤	

12 (1) Though[Although] it rained a lot, we enjoyed our holiday.

(2) Even though it was cold, I felt very happy today.

(3) Since[As/Because] Laura is very kind, she is loved by all of them.

(4) He learned that he had been chosen to play Harry Potter.

(5) The play had already started when we arrived..

13 ①, ④	14 saying	15 ②	16 ④
17 ⑤	18 and he		
19 (A) the stairs (B) the elevator			
20 ①	21 ⑤		

01 주어진 단어는 반의어 관계이다. whole 전체의 partial 부분의 common 흔한 rare 드문

02 ② flood는 'a very large amount of water that covers an area 한 지역을 덮는 아주 많은 양의 물'이라고 해야 한다.

03 ① 장난삼아 as a joke ② 격렬하게 violently ③ 반응하다 react ④ 붕괴하다 collapse ⑤ 가다 make one's way

04 • pull over 길 한쪽으로 차를 대다 • over ~ ~ 이상 • tip over 넘어지다

05 폭염에 대한 주의 사항을 이야기하고 이어서 또 다른 주의 사항을 더하는 것으로 보아 앞에 제시된 것 이외에 또 다른 것이 있는지 묻는 말이 적절하다.

06 더위에 대한 대응 방안으로 폭염이 왔을 때는 시원한 건물로 들어가는 것이 적절한 방법이다.

07 "~도 마찬가지이다"는 "So+동사+주어."이다. 앞의 문장에 be동사가 있으면 be동사를 쓰고, 일반동사가 있을 때는 do/does/did를 쓴다.

08 ⓑ "Yes, actually the wind has made the fires worse." 라는 대답으로 보아 "산불이 끝났니?"가 아니라 "여전히 산불이 계속되니?"에 해당하는 "Are the fires still going on?"이 적절하다.

09 ⑤ "About 400 people are missing in that area."는 그 지역에서 400명 정도가 실종되었다는 의미이기 때문에 찾을 수 없었다.

10 I had to go and greet him though I didn't want to. 내용상 주절과 종속절이 서로 상반되므로 though가 적절하다.

11 첫 번째 빈칸에는 식당에 둔 것이 알게 된 것보다 앞서므로 과거완료를 이용하고, 두 번째 빈칸에는 서로 상반되는 내용이 나오므로 though를 이용한다.

12 (1) Despite 다음에는 '구'가 나오고 Though[Although] 다음에는 '절'이 나온다. (2) As though: 마치 …인 것처럼 Even though: 비록 …일지라도, 설사 …이라고 할지라도 (3) 뒤에 나오는 절의 이유가 나오고 있으므로 이유를 나타내는 절을 이끄는 Since나 As, Because 등이 적절하다. (4) 알기 전에 먼저 선택된 것이므로 과거완료로 쓰는 것이 적절하다. (5) 도착하기 전에 시작된 것이므로 과거완료로 쓰는 것이 적절하다.

13 ② Soon I realized that I had left my report at home. ③ Although I had done many earthquake drills in school, I had never thought I'd experience a real earthquake. ⑤ I woke up suddenly because[as] my bed was shaking.

14 keep ~ing: 계속해서 ~하다

15 (A)와 ②: (자격·기능 등이) …로(서)(전치사) ① …하는 대로(접속사) ③ …하는 동안에(접속사) ④ [비례] …함에 따라, …할수록(접속사) ⑤ as ~ as …에서, 앞의 as가 지시부사, 뒤의 as는 접속사

16 ①과 ②: 지각동사(see)+목적어+현재분사 또는 원형부정사 ③ every second = every moment: 매 순간 ④ 지각동사(hear)+목적어+원형부정사 또는 현재분사로 써야 하므로 breaking으로 고치는 것이 적절하다. ⑤ start는 to부정사와 동명사를 모두 목적어로 취하는 동사이다.

17 ⓐ와 ⑤: 기울어지다, tip over 넘어뜨리다, 넘어지다 ① (뾰족한) 끝 ② (실용적인, 작은) 조언 ③, ④: 팁, 봉사료

18 계속적 용법의 주격 관계대명사는 '접속사+주어'로 바꿔 쓸 수 있다.

19 글쓴이의 아빠는 엄마에게 전화해서 건물 밖으로 나오라고 말했고, '엘리베이터' 대신 '계단'을 이용하라고 말했다.

20 앞의 내용과 상반되고 대조적인 내용이 주절에 이어지므로 Although가 가장 적절하다.

21 글쓴이는 지진을 겪은 이후부터 지진 대피 훈련에 진지하게 임하기 시작했다.

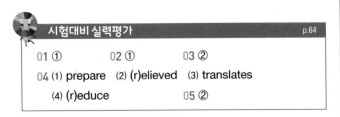

Lesson 4

My Roles in Society

시험대비 실력평가   p.64

01 ①　　　02 ①　　　03 ②

04 (1) prepare　(2) (r)elieved　(3) translates

(4) (r)educe　　　05 ②

01 '어떤 다른 사람을 대신해 말하거나 결정하도록 선택된 사람'을 가리키는 말은 representative(대표[대표자])이다.

02 ①번 문장에서 return은 '반납하다'를 뜻한다.

03 주어진 문장에서 vision은 통찰력 또는 비전을 의미하며 이와 같은 의미로 쓰인 것은 ②번이다. 나머지는 모두 시야, 시력을 가리킨다.

04 prepare: 준비하다, relieved: 안도하는, translate: 번역하다, reduce: 줄이다

05 take sides: 편들다, take care of: ~을 돌보다, work out: 해결하다, work on: 공들여 일하다

서술형 시험대비   p.65

01 creation

02 (1) let down　(2) was stuck in　(3) come up

03 (1) ensure　(2) valued　(3) logical　(4) reasoning

(5) analyze

04 (1) Why don't you run for class representative?

(2) I have no doubt that you will be elected if you run.

(3) I'm in charge of making the presentation materials.

(4) Many people believe that the best leaders lead by example.

05 (1) The brothers get along with each other.

(2) The king would like to lead by example.

(3) Let's come up with a new idea to end water pollution.

01 주어진 단어는 형용사와 명사의 관계를 나타낸다.

02 let down: 실망시키다, be stuck in: ~에 갇히다, come up: 발생하다, 생기다

03 analyze: 분석하다, logical: 논리적인, ensure: 반드시 ~하게 하다, ~을 보장하다, valued: 귀중한, reasoning: 추리, 추론

05 get along with: ~와 잘 어울리다, lead by example: 솔선수범하다, come up with: 생각해 내다

교과서 Conversation

핵심 Check   p.66~67

1 ⑤

2 I have no doubt that it will be very helpful.

3 (B) – (C) – (A)

교과서 대화문 익히기

Check(√) True or False   p.68

1 T　2 F　3 F　4 T

교과서 확인학습   p.70~71

Listen & Talk 1 A
problem / matter / on Saturday evening, What should I do / decision / miss

Listen & Talk 1 B
What's the matter / happened / had a fight, stuck in, what to do / why / big deal, some, misunderstanding / Why don't / can't take sides / works out

Listen & Talk 1 C
What's the matter / asked me to help him / return some books, presentation, prepare / do / let down / how about meeting, everything, help / help me out

Listen & Talk 2 A
Sports Day / good at taking photos, have no doubt that

Listen & Talk 2 B
divided, into, be responsible for, translate, edit, in charge of, I have no doubt that, who

Listen & Talk 2 C
excited, field trip / in charge of / taking pictures / some research / write our field trip report / have no doubt that, turn out

시험대비 기본평가   p.72

01 ②　　　02 doubt　　　03 ⑤

01 상대방의 긍정적인 발언데 대해 동의하는 것이므로 'So+조동사+주어' 형태가 알맞다.

02 I have no doubt that ~.: ~이라는 것에 의심의 여지가 없다.

03 토요일에 지수가 어떻게 할지는 아직 결정하지 못하였다.

시험대비 실력평가 p.73~74

01 ③　　　　02 ⑤

03 I have no doubt that you will take some wonderful pictures.

04 ④　　　05 ③　　　06 ③

07 I have no doubt that our project will turn out well.

08 He is going to do some research on the museum.

09 Emma will be in charge of writing the field trip report.

10 ⓒ → are printed　　　11 ③

01 문제가 무엇인지 묻는 표현으로 'Is there something wrong?'과 바꾸어 쓸 수 있다.

02 지수가 토요일에 무엇을 할지는 대화를 통해 알 수 없다.

04 주어진 문장은 상대방의 어려움을 이해하는 표현이므로 친구들이 싸워서 중간에 끼어 어찌할 바를 모르고 있다는 준수의 대화에 이어질 말로 적절하다.

05 have a fight: 다투다, 싸우다, make up with: 화해하다, take sides: 편들다, work out: 해결하다

06 위 대화를 통해 재우와 윤호가 언제 싸웠는지는 알 수 없다.

07 I have no doubt that ~.: ~할 거라고 믿는다. ~할 거라고 확신한다.

08 세진이는 박물관에 대해 조사를 할 것이다.

09 견학 보고서 작성을 담당한 사람은 Emma이다.

10 수동태로 'be p.p' 형태가 알맞다.

11 A 그룹은 한국어 이야기를 영어로 번역할 것이다.

서술형 시험대비 p.75

01 They are going to make a picture book for children in other countries and send copies of the book to them.

02 Group B is in charge of making drawings for the book and edit it.

03 They have to send them to the children.

04 (A) help him with his homework　(B) let down
(C) to return some books
(D) meet Nick to work on the presentation
(E) I need to prepare for an exam at night
(F) on Thursday

01 Send Our Stories project는 외국의 아이들을 위한 그림책을 만들어 보낸다.

02 그룹 B는 책의 그림을 그리고 편집을 담당한다.

03 책이 인쇄되면 학생들은 아이들에게 책을 보내야 한다.

04 오늘 나는 Nick에게 정말로 고마웠다. 내 동생이 내게 이번 주 수요일에 숙제를 도와줄 것을 요청했을 때, 나는 도와줄 수 없다고 말했다. 내 남동생은 실망한 것처럼 보여 나는 미안함을 느꼈다. 사실, 나는 이번 주 수요일에 해야 할 일이 많았다. 나는 도서관에 책을 반납하러 가야 하고 발표 준비를 위해 Nick을 만나야 한다. 그 다음에, 나는 밤에 시험을 위해 준비해야 한다. 내가 이것에 대해 Nick에게 이야기했을 때, 그는 우리의 만남 일정을 연기할 것을 제안했다. 그는 나를 이해해 주었고, 우리는 우리의 발표를 위해 목요일에 만나기로 결정했다. 그가 얼마나 친절한지! Nick 덕분에, 나는 동생을 도와 줄 수 있다.

Grammar
교과서

핵심 Check p.76~77

1 (1) if　(2) whether

2 (1) will be held　(2) should be handled

시험대비 기본평가 p.78

01 ④　　　　02 ①　　　　03 ③

04 (1) will be sent by me tomorrow
(2) must not be forgotten
(3) can it be done

01 wonder의 목적어가 나와야 하는데 '~인지 (아닌지)'라는 의미로 명사절을 이끄는 접속사 if가 적절하다.

02 조동사가 있는 문장의 수동태는 '조동사+be+과거분사'의 형태로 나타낸다.

03 불확실하거나 의문시되는 사실을 나타내는 접속사 if가 적절하다. that을 쓸 경우에는 그 뒤에 확실한 내용을 담고 있는 절이 나온다.

04 (1) 조동사가 있는 문장의 수동태는 '조동사+be+과거분사'의 형태로 나타낸다. (2) 조동사가 있는 문장의 수동태의 부정문은 '조동사+not+be+과거분사'의 형태로 나타낸다. (3) 조동사가 있는 문장의 수동태의 의문문은 '조동사+주어+be+과거분사 ~?'의 형태로 나타낸다.

01 ②　　02 ②　　03 ⑤
04 (1) if　(2) whether　(3) whether　(4) will be
　　(5) can be　(6) will not be　(7) appear
　　(8) resemble
05 I don't know if she likes Italian food or not.
06 (1) if[whether]　(2) can be understood
　　(3) must be made
07 ③　　08 ①　　09 ③
10 The plan had to be postponed because of cost.
11 ①　　12 ⑤　　13 ④　　14 ④
15 ②, ④
16 (1) Joan asked if[whether] I want to go to the
　　party.
　　(2) It depends on whether it applies directly to
　　your job.
　　(3) You'll have to choose whether to buy it or not.
　　(4) The beautiful clothes will be put on right now.
　　(5) Problems will occur as a result of human life.

01 ① I don't want to know if something happened. ③ Matthew asked Vivian if she wanted to go back home or not. ④ I'm not sure if Ted won the speech contest. ⑤ Let me know if she will bring some food.

02 This essay will have to be completely rewritten. 조동사가 있는 문장의 수동태는 '조동사+be+과거분사'의 형태로 나타낸다.

03 조동사가 있는 문장의 수동태는 '조동사+be+과거분사'의 형태로 나타낸다.

04 (1) 불확실하거나 의문시되는 사실을 나타내는 접속사 if가 적절하다. (2) 내용상 '~인지 (아닌지)'라는 의미의 접속사 whether가 적절하다. (3) 바로 뒤에 'or not'이 이어지고 있으므로 whether가 적절하다. (4) if가 명사절을 이끌고 있으므로 미래시제는 미래시제로 나타내야 한다. (5)~(6) 조동사가 있는 문장의 수동태는 '조동사+be+과거분사'의 형태로 나타내며, 부정문은 '조동사+not+be+과거분사'의 형태로 쓴다. (7) appear는 자동사이므로 수동태로 쓰이지 않는다. (8) resemble은 타동사이지만 상태를 나타내는 말로 수동태로 쓰이지 않는다.

05 '~인지 (아닌지)'라는 의미의 접속사 if가 나오므로 'I don't know'를 쓰고 'if+주어+동사'의 어순으로 쓴 후 'or not'을 문장의 마지막에 써야 한다.

06 (1) asked의 목적어를 이끄는 if나 whether가 적절하다. (2), (3) 조동사가 있는 문장의 수동태는 '조동사+be+과거분사'의 형태로 나타낸다.

07 첫 번째 빈칸에는 see의 목적어를 이끄는 if나 whether가 적절하다. 두 번째 빈칸에는 조동사가 있는 문장의 수동태의 부정문

은 '조동사+not+be+과거분사'의 형태로 나타내는 것이 적절하다.

08 조동사가 있는 문장의 수동태는 '조동사+be+과거분사'의 형태로 나타낸다.

09 불확실하거나 의문시되는 사실을 나타내는 접속사 if나 whether가 적절하며, 뒤에는 '주어+동사'의 절이 나와야 한다.

10 조동사가 있는 문장의 수동태는 '조동사+be+과거분사'의 형태로 나타낸다.

11 check의 목적어를 이끄는 if나 whether가 적절하며 whether는 'or not'이 바로 뒤에 나올 때 쓰일 수 있지만 if는 그럴 수 없다.

12 능동태를 수동태로 바꿀 때, 목적어를 주어로 쓰고, 주어는 'by+목적격'으로 쓰며(일반인의 경우 보통 생략함.), 동사는 조동사가 있는 경우 '조동사+be+과거분사'의 형태로 쓴다.

13 ④번은 뒤에 or not이 이어지므로 if는 들어갈 수 없고 whether가 들어가야 하지만 나머지는 모두 if나 whether가 들어갈 수 있다.

14 know의 목적어가 나와야 하는데 '~인지 (아닌지)'라는 의미로 사실의 여부를 확인하거나 불확실함을 나타내는 명사절을 이끄는 접속사 if가 적절하다.

15 ② Very little of the house may remain after the fire. remain은 자동사로 수동태로 쓰지 않는다. ④ Do you know if Cathy will come home soon? if절은 간접의문문을 이끄는 것이므로 '주어+동사'의 어순이 되어야 한다.

16 (1) 사실의 여부를 확인하거나 불확실함을 나타내는 명사절을 이끄는 접속사 if나 whether가 적절하다. (2) if는 전치사의 목적어로 쓰인 명사절을 이끌지 못하므로 if 대신에 whether로 써야 한다. (3) whether는 to부정사와 함께 쓰일 수 있지만 if는 그럴 수 없으므로 if 대신에 whether로 써야 한다. (4) The beautiful clothes가 주어이므로 수동태로 써야 하고, 조동사가 있는 문장의 수동태는 '조동사+be+과거분사'의 형태로 쓴다. (5) occur는 자동사이므로 수동태로 쓰이지 않는다.

01 (1) The final match may be watched by about a
　　million people.
　　(2) The value of regular exercise should not be
　　underestimated (by us).
　　(3) The robots can be made to work faster in the
　　future (by us).
　　(4) This math problem can't be solved by anyone.
02 Ask her if[whether] she watches TV every night.
03 (1) if[whether] Jake draws a picture
　　(2) will be taken
04 (1) if[whether] you like　(2) how I should respond

05 (1) I want to know if my study plans are effective.

(2) I want to check if I can view the content of the site.

(3) I am not sure if she runs fast enough.

06 (1) Whether I believe you or not is important.

(2) My heart raced, not knowing whether or not my son was alive.

(3) He seemed undecided whether to go or stay.

(4) My lost card might be used illegally.

(5) Ghosts can appear in visible form in the world of the living.

(6) The tree had to be sawn down.

07 (1) may be affected   (2) will be released

08 (1) He asked me if[whether] I saw his backpack.

(2) No one can tell if[whether] he is serious or not.

(3) Let's see if[whether] anyone lives in that house.

(4) The room won't be cleaned until 2 p.m.

(5) Their voices can be heard from here.

(6) He shall be missed by us all

01 (1), (2) 능동태를 수동태로 바꿀 때, 능동태의 목적어를 수동태의 주어로 쓰고, 주어는 'by+목적격'으로 문장의 뒤에 쓰며(보통 일반인의 경우 생략함.), 동사는 조동사가 있는 경우 '조동사+be+과거분사'의 형태로 쓴다. (3) 사역동사 make의 목적격 보어로 쓰인 동사원형이 수동태에서 to부정사로 바뀌는 것에 주의한다. (4) No one이 수동태에서 not anyone으로 바뀌는 것에 주의한다. (by 이하가 일반인을 의미하므로 생략 가능한 문장인데, 부정의 뜻을 나타내야 하므로 no를 'not+any'로 보아 not을 앞으로 보내야 한다.)

02 목적어가 되는 명사절을 if[whether]로 시작하는 간접의문문으로 바꾼다.

03 (1) 명사절을 이끄는 if나 whether를 이용하여 '주어+동사'의 어순으로 쓴다. (2) 'some wonderful pictures'가 주어이므로 수동태를 이용하고 '조동사+be+과거분사'의 형태로 쓴다.

04 간접의문문에서 의문사가 없는 경우에는 'if[whether]+주어+동사'의 어순으로 쓰지만 의문사가 있을 경우 '의문사+주어+동사'의 어순으로 쓴다.

05 '~인지 (아닌지)'라는 의미의 접속사로 쓰이는 if를 이용하여 'if+주어+동사'의 어순으로 쓴다. if 뒤에 오는 절은 의문사가 없는 간접의문문이다.

06 (1) 문두에서 주어를 이끄는 역할을 하고 있으므로 If를 Whether로 고치는 것이 적절하다. (2) 바로 뒤에 or not이 나오고 있으므로 if를 whether로 고치는 것이 적절하다. (3) whether 다음에는 to부정사를 쓸 수 있지만 if는 쓸 수 없으므로 if를 whether로 고치는 것이 적절하다. (4) 조동사가 있는 문장의 수동태는 '조동사+be+과거분사'의 형태로 쓴다. (5) appear는 자동사이므로 수동태로 쓰이지 않는다. (6) The tree가 주어

이므로 수동태가 되어야 하고, had to가 있으므로 'had to be sawn'의 형태로 써야 한다.

07 Manufacturing processes와 The new model이 주어이므로 수동태로 써야 하고, 조동사가 있으므로 '조동사+be+과거분사'의 형태로 쓴다.

08 (1) if나 whether를 추가하여 'if[whether]+주어+동사'의 어순으로 쓴다. (2), (3) 'if나 whether를 추가하여 쓴다. (4), (5) 조동사가 있는 문장의 수동태는 '조동사+be+과거분사'의 형태로 쓰므로 be를 추가한다. (6) 수동태에서 행위자를 나타낼 때 쓰이는 'by+목적격'의 by를 추가한다.

교과서 Reading

확인문제	p.84

1 T 2 F 3 T 4 T 5 F

확인문제	p.85

1 T 2 F 3 T 4 F 5 T 6 F

확인문제	p.86

1 T 2 F 3 T 4 F 5 T 6 F

교과서 확인학습 A p.87~89

01 We Are All
02 coming up
03 Why don't you
04 No way
05 right person
06 thought about
07 Why not
08 Come on
09 special qualities
10 can be called
11 What
12 good leadership qualities
13 friendly, outgoing
14 get along
15 will be elected
16 good leadership qualities
17 has ever told
18 Why
19 trying to be
20 however
21 become a leader
22 don't know
23 a vision, to motivate others
24 any of those things
25 wonder if
26 wrong
27 other leadership qualities
28 do some research online
29 what
30 Builders
31 feels valued
32 positive environment

33 to talk to
34 Logical Analysts
35 reasoning skills
36 Analyze
37 achieve the team's goals
38 Hands-Off Managers
39 on their own
40 try to control
41 it is needed
42 Strict Directors
43 everyone's role
44 on time
45 each step
46 Quiet Supporters
47 by example
48 shine instead
49 Meet, needs
50 Creative Thinkers
51 Approach
52 Come up with
53 differently from
54 realized the reason
55 belong to, come up
56 call for
57 unique situation
58 different responsibilities
59 more confident
60 some of the qualities
61 pick me
62 let's try

교과서 확인학습 B   p.90~92

1 We Are All Leaders

2 Brian: The election is coming up.

3 Why don't you run for class representative, Yumi?

4 Yumi: No way.

5 I'm not the right person for that position.

6 I've never thought about running.

7 Brian: Why not?

8 Yumi: Come on, Brian.

9 Leaders have special qualities.

10 I don't think a person like me can be called a leader.

11 Brian: What do you mean?

12 I think you have very good leadership qualities.

13 You're really friendly and outgoing.

14 You also help people get along.

15 I have no doubt that you will be elected if you run..

16 Brian told me this afternoon that I have good leadership qualities.

17 No one has ever told me that before.

18 Why does he think so?

19 Maybe he was just trying to be nice.

20 When he said that to me, however, I started to think.

21 Can I really become a leader?

22 I don't know.

23 I think leaders should have a vision, clear goals, and the ability to motivate others.

24 I don't have any of those things.

25 Then I suddenly started to wonder if these are the only qualities that make a good leader.

26 Maybe I'm wrong.

27 Maybe there are other leadership qualities.

28 So I decided to do some research online.

29 Here's what I found!

30 GREEN LEADERS: "Team Builders"

31 Ensure that the team feels valued

32 Create a positive environment

33 Are friendly and easy to talk to

34 RED LEADERS: "Logical Analysts"

35 Have good reasoning skills

36 Analyze problems and situations

37 Think of the most effective ways to achieve the team's goals

38 PURPLE LEADERS: "Hands−Off Managers"

39 Allow others to work on their own

40 Do not try to control people

41 Give advice only when it is needed

42 ORANGE LEADERS: "Strict Directors"

43 Make everyone's role clear

44 Make sure everything is finished on time

45 Ensure each step is done properly

46 YELLOW LEADERS: "Quiet Supporters"

47 Lead by example

48 Let the team members shine instead

49 Meet the team members' needs

50 BLUE LEADERS: "Creative Thinkers"

51 Approach problems in new ways

52 Come up with fresh ideas

53 Deal with tasks differently from others

54 I was surprised that there are actually many different leadership styles, but soon I realized the reason.

55 We belong to many different groups, and many different situations can come up in our lives.

56 They all call for different leadership styles.

57 Each group's unique situation determines the best leadership style.

58 "I am a part of many different groups, and I have different responsibilities in each group."

59 After reading everything, I became more confident.

60 I discovered that I have some of the qualities of a "green leader."

61 If my classmates think a green leader would make our class better, they might pick me to be class representative!

62 Okay, let's try it!

16 정답 및 해설

01 (A) don't   (B) Why not   (C) if   02 ②

03 ④   04 ②   05 I read

06 unique situation   07 ②

08 which → what

09 red leaders 또는 logical analysts

10 (A) on their own   (B) control   (C) it is needed

11 ④   12 if[whether]   13 ⑤

14 with   15 ②   16 to shine → shine

17 don't mind whether → make sure 또는 ensure

18 to   19 ③

20 (A) different leadership styles   (B) unique
    (C) best leadership style

21 ⑤   22 ③

23 a vision, clear goals, and the ability to motivate
    others

24 ③   25 be elected   26 ④

27 I'm not the right person for that position.

28 ③   29 Ensure   30 ④

31 (A) creative thinkers   (B) fresh ideas
    (C) differently from

---

01 (A) '반 대표에 입후보하는 게 어때?'라고 해야 하므로 don't
가 적절하다. Why don't you 동사원형?: ~하는 게 어때?,
(B) '왜 입후보하는 것에 대해 생각해 본 적이 없어?'라는 뜻이
므로 'Why not'이 적절하다. (C) '만약 네가 입후보한다면'이
라고 해야 하므로 if가 적절하다. whether: ~인지 아니지

02 ⓐ와 ③, ⑤: 경험 용법, ①, ④: 계속 용법, ②: 완료 용법

03 자기 같은 사람이 리더로 불릴 수 있다고 생각하지 않는다고 말
한 사람은 '유미'이다. ① propose: 제안하다

04 call for = require = need = demand = want: 요구하다,
② stand for: ~을 상징하다, ~을 의미하다

05 reading을 '주어+동사'로 바꿔 쓰는 것이 적절하다.

06 각 집단의 '독특한 상황'이 최고의 지도력 유형을 결정한다.

07 녹색 리더는 팀이 반드시 가치 있다고 느끼게 하고 긍정적인 환
경을 조성하고 친절하고 말을 걸기 쉬운 유형이므로 '팀 조직자'
가 적절하다. ⑤ carefree: 근심 걱정 없는, 속 편한

08 선행사를 포함하는 관계대명사 what을 쓰는 것이 적절하다.

09 문제와 상황들을 분석하는 리더들은 '빨간색 리더' 또는 '논리적
분석가'들이다.

10 보라색 리더는 다른 사람들이 '스스로' 일하도록 해 주고, 사람
을 '통제하려고' 하지 않고, '필요할 때만' 조언한다.

11 앞에 나오는 내용과 상반되는 내용이 뒤에 이어지므로
however가 가장 적절하다. ② 게다가, 더욱이, ③ 뿐만 아니
라, 더욱이, ⑤ 즉[말하자면]

12 의문사가 없을 때 접속사 if[whether]를 사용하여 간접의문문
으로 고치는 것이 적절하다.

13 이 글은 '좋은 리더를 만드는 자질들이 무엇인가'에 관한 글이므
로, 주제로는 ⑤번 '리더가 가져야 하는 자질들'이 적절하다.

14 ⓐ come up with: 찾아내다, 내놓다, ⓑ deal with: 다루다,
처리하다

15 strict = severe = stern = rigid = rigorous: 엄격한, ②
easy-going: 태평스러운, 안이한, 게으른

16 사역동사 let+목적어+원형부정사

17 주황색 리더는 모든 일이 제때 끝날 것을 '확실히 하는' 엄격한
감독관이다.

18 belong to: ~에 속하다

19 '한 번 해보자'라고 하는 이어지는 내용으로 보아 모든 것을 읽
고 나서, 나는 더 '자신감'이 생겼다고 하는 것이 적절하다.
confident: 자신 있는, ① 관대한, ② 겸손한, ④ 불안해 하는,
염려하는, ⑤ 이기적인

20 '서로 다른 지도력 유형들'을 요구하는 다른 많은 상황들이 우리
인생에서 발생할 수 있고, 우리가 속한 각 집단의 '독특한' 상황
이 '최고의 지도력 유형'을 결정하기 때문이다.

21 이 글은 '각 집단의 독특한 상황이 최고의 지도력 유형을 결정한
다.'는 내용의 글이므로, 제목으로는 ⑤번 '최고의 지도력 유형
은 상황에 따라 다르다'가 적절하다.

22 주어진 문장의 'don't know'에 주목한다. ③번 앞 문장의 질문
에 대한 답을 모른다는 것이므로 ③번이 적절하다.

23 '비전, 명확한 목표, 그리고 다른 사람들에게 동기를 부여할 능
력'을 가리킨다.

24 '다른 지도력 자질들이 있는지도 모른다. 그래서 나는 온라인으
로 조사해 보기로 결심했다'고 말했기 때문에 뒤에 올 내용으로
는 '지도력 자질들에 대해 유미가 온라인으로 행한 조사'가 적절
하다.

25 '당선될 것'이라고 해야 하므로, 수동태로 쓰는 것이 적절하다.

26 (A)와 ④: (특히 미국에서, 선거에) 출마[입후보]하다, ① (~
에) 급히 가다, 달려가다(for, to), run for the doctor: 의사를
부르러 급히 가다, ② (탈것이) 달리다, (버스·배 따위의) 편이
있다, ③ ~을 경영하다, 관리하다, ⑤ (연극·영화의) 장기 공연
[상영]

27 the right person: 적절한 사람

28 노란색 리더는 솔선수범하고 팀원들이 대신 빛나도록 해 주고
팀원들의 요구 사항을 충족시켜주므로 조용한 '지지자'라고 하는
것이 적절하다. ① 경쟁자, ② 상대, 반대자, ④ 도전자, ⑤ 경
쟁자

29 make sure = ensure 반드시 ~하게 하다, 확실하게 하다

30 (B)와 ④: 단계, ① (발)걸음, ② 걸음걸이, ③ 밟다, 딛다, ⑤
디딤판, 계단

31 파란색 리더는 새로운 방식으로 문제들에 접근하고 '신선한 아
이디어를' 떠올리고, 그리고 다른 사람들과 '다르게' 일을 처리하
는 '창조적 사상가'이다.

17

01 How[What] about   02 class representative

03 (A) special qualities   (B) class representative

04 (A) clear   (B) properly   (C) Approach

05 (A) Strict Directors   (B) on time   (C) properly

06 creative thinkers → quiet supporters   07 none

08 that → if[whether]

09 She thinks leaders should have a vision, clear goals, and the ability to motivate others.

10 Each group's unique situation determines the best leadership style.

11 green leader   12 representative

---

01 Why don't you+동사원형 ~?= How[What] about ~ing?: ~하는 게 어때?

02 '반 대표'를 가리킨다.

03 유미는 리더들은 '특별한 자질'을 갖추고 있고, 자신은 '반 대표'에 적합한 사람이 아니라고 말한다. suitable: 적합한

04 (A) 목적격보어에 해당 하므로 형용사 clear가 적절하다. (B) 동사 is done을 수식하므로 부사 properly가 적절하다. (C) approach는 타동사로 전치사 없이 목적어를 써야 하므로 Approach가 적절하다. approach = come up to

05 주황색 리더는 모두의 역할을 분명하게 해 주고, 모든 일을 '제 때' 끝날 것을 확실히 하고, 그리고 각 단계가 '적절히' 이행되도록 하는 '엄격한 감독관'이다.

06 노란색 리더는 솔선수범하고, 팀원들이 대신 빛나도록 해 주고, 그리고 팀원들의 요구 사항을 충족시켜 주는 '조용한 지지자'이다.

07 not ~ any는 '아무것도 ~ 아니다'라는 의미로 전체부정을 나타낸다. not과 any가 결합된 none을 써서 부정형을 나타내는 것이 적절하다.

08 that 뒤에는 확실한 내용이 나와야 하므로, '~인지 아닌지'의 의미를 가지는 접속사 if[whether]를 사용하여 wonder의 목적어에 해당하는 절을 이끌게 하는 것이 적절하다.

09 유미는 리더가 비전, 명확한 목표, 그리고 다른 사람들에게 동기를 부여할 능력을 가지고 있어야 한다고 생각한다.

10 the best leadership style: 최고의 지도력 유형

11 모든 것을 읽고 나서, 유미는 '녹색 리더'의 자질들 중 일부분을 가지고 있다는 것을 알게 되었다.

12 representative: 대표(자), 다른 사람이나 사람들의 집단을 대표하여 행동하거나 결정을 내리도록 선택된 사람

01 illogical   02 ⑤   03 ⑤

04 (1) in charge of   (2) take sides   (3) is good at

---

05 (1) She and I belong to different groups.

   (2) This work calls for a high level of knowledge.

   (3) I tried my best to meet their needs.

06 ④

07 (A) making the presentation materials

   (B) presentation materials

08 ⑤   09 take sides

10 ⓒ → misunderstanding   11 ③   12 ⑤

13 ②   14 ⑤   15 ⑤   16 ⑤

17 can be adopted   18 ①

19 ⓐ, ⓒ, ⓓ, ⓕ   20 ②

21 Why haven't you (ever) thought about running?

22 ②, ⑤

23 many different groups and situations

24 If my classmates think a green leader would make our class better

25 ①, ④   26 yellow   27 ④

28 아무도 재활용물품 분리를 원치 않을 때 유나가 그것을 분리했고, 글쓴이가 감명 받아서 그녀를 돕기 시작했다.

29 ③

---

01 주어진 단어는 반의어 관계를 나타낸다. logical: 논리적인, illogical: 비논리적인

02 '누군가나 무언가에 가까이 가다'를 가리키는 말은 approach(접근하다)이다.

03 outgoing: 외향적인

04 be in charge of: ~을 담당하다, take sides: 편을 들다, be good at: ~을 잘하다

05 belong to: ~에 속하다, call for: 필요로 하다, 요구하다, try one's best: 최선을 다하다

06 어떠한 문제가 있는지 묻는 질문에 도움이 많이 된다는 대답은 어색하다.

08 민수는 발표 자료를 만드는 것을 잘한다.

09 take sides: 편을 들다

10 전치사 뒤에 명사가 이어지므로 misunderstanding이 적절하다.

11 준수가 보기에 재우와 윤호는 그다지 대단하지 않은 일로 싸웠다.

12 주어진 문장은 수요일에 바쁜 Mandy를 위해 목요일에 만남을 제안하며 이에 대한 감사의 표현이 이어지는 ⓔ번이 가장 적절하다.

13 disappointed: 실망한, satisfied: 만족한, amused: 즐거운

14 대화를 통해 Mandy가 무슨 시험을 준비해야 하는지 알 수 없다.

15 ⑤번을 제외한 나머지는 모두 확실성을 나타낸다.

16 His case가 주어이고 next week이 있으므로 조동사 will이

있는 수동태로 'will+be+과거분사'의 형태가 적절하다.

17 조동사가 있는 수동태는 '조동사+be+과거분사'의 형태로 쓴다.

18 ①에는 to부정사가 바로 이어서 나왔으므로 whether가 적절하다. 나머지는 모두 if나 whether를 쓸 수 있다.

19 ⓑ that → if[whether] ⓔ forget → be forgotten

20 run for: ~에 입후보하다

21 '왜 입후보하는 것에 대해 생각해 본 적이 없어?'라는 뜻이다. not+ever = never

22 actually = in fact = as a matter of fact: 사실(은), ① 물론, ③ 게다가, ④ 대신에

23 '서로 다른 많은 집단과 상황들'을 가리킨다.

24 If: '만약 ~한다면'을 의미하는 조건을 나타내는 접속사

25 deal with = treat = handle: 다루다, 처리하다, ② ~을 돌보다, 시중들다, ③ 들고[데리고] 있다, 나르다, ⑤ ~을 매매하다

26 Chris는 '노란색' 유형의 리더에 해당한다.

27 파란색 리더들은 '새로운 방식으로' 문제들에 접근한다.

28 다음에 이어지는 일화를 소개하는 것이 적절하다.

29 ⓑ와 ③: 강조 용법, ①, ⑤: 재귀적 용법, talk to oneself: 혼잣말하다, ②, ④: 관용 용법, by oneself: 홀로, for oneself: 혼자 힘으로

단원별 예상문제
p.106~109

01 (1) properly　(2) approaching　(3) wonder
　 (4) determines　(5) confident

02 (E) → (C) → (A) → (D) → (B)　　　　03 ⑤

04 ①　　　05 ⑤　　　06 ①　　　07 ③

08 He asked her to help him with his homework.

09 She was supposed to meet Nick to work on their presentation.

10 He suggested meeting on Thursday for their presentation.

11 ③　　　12 ④　　　13 ②

14 I don't have any of those things.

15 ③　　　16 ④　　　17 blue　　　18 ①

19 ②　　　20 ④

21 Because there are actually many different leadership styles.

---

01 approach: 접근하다, confident: 자신감 있는, determine: 결정하다, wonder: 궁금해하다, properly: 적절하게 potential: 잠재력, 가능성

02 (E) 각자 맡은 일 확인 → (C) 사진 담당 대답 → (A) 세진이 맡은 일 확인 → (D) 대답 및 Emma의 맡은 일 확인 → (B) 대답 및 준비 확인

03 주어진 문장은 역할을 바꾸자는 수진의 제안에 대한 반응으로 ⓔ번에 들어가기에 적절하다.

04 고민이 해결되었으므로 relieved(안심이 되는)가 적절하다.

05 수진이가 몇 번 발표를 했는지는 알 수 없다.

06 주어진 문장 다음에 세 그룹에 대한 설명이 나와야 하므로 ⓐ가 적절하다.

07 (A) respond: 반응하다, responsible: 책임감 있는, (B) translate: 번역하다, transfer: 옮기다, (C) receive: 받다, send: 보내다

08 Mandy의 남동생은 이번 주 수요일에 숙제를 도와줄 것을 요청하였다.

09 Mandy는 도서관을 다녀온 후 발표 준비를 위해 Nick을 만나기로 되어 있었다.

10 Nick은 발표 준비를 위해 목요일에 만날 것을 제안했다.

11 첫 번째 문장에서는 '~인지 (아닌지)'라는 의미의 접속사로 불확실하거나 의문시되는 사실을 나타낼 때 쓰이는 if나 whether가 적절하다. 두 번째 문장에서는 조동사가 있으므로 '조동사+be+과거분사'의 형태로 쓴다.

12 ① They will check whether[if] stores in school zones sell unhealthy food to children. ② I was anxious about whether I failed the exam or not. ③ Try this product for a week and decide whether or not you want to buy it. ⑤ I wonder if[whether] you are going to attend the meeting.

13 'belong'은 자동사로 쓰이므로 수동태로 쓸 수 없다.

14 not ~ any는 '아무것도 ~ 아니다'라는 의미로 전체 부정을 나타낸다.

15 유미는 '내가 정말 리더가 될 수 있을까? 나는 모르겠다.'라고 했지만, '자신이 리더가 될 수 없다고 생각한다.'는 말은 언급되어 있지 않다.

16 ⓐ와 ④: (요구 따위를) 채우다, 만족[충족]시키다, ①, ⑤ 만나다, ② (길·강 등이) ~와 만나다, 교차하다, 합류하다, ③ (흔히 불쾌한 일을) 만나다[겪다]

17 Jennifer는 '파란색' 유형의 리더에 해당한다.

18 주황색 리더가 어떻게 모두의 역할을 분명하게 해주는지는 알 수 없다. ② They are orange leaders. ③ Yes. ④ It is "Creative Thinkers." ⑤ They approach problems in new ways.

19 주어진 문장의 They에 주목한다. ②번 앞 문장의 'many different groups and many different situations'를 받고 있으므로 ②번이 적절하다.

20 이 글은 '각 집단의 독특한 상황이 최고의 지도력 유형을 결정한다.'는 내용의 글이므로, 주제로는 ④번이 적절하다.

21 실제로 서로 다른 많은 지도력 유형들이 있기 때문이다.

01 Because they had some kind of misunderstanding.

02 He recommends that Junsu meet with his friends and talk about the problem.

03 Because Jaewoo and Yunho are (both) good friends of his.

04 (1) Reservations must be made through the online system (by people).

(2) This item can be used in a variety of ways (by them).

(3) By whom can the most beautiful clothes be made for me?

(4) Medicine cannot cure some diseases.

(5) Only wise people can see them.

05 (1) Before you leave, you should check if you turned off the tap.

(2) My mom asked me if I would have dinner.

(3) I don't know if he is strong.

06 I want to know whether or not I will get taller.
또는 I want to know if I will get taller or not.

07 No way.

08 I don't think a person like me can be called a leader.

09 (A) be elected   (B) leadership qualities

10 advice

11 purple leaders 또는 hands-off manager

01 재우와 윤호 사이에 어떤 오해가 생겼다.

02 Smith 선생님은 준수에게 친구들을 만나 문제에 대해 이야기해 볼 것을 추천한다.

03 재우와 윤호 모두 준수의 좋은 친구들이므로 편을 들 수 없다.

04 조동사가 있는 수동태는 '조동사+be+과거분사'의 형태로 쓴다.

05 '~인지 (아닌지)'라는 의미의 접속사로 쓰이는 if를 이용한다. if 뒤에 오는 절은 의문사가 없는 간접의문문으로 'if+주어+동사'의 어순으로 쓴다. (2)에서 if를 이용하라고 했으므로 간접의문문으로 써야 하는데 you가 I로 바뀌어야 하고, will을 시제에 맞추어 would로 바꾸어야 하는 것에 주의한다.

06 whether는 'or not'이 바로 뒤에 나올 때 쓰일 수 있지만 if는 그럴 수 없다. 'whether[if] ~ or not'의 형태로는 쓸 수 있다.

07 no way: 절대로[결코] 아니다[안 되다]

08 수동태(be p.p.) 앞에 조동사 can을 써서 조동사의 수동태 문장으로 쓰는 것이 적절하다.

09 Brian은 유미가 매우 좋은 '지도력 자질들'을 갖추고 있기 때문에 그녀가 반 대표에 입후보한다면 '당선될' 거라고 확신한다.

10 '조언'을 가리킨다.

11 다른 사람들이 스스로 일하도록 해 주는 리더들은 '보라색 리더' 또는 '방임적 관리자'들이다.

|모범답안|

01 (A) stuck   (B) what to do

(C) they had some kind of misunderstanding

(D) meet together and talk about it

(E) they're both good friends of mine

02 (1) They will be unpacking the boxes.

(2) The boxes will be being unpacked by them.

01 오늘 나는 재우와 윤호를 걱정했다. 그들이 싸워서 나는 중간에 끼어버렸다. 나는 무엇을 해야 할지 몰라서 Smith 선생님과 그것에 대해 이야기를 했다. 나는 그들이 왜 싸웠는지 알고 있었다. 나에게는 대단한 일도 아닌 것 같았지만 그들은 약간의 오해가 있었던 같았다. 나의 이야기를 들으신 후, Smith 선생님은 내게 함께 만나 이야기해 볼 것을 조언하셨다. 나는 선생님의 의견에 동의해서 그렇게 해 보기로 결심했다. 그들은 모두 나의 좋은 친구들이기 때문에 나는 어느 편도 들 수 없다. 나는 모든 것이 곧 해결되길 바란다.

01 positive　　　　　　　　　02 ①

03 (1) His message to the students was very clear.

(2) My goal is just to finish the race.

(3) The teacher told us a story to motivate us.

04 ④

05 She doesn't want to miss her best friend's birthday party.

06 She advises Jisu to talk about it with her dad.

07 ⑤　　　　　08 I'm stuck in the middle.

09 ②　　　　　10 ⑤

11 my brother seemed let down　　　12 ⑤

13 ②, ⑤　　　14 ③　　　　15 ④

16 (1) The job must be done by you by Tuesday.

(2) This book should be read by everyone.

(3) I have no doubt that you will be elected if you run.

(4) I'm not sure if we can use this coupon.

(5) How can you tell whether the machine is working?

(6) The boy wanted to check if the monster was alive or dead.

17 ③, ④　　　18 ⑤　　　　19 ④

20 is needed　　　　　　　　21 ②

22 (A) Team Builders   (B) positive environment
(C) friendly

23 impressive → effective　　24 ①　　　25 ②

26 Sumin gave each of us a different cleaning task after the event.

27 my partner Sumin is an orange leader

01 주어진 단어는 반의어 관계를 나타낸다. negative: 부정적인, positive: 긍정적인

02 '무언가를 이해하기 위해 그것의 모든 부분을 깊이 연구하다'를 뜻하는 말은 analyze(분석하다)이다.

03 motivate: 동기를 부여하다, goal: 목표, clear: 명확한

04 주어진 문장은 어려운 결정이라는 것을 나타내고 있으므로 (D)에 들어가는 것이 적절하다.

05 지수는 그녀의 가장 친한 친구의 생일 파티를 놓치고 싶지 않다.

06 엄마는 지수에게 아빠와 이야기해 볼 것을 조언한다.

07 나머지는 모두 조언을 나타내지만 ⑤번은 의심을 나타낸다.

08 be stuck in: ~에 갇히다

09 친한 친구들이 싸워서 걱정하였다가 Smith 선생님의 조언을 듣고 안도함을 알 수 있다.

10 밑줄 친 (A)는 고민이나 불만족을 묻는 표현으로 ⑤번을 제외한 나머지 표현으로 바꾸어 물어볼 수 있다.

11 let down: 실망한.

12 Mandy는 Nick과 발표 준비를 목요일에 하고 수요일에 동생을 도와줄 것이다.

13 ① I want to know if[whether] there are ghosts in the world. ③ Some friends have asked me whether or not I'd write a novel. ④ Membership fees should be paid to the secretary.

14 바로 뒤에 or not이 나오고 있으므로 if를 whether로 고치는 것이 적절하다.

15 '소유'를 나타내는 'have' 동사는 수동태로 쓰이지 않음에 주의한다.

16 (1)~(3) 조동사가 있는 문장의 수동태는 '조동사+be+과거분사'의 형태로 쓴다. (4)~(6) if나 whether는 불확실하거나 의문시되는 사실을 나타내는 접속사로, 'if[whether]+주어+동사'로 쓰인다.

17 ③ You should check whether or not you locked the door. ④ Beth wants to know if the problem can be solved.

18 ⓐ, ⓑ, ⓒ: I have good leadership qualities. ⓓ, ⓔ: a vision, clear goals, and the ability to motivate others, ⓕ a vision, clear goals, and the ability to motivate others 이외의 다른 지도력 자질들

19 (A)와 ①, ②, ③, ⑤: 관계대명사, ④ 접속사

20 when people need it을 수동태로 고친 것이므로 'is needed'가 적절하다. when it[advice] is needed: 충고가 필요할 때만

21 (A)와 ②: 형용사적 용법, ①, ④: 부사적 용법, ③, ⑤: 명사적

용법

22 녹색 리더는 팀이 반드시 가치 있다고 느끼게 하고, '긍정적인 환경'을 조성하고, 그리고 '친절하고' 말을 걸기 쉬운 '팀 조직자'이다.

23 빨간색 리더는 좋은 추론 기술을 갖고 있고 팀의 목표를 성취하는 가장 '효과적인' 방법들을 생각하는 논리적 분석가이다. impressive: 인상적인, 인상[감명] 깊은

24 ⓐ belong to: ~에 속하다, ⓑ call for: ~을 필요로 하다

25 유미는 실제로 서로 다른 많은 지도력 유형들이 있어서 놀랐지만, 곧 그 이유를 '깨달았다.'

26 '수민이가 우리 각자에게 행사가 끝난 뒤에 각각 다른 청소 임무를 준 것'이 ⓐ의 예에 해당한다.

27 '내 짝 수민이가 주황색 리더인 것'을 가리킨다.

Environmental Innovations

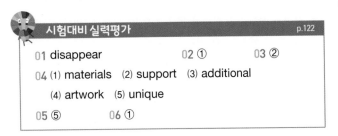

시험대비 실력평가
p.122

01 disappear   02 ①   03 ②
04 (1) materials   (2) support   (3) additional
    (4) artwork   (5) unique
05 ⑤   06 ①

01 주어진 단어는 반의어 관계를 나타낸다. appear: 나타나다, disappear: 사라지다

02 '건물을 디자인하는 사람'을 가리키는 말은 architect(건축가) 이다.

03 suggestion: 제안

04 support: 지지하다, material: 재료, additional: 추가적인, unique: 독특한, artwork: 예술 작품

05 보기에 주어진 bright은 '똑똑한, 영리한'을 의미하며 이와 같은 의미로 쓰인 것은 ⑤번이다. 나머지는 모두 '밝은, 빛나는, 근사한'을 뜻한다.

06 in harmony: 조화하여, in addition to: ~ 이외에도, in my view: 내 생각에는

서술형 시험대비
p.123

01 incredible
02 (1) explanation   (2) damage   (3) prevent
    (4) surface   (5) statue
03 (1) hold a cooking contest
    (2) (r)aise (a)wareness   (3) make a suggestion
    (4) (b)ored with
04 (1) *Hanok* is a Korean traditional structure made of wood.
    (2) We are going to learn how the direction of water flow has changed.
    (3) Creativity and innovation are keys to success.
    (4) Don't throw away the trash on the street.

01 주어진 단어는 반의어 관계를 나타낸다. credible: 믿을 만한, incredible: 믿기 힘든

02 surface: 표면, statue: 조각상, explanation: 설명, damage: 손상시키다, prevent: 막다, 예방하다

03 hold a contest: 대회를 개최하다. raise awareness: 인식을

높이다; make a suggestion: 제안을 하다, get bored with: ~에 지루해지다

05 structure: 구조(물), flow: 흐름, innovation: 혁신, throw away: 버리다

[교과서] Conversation

핵심 Check
p.124~125

1 In my opinion, we should bring reusable bags when we go shopping.

2 ③

교과서 대화문 익히기

Check(√) True or False
p.126

1 T   2 F   3 T   4 F

교과서 확인학습
p.128~129

Listen & Talk 1 A

plastic bags / environment, plastic bags / In my opinion, reusable bags

Listen & Talk 1 B

up, going up / take the stairs / all the way / save, protect the environment / one elevator ride / adds up, In my opinion, taking care of / have a point

Listen & Speak 1 C

make a suggestion, throw, away, recycling, resources, protect, in my opinion, trash cans, place, colored recycling bins, remind, separate

Listen & Talk 2 A

holding / What kinds of / theme, raise students' awareness / wait to see it

Listen & Talk 2 B

article / plastic bag, made, of / amazing / breaks down, soil, disappears / reduce plastic waste / company, wait to use

Listen & Talk 2 C

sheep park / interesting / protect the environment / How can / chemicals, unwanted plants / chemicals / bright, wait to

Do It Yourself

In my opinion, any more / bored with / using / how to do it / interesting, to make

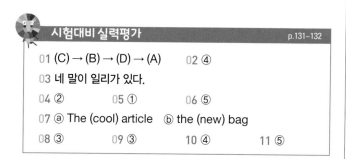

시험대비 기본평가   p.130

01 ⑤   02 ⑤   03 ③

04 reusable

01 밑줄 친 (A)는 희망이나 기대를 표현하지만, ⑤번은 지루함을 나타낸다.

03 ③번을 제외하고는 모두 동의의 표현이다.

04 '한 번 이상 사용될 수 있는'을 가리키는 말은 reusable(재사용할 수 있는)이다.

시험대비 실력평가   p.131~132

01 (C) → (B) → (D) → (A)   02 ④

03 네 말이 일리가 있다.

04 ②   05 ①   06 ⑤

07 ⓐ The (cool) article   ⓑ the (new) bag

08 ③   09 ③   10 ④   11 ⑤

01 (C) 사진 대회 개최 계획 설명 → (B) 대회에 대한 구체적 질문 → (D) 주제 설명 및 대회 개최 이유 설명 → (A) 기대감 표현

02 (A)는 목적을 나타내는 부사적 용법의 to protect, (B)는 주어가 the energy로 3인칭 단수이므로 adds, (C)는 주어로 동명사 taking이 적절하다.

04 수진은 지호에게 엘리베이터를 타고 갈 것을 제안했다.

05 앞 문장과 상반되는 내용이 이어지므로 '그러나, 하지만'을 뜻하는 however가 적절하다.

06 위 대화에서 학생들이 종이는 어느 색의 분리수거함에 버려야 하는지 알 수 없다.

08 (A) amazing: 놀라운, amazed: 깜짝 놀란, (B) 주어가 The bag으로 3인칭 단수이므로 disappears, (C)는 help의 목적어로 원형부정사 reduce가 알맞다.

09 따뜻한 물속에서는 3분 만에 사라진다.

10 (A) pollute: 오염시키다, pollution: 오염, (B) raise: 올리다, 끌어올리다, rise: 일어나다, (C) I can't wait to+동사원형: ~이 기대된다

서술형 시험대비   p.133

01 (A) seeing the photo contest   (B) Minsu's club

    (C) raise students' awareness of environmental problems

---

02 It is mostly made of corn.

03 It breaks down in soil in only three months.

04 It helps protect the environment by reducing the amount of plastic waste.

05 C. cold → warm

06 (B) → (C) → (A) → (E) → (D)

01 소라는 사진 대회를 보기를 기대하고 있다. 이것은 민수의 동아리에 의해 다음 주에 개최될 것이다. 주제는 세계의 환경오염이다. 그것은 환경 문제에 대한 학생들의 인식을 향상시키기 위해 계획되었다.

02 새로운 봉지는 주로 옥수수로 만들어진다.

03 새로운 봉지는 흙 속에서 3달 만에 분해된다.

04 새로운 봉지는 플라스틱 쓰레기를 줄이는 데 도움이 된다.

06 (B) 계단 이용 제안에 대한 거절 → (C) 설득 및 에너지 절약의 필요성을 설명 → (A) 상대방의 의견에 반박 → (E) 인정 및 자신의 의견 설명 → (D) 상대방의 주장에 동의

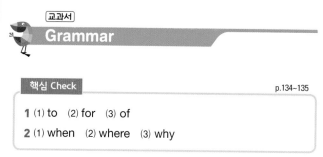

교과서
Grammar

핵심 Check   p.134~135

1 (1) to   (2) for   (3) of

2 (1) when   (2) where   (3) why

시험대비 기본평가   p.136

01 ④   02 ③   03 ③

04 (1) to write   (2) her   (3) for   (4) why   (5) where

   (6) when

01 It을 가주어로 하고 to부정사를 진주어로 하며 의미상의 주어로 'for him'을 쓴 ④번이 적절하다.

02 관계부사 how는 선행사 the way와 함께 쓰지 않고 반드시 둘 중의 하나만 써야 한다.

03 to부정사의 의미상의 주어가 일반적인 사람일 경우는 보통 생략한다.

04 (1) 진주어로 to부정사가 적절하다. (2), (3) to부정사의 의미상의 주어는 to부정사 바로 앞에 'for+목적격'으로 나타낸다. (4) 선행사가 the reason이므로 관계부사 why가 적절하다. (5) 선행사가 a village이므로 관계부사 where가 적절하다. (6) 선행사가 the day이므로 관계부사 when이 적절하다.

01 ④　　　　02 ②　　　　03 ③

04 (1) to wake　(2) for　(3) of　(4) why　(5) when

   (6) which　(7) how

05 where　　　06 ①　　　07 ②　　　08 ⑤

09 It was hard for them to make Gimchi.

10 ④　　　　11 ③　　　　12 ⑤

13 (1) the time 또는 when　(2) the reason 또는 why

14 (1) For him to live without her even for a single day

    was really hard.

  (2) I suppose it was rude of me to listen to a

    private conversation.

  (3) It is very important for him to make a decision

    soon.

  (4) We should find a place where we can be safe!

  (5) Do you know the reason why John left so

    early?

  (6) I have to say I like the way he solved the

    situation.

15 ①, ④　　　16 (1) ⓑ, ⓒ, ⓔ　(2) ⓐ, ⓓ, ⓕ　17 ⑤

01 ① It was very kind of you to meet me. ② It is easy to catch a disease in winter. ③ It's good for children to do things on their own sometimes. ⑤ It was great for Kevin to rest for a week.

02 선행사가 'the reason'이므로 관계부사 why가 적절하다.

03 선행사로 'the year'가 있으므로 '시간'을 나타내는 when이 적절하다. 가주어로 It이 나와 있고 진주어로 to부정사가 나와 있으므로 빈칸에는 to부정사의 의미상의 주어가 나와야 한다. 사람의 성향이나 성격을 나타내는 형용사가 아니므로 for가 적절하다.

04 (1) 진주어로 to부정사가 적절하다. (2) to부정사의 의미상의 주어는 to부정사 바로 앞에 'for+대명사의 목적격'으로 나타낸다. (3) 문장에 쓰인 형용사가 사람의 성향이나 성격을 나타내는 말일 때는 'for+목적격'이 아니라 'of+목적격'으로 쓴다. (4) 선행사로 the reason이 나왔으므로 관계부사 why가 적절하다. (5) 선행사로 the day가 나왔으므로 관계부사 when이 적절하다. (6) 선행사로 the house가 나왔지만 관계사절에서 in의 목적어가 없으므로 관계대명사 which가 적절하다. (7) 선행사 the way와 how를 함께 쓰지 않으므로 how가 적질하다.

05 'a small town'을 선행사로 하는 관계부사 where가 적절하다.

06 It is very important for me to make the fans happy.
*cane: 지팡이

07 주어진 문장과 ②번은 시간을 선행사로 하는 관계부사이다. ① 의문부사, ③ 의문대명사, ④ 명사, ⑤ 접속사

08 선행사가 'the house'이므로 관계부사 where를 쓰거나 'in which'로 쓰는 것이 적절하며 in은 관계절의 마지막에 써도 좋

다. 'This is the house. + I used to live in the house.'를 관계부사를 이용하여 한 문장으로 만든 것이다.

09 'It ~ for ... to부정사' 구문을 이용하여 쓴다.

10 선행사가 the beach이므로 장소를 나타내는 관계부사 where를 이용한다.

11 가주어로 It을 쓰고 to부정사의 의미상의 주어로 사람의 성향이나 성격을 나타내는 형용사가 아니므로 for를 쓴다.

12 to부정사의 의미상의 주어는 to부정사 바로 앞에 'for+목적격'으로 나타내지만 사람의 성품·성격을 나타내는 형용사가 보어로 쓰이면 의미상의 주어로 'of+목적격'을 쓴다.

13 선행사가 'the time', 'the place', 'the reason'처럼 일반적인 뜻을 나타낼 때 선행사나 관계부사 중 하나를 생략할 수 있다.

14 (1) 의미상의 주어로 For him을 쓴다. (2) 보어로 쓰인 형용사가 사람의 성향, 성격을 나타내는 말이므로 'for+목적격'이 아니라 'of+목적격'으로 쓴다. (3) 의미상의 주어가 'for+목적격'이 나왔으므로 진주어로 to부정사를 쓴다. (4) a place가 선행사로 나왔고 관계사에 이끌리는 절이 완전하므로 관계부사 where로 고치거나 전치사 in을 which 앞이나 관계사절의 끝에 써 주어야 한다. (5) 'The reason'이 선행사이므로 which를 why로 고치는 것이 적절하다. (6) 'the way how'는 쓸 수 없으므로 the way 또는 how를 생략하거나 how를 that이나 'in which'로 고쳐야 한다.

15 ① of her로 의미상의 주어가 나와 있으므로 to부정사가 적절하다. ④ 관계사에 이끌리는 절이 완전하므로 which를 where로 고쳐야 한다.

16 ⓑ, ⓒ, ⓔ: '가주어 It, 진주어 to부정사' 구문 ⓐ, ⓓ, ⓕ: 'It ~ that 강조' 구문 ⓕ는 what을 강조한 'It was what that he wanted you to do.'를 의문문으로 한 것이다.

17 'the reason'이 선행사이므로 관계부사 why가 적절하다.

01 (1) us to　(2) of them to

02 (1) I like the café where we had tea yesterday.

  (2) May I ask you the reason why you decided to

    leave Seoul?

  (3) The bags were too heavy for us to carry.

  (4) It took a few weeks for the workers to repair

    the street.

  (5) It was brave of her to go abroad alone.

03 (1) the way she could solve

  (2) where I want to go

04 (1) for me to wake　(2) of you to remember

05 (1) They made an underwater museum away from

    the places where sea life was dying.

  (2) I can't forget the day when I won the class

    election.

(3) They talked about how he scored the goal in the final match.

(4) That is the reason why I like documentaries.

06 (1) of us → for us　　(2) for you → of you

(3) for him → of him　　(4) to not → not to

07 (1) where → when

(2) which → why 또는 for which

(3) the way how → the way 또는 how, 또는 the way that 또는 the way in which

(4) in 생략 또는 when → which

08 (1) I explained the reason why I left the party early. / I explained the reason for which I left the party early.

(2) He regrets the way he lived his life. / He regrets how he lived his life. / He regrets the way that he lived his life.

01 'It(가주어) ~ for[of] ...(의미상의 주어) 진주어(to부정사)' 구문을 이용한다.

02 (1) 선행사 'the café'에 맞는 관계부사 where를 이용하여 배열한다. (2) 선행사 'the reason'에 맞는 관계부사 why를 이용하여 배열한다. (3)~(5) 'It(가주어) ~ for(of) …(의미상의 주어) 진주어(to부정사)' 구문을 이용한다.

03 (1) 'the way'가 선행사로 나왔으므로 how를 쓰면 안 되는 것에 주의한다. (2) 'the place'를 선행사로 하는 관계부사 where를 이용한다.

04 'It(가주어) ~ for[of] ...(의미상의 주어) 진주어(to부정사)' 구문을 이용한다.

05 (1) 선행사 'the places'에 맞는 관계부사 where를 이용하여 연결한다. (2) 선행사 'the day'에 맞는 관계부사 when을 이용하여 연결한다. (3) 선행사가 'the way'이므로 how를 이용하여 연결한다. (4) 선행사 'the reason'에 맞는 관계부사 why를 이용하여 연결한다.

06 (1) to부정사의 의미상의 주어는 to부정사 바로 앞에 'for+목적격'으로 나타낸다. (2) 문장에 쓰인 형용사가 사람의 성향, 성격을 나타내는 말일 때는 의미상의 주어로 'of+목적격'으로 쓴다. (3) 의미상의 주어로 'of+목적격'이 적절하다. (4) to부정사의 부정은 to부정사 앞에 not이나 never를 써서 'not[never]+to부정사'로 나타낸다.

07 (1) 'the day'가 선행사이므로 where를 when으로 고치는 것이 적절하다. (2) 'The reason'이 선행사이므로 which를 why나 'for which'로 고치는 것이 적절하다. (3) 'the way how'는 쓸 수 없으므로 the way나 how를 생략하거나 how를 that이나 'in which'로 고쳐야 한다. (4) 관계사절의 마지막에 있는 in을 생략하거나 when을 which로 고쳐 쓴다.

08 (1) 선행사가 '이유'를 나타낼 때 관계부사는 why를 쓰며 여기서 why는 'for which'로 바꿔 쓸 수 있다. for를 관계사절 끝에 쓸 수도 있다. (2) 선행사가 '방법'을 나타낼 때 관계부사는 how를 쓰며 이때 how와 함께 the way를 쓰지 않는다는 것을 주의한다. the way나 how 또는 the way that이나 the way in which를 쓴다.

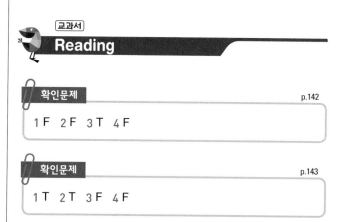

교과서 Reading

확인문제　　　　　　　　　　　　p.142

1 F　2 F　3 T　4 F

확인문제　　　　　　　　　　　　p.143

1 T　2 T　3 F　4 F

교과서 확인학습 A　　　　　　　p.144~145

01 for us to find ways　　02 creative, to save

03 underwater museum

04 meet, professor, listen to

05 where, tourists travel

06 the most popular, to do, is, at

07 However, are, damaging parts, near

08 To prevent this, something interesting

09 if, attracted, to, dying areas, to get better

10 made, underwater, away from, where, dying

11 about, meters below, contains, statues

12 gare made from, that support

13 provide, for, to live on

14 will grow on, which will make, unique

15 want people to see, on

16 how rich sea life is, how important it is

17 husing, to protect, on land

18 what, says about　　19 throughout the year

20 need, which uses, contributes to

21 That's why, have begun to, that use less, are still

22 For example, are designed to have

23 it, for outside air to move

24 natural, how these buildings stay cool

25 In addition to making

26 provides, protects, from direct sunlight, keeps

27 not only help, but also provide, with

28 goals, new style, architecture

29 will keep coming up with

30 Every field has, protecting

31 With, will be able to live together, far into

1 It is important for us to find ways to protect the environment.

2 Some people have found creative ways to save the earth.

3 One example is an underwater museum in Cancun, Mexico.

4 Let's meet Dr. Rosa Allison, an art professor, and listen to her explanation about the special museum.

5 Rosa: Cancun is a city where 4.8 million tourists travel every year.

6 One of the most popular activities to do there is looking at the area's beautiful sea life underwater.

7 However, tourist activities are seriously damaging parts of the sea near Cancun.

8 To prevent this, artists did something interesting.

9 They thought if they attracted tourists to a different part of the sea, the dying areas could have time to get better.

10 They made an underwater museum away from the places where sea life was dying.

11 It's about 14 meters below the surface and contains 500 statues.

12 The statues are made from materials that support sea life.

13 They provide additional places for plants and animals to live on.

14 Over time, many types of sea life will grow on the statues, which will make the artwork unique.

15 The artists want people to see a variety of sea life on the statues.

16 If people realize how rich sea life is, they will understand how important it is to save the sea.

17 In Singapore, people are using architecture to protect the environment on land.

18 Let's hear what Rajesh Khan, an architect, says about eco-friendly buildings.

19 Rajesh: Singapore is hot throughout the year.

20 Most buildings need air conditioning, which uses a lot of energy and contributes to climate change.

21 That's why architects in Singapore have begun to design eco-friendly buildings that use less air conditioning but are still cool inside.

22 For example, many buildings in Singapore are designed to have an open structure.

23 This structure makes it possible for outside air to move throughout a building.

24 This natural air flow is how these buildings stay cool.

25 In addition to making open structures, architects add large gardens.

26 This greenery provides shade and protects parts of the building from direct sunlight, which keeps the building cooler.

27 Eco-friendly buildings like these not only help protect the environment, but also provide people with a good quality of life.

28 Those are the goals of this new style of architecture.

29 Hopefully, architects will keep coming up with new eco-friendly ideas.

30 Every field has different ways of protecting the environment.

31 With more innovation, humans and nature will be able to live together in harmony far into the future.

01 ③   02 museum   03 ⑤

04 4.8 million tourists visit Cancun every year.

05 ③   06 ④

07 The artists want people to see a variety of sea life on the statues.

08 ④   09 ②

10 Most buildings in Singapore need air conditioning.

11 ②   12 ③

13 Every field has different ways of protecting the environment.

14 ④   15 ⑤

16 Many types of sea life will grow on the statues over time.

17 ②

18 They are made from materials that support sea life.

19 ⑤   20 ②   21 ⑤   22 ③

23 ⑤

01 멕시코 칸쿤에 있는 수중 박물관을 가리키는 말이다. 따라서 ③번이 적절하다.

02 많은 예술 작품 혹은 역사적 물건들과 같은 귀중하고 흥미로운 물건들이 보관되고 연구되고 대중에게 전시되는 건물은 '박물관 (museum)'이다.

03 칸쿤에서 할 수 있는 가장 인기 있는 활동 중 하나는 바닷속의

아름다운 해양 생물을 관찰하는 것이지만 이러한 관광 활동들이 칸쿤 근처의 바다 일부를 심각하게 훼손시킨다는 연결이 자연스럽다.

04 칸쿤은 매년 480만 명의 관광객이 여행하는 도시라고 하였다.

05 해양 생물이 죽어가는 지역으로부터 떨어진 곳에 만들었다고 하였다.

06 예술작품이 독특한 것이므로 make를 5형식 동사로 썼음을 알 수 있다. 따라서 목적격 보어로 형용사를 써야 한다.

07 예술가들은 사람들이 그 조각상들에서 살고 있는 다양한 해양 생명체들을 보길 원한다.

08 주어진 문장의 This structure는 an open structure를 의미한다. 따라서 ④번에 들어가는 것이 가장 자연스럽다.

09 싱가포르는 연중 더운 곳이라고 하였다.

10 싱가포르에 있는 대부분의 건물들은 에어컨 가동이 필요하다고 하였다.

11 이어지는 문장에서 '이러한 녹지 공간(this greenery)'이 그늘을 제공한다고 하였으므로 ②번이 가장 적절하다.

12 글의 내용으로 보아 친환경 건물에 관한 글이 선행했음을 알 수 있다.

13 of의 목적어로 동명사 protecting을 쓰는 것에 유의한다.

14 빈칸 (A)에는 진주어를 이끄는 to find가 들어가는 것이 적절하다. ④번에는 enjoy의 목적어인 동명사 finding이 적절하다.

15 몇몇 사람들이 지구를 구하기 위한 창의적인 방법을 찾았다고 말하며, 그 예로 멕시코 칸쿤에 있는 수중 박물관을 들고 있다. 따라서 ⑤번이 가장 적절하다.

16 시간이 흐르면서 많은 형태의 바다 생명체들이 그 조각상에서 자라게 될 것이라고 하였다.

17 칸쿤 근처의 바다 일부는 관광 활동들로 인해 훼손되었다고 하였다. 따라서 ②번이 가장 적절하다.

18 해저 박물관에 있는 조각상들은 해양 생물에게 도움이 되는 재료들로 만들어졌다고 하였다.

19 칸쿤 근처의 바다 일부가 심각하게 훼손되어 예술가들은 그곳에서 멀리 떨어진 곳에 해저 박물관을 만들어 사람들을 유인하려 하였다.

20 건축가들은 개방형 구조를 만드는 것 외에도 큰 정원을 더한다는 의미가 자연스럽다. 따라서 '~에 더하여, ~일 뿐만 아니라'라는 의미로 쓰이는 ②번이 가장 적절하다. regardless of: ~에 상관없이

21 글의 내용에 따르면 먼 미래에 인간과 자연이 함께 조화를 이루며 살아갈 수 있을 것이라고 말하는 것이 자연스럽다. 따라서 isolation을 harmony라고 쓰는 것이 적절하다.

22 사람들에게 양질의 삶을 제공하면서 동시에 환경을 보호하는 것을 돕는 친환경적인 건축 양식을 의미한다.

23 친환경적인 건물들이 사람들에게 양질의 삶을 제공한다고 하였다.

01 It is important for us to find ways to protect the environment.

02 It is located in Mexico.

03 It is looking at the area's beautiful sea life underwater.

04 관광 활동들이 칸쿤 근처의 바다 일부를 심각하게 훼손시키는 것

05 It was to give the dying areas time to get better.

06 materials that support sea life, additional places, plants and animals can live

07 It contains 500 statues.

08 Many types of sea life will make the statues unique.

09 eco-friendly

10 It uses a lot of energy and contributes to climate change.

11 outside air, move throughout a building

12 개방형 구조의 건물, 큰 정원이 있는 건물

13 Hopefully, architects will keep coming up with new eco-friendly ideas.

14 They provide shade and protect parts of the building from direct sunlight.

01 '환경을 보호할 수 있는 방법을 찾는 것'의 주체는 '우리'이므로 의미상의 주어로 'for+목적격'을 쓰는 것에 유의한다.

02 칸쿤은 멕시코에 위치해 있다.

03 칸쿤에서 할 수 있는 가장 인기 있는 활동 중 하나는 그 지역의 바닷속의 아름다운 해양 생물을 관찰하는 것이다.

04 앞 문장을 가리키는 말이다.

05 해저 박물관을 만든 목적은 해양 생물이 죽어가는 지역에 호전될 시간을 주는 것이었다.

06 해석: 해양 생물에게 도움이 되는 재료들로 만들어진 것에 더하여, 조각상은 식물과 동물이 살 수 있는 추가적인 장소를 제공할 수 있다.

07 해저 박물관에는 500개의 조각상이 있다고 하였다.

08 많은 형태의 바다 생명체들이 그 조각상에서 자라게 될 것이며, 이것이 그 예술 작품을 독특하게 만들 것이라고 하였다.

09 육지의 환경을 보호하기 위한 건축물을 설명하면서 친환경적인 건물들을 소개하고 있으므로 eco-friendly라고 쓰는 것이 가장 적절하다.

10 많은 에너지를 사용하고 기후 변화의 원인이 되는 것이 에어컨 사용의 문제이다.

11 건물의 개방형 구조는 외부 공기가 건물을 관통하는 것을 가능케 한다. enable+목적어+to V: 목적어가 V하는 것을 가능하게 하다

12 앞서 소개한 개방형 구조 건물과 큰 정원이 있는 건물을 가리키

는 말이다.

13 '계속해서 ~하다'는 keep+Ving이며, come up with는 '~을 생각해 내다'라는 의미이다. 따라서 keep coming up with라고 쓰는 것에 유의한다.

14 건물의 큰 정원은 그늘을 제공하고 직사광선으로부터 건물의 부분들을 지켜준다고 하였다.

01 environmental   **02** ①   **03** ②

04 (1) architect   (2) architecture   (3) additional
     (4) plastic bag

05 ④   **06** ③

07 (1) You have a point.
     (2) What do you think have contributed to your
        good health?
     (3) We should live in harmony with other people.

08 ④   **09** ⑤   **10** ⓓ → needed

11 (A) a sheep park   (B) unwanted plants
     (C) chemicals

12 I can't wait to see it!

13 It's pollution around the world.

14 It's because they want to raise students'
     awareness of environmental problems.

15 It's because elevators use lots of energy and he
     believes that they need to save energy to protect
     the environment.

16 They are going to the science room.

17 ④   **18** the way she has to follow

19 ②   **20** ④

21 (1) I want to go to a place where I can breathe
       fresh air.
     (2) Lunch break at school is the time when Junho
       can play soccer with his friends.
     (3) I know the reason why the manhole covers are
       round.
     (4) My mom doesn't like how my sister drives.

22 how rich sea life is

23 ③   **24** ③   **25** ⑤

26 ②번 → That's why   **27** with   **28** ③

29 Eat Your Cup and Save the Earth!

30 컵을 사용한 후 먹는 것

01 주어진 단어는 명사와 형용사 관계를 나타낸다. environmental: 환경적인

02 '어느 지역의 전체적인 날씨'를 가리키는 말은 climate(기후)이다.

03 incredible: 믿기 힘든, 믿을 수 없는

04 architect: 건축가, architecture: 건축, additional: 추가적인, plastic bag: 비닐봉지

05 보기와 나머지 company는 '회사'를 뜻하지만, ④번은 '친구, 동료'를 뜻한다.

06 ride: 타다; 탑승

07 contribute to: ~에 기여하다, (~의) 원인이 되다, in harmony with: ~와 조화하여

08 주어진 문장은 오래된 가방들이 지겹다는 말에 해 줄 조언으로 적절하므로 (D)가 적절하다.

10 화학 물질이 필요하지 않다는 의미로 수동태가 알맞다.

11 나는 미희네 집 근처에 있는 양 공원에 갔다. 동물들을 보는 것이 즐거웠다. 더욱이, 그들은 잡초를 먹는다. 이것은 잡초를 없애기 위해 화학 물질을 사용하는 것을 줄이는데 도움이 될 수 있다.

12 I can't wait to+동사원형

13 사진 대회의 주제는 세계의 환경 오염이다.

14 학생들의 환경 문제에 대한 인식을 높이기 위해 대회를 개최한다.

15 지호는 수진에게 엘리베이터가 많은 에너지를 사용하고 그들이 에너지를 절약하고 환경을 보호해야 한다고 생각하기 때문에 계단으로 갈 것을 제안했다.

16 수진과 지호는 과학실에 가고 있다.

17 to부정사의 의미상의 주어는 to부정사 바로 앞에 'for+목적격'으로 나타내지만 보어로 쓰인 형용사가 사람의 성향, 성격을 나타내는 말일 때는 'for+목적격'이 아니라 'of+목적격'으로 쓴다.

18 'the way'가 선행사로 나왔으므로 how를 쓰면 안 되는 것에 주의한다.

19 ②에는 사람의 성격이나 성질을 나타내는 형용사(foolish)가 왔으므로 의미상의 주어로 'of+목적격'이 적절하다. 나머지는 모두 'for+목적격'이 적절하다.

20 의미상의 주어 앞에 전치사 for가 있으므로 빈칸에는 사람의 성격을 나타내는 형용사인 brave는 알맞지 않다.

21 (1) 선행사 'a place'에 맞는 관계부사 where를 이용하여 연결한다. (2) 선행사 'the time'에 맞는 관계부사 when을 이용하여 연결한다. (3) 선행사 'the reason'에 맞는 관계부사 why를 이용하여 연결한다. (4) 선행사가 'the way'이므로 how를 이용하여 연결한다.

22 간접의문문의 어순은 '의문사+주어+동사'이며, how는 rich를 수식하고 있으므로 'how rich sea life is'라고 쓰는 것이 적절하다.

23 관광객들을 바다의 다른 쪽으로 유인하기 위해 만든 것이 주어진 문장에 제시된 해저 박물관이며 이것은 해수면에서 14미터 아래에 있다는 연결이 자연스러우므로 ③번이 가장 적절하다.

24 (A)는 to부정사의 형용사적 용법이다. ①, ② 부사적 용법 중 목적 ③ 형용사적 용법 ④ 명사적 용법 중 진주어 ⑤ 명사적 용법 중 보어

25 예술가들은 사람들이 조각상들에서 살고 있는 다양한 해양 생명체들을 보고 해양 생물이 얼마나 풍부한지 인지한다면 바다를 지키는 것이 얼마나 중요한지 이해할 것이라고 하였다. 따라서 ⑤번이 글의 내용과 일치한다.

26 앞 문장에 대한 결과를 이끌고 있으므로 That's why라고 쓰는 것이 적절하다.

27 provide A with B: A에게 B를 제공하다, come up with: ~을 생각해 내다

28 개방형 구조는 외부 공기가 건물을 관통하는 것을 가능하게 한다.

29 글의 내용은 먹을 수 있는 컵을 사용하여 지구를 구하라는 것이다.

30 앞 문장의 내용을 가리키는 말이다.

단원별 예상문제
p.160~163

01 (B) → (C) → (A)　　02 ⑤　　03 ⑤
04 ⑤　　05 ④　　06 ④
07 separate
08 I'm looking forward to visiting the park!
09 ④　　10 when　　11 ④　　12 ③
13 ⓒ, ⓔ, ⑨
14 (1) He grew up in a city where violence was rare.
　(2) It took three hours for me to write the report.
15 An underwater museum is used to protect the environment.
16 ②　　17 ④　　18 ⑤　　19 ②
20 ⑤　　21 They add large gardens.

01 (B) 의견 언급 → (C) 동의 및 비닐봉지 사용을 줄이기 위한 방법 질문 → (A) 의견 말하기

02 의견을 묻는 질문에 기대감을 표현하는 것은 어색하다.

03 주어진 문장은 수진의 '엘리베이터를 한 번 탄다고 그렇게 많은 에너지를 사용하지 않는다'는 주장에 반박하는 말로 적절하므로 (E)에 들어가야 한다.

04 대화를 통해 한 번 엘리베이터를 타는 것이 얼마나 많은 에너지를 사용하는지는 알 수 없다..

05 (A) instead는 부사, instead of+명사구, (B) 주어 역할을 하는 동명사 recycling, (C) 부사가 적절하므로 properly가 알맞다.

06 소년은 재활용을 권장하기 위해 학교에 있는 쓰레기통의 개수를 줄이는 것이 필요하다고 생각한다.

07 '무언가를 다른 부분이나 다른 그룹으로 나누다'라는 뜻을 나타내는 말은 separate(분리하다)이다.

08 can't wait to+동사원형 = look forward to+ing

10 'the day'를 선행사로 하는 관계부사 when이 적절하다.

11 ① It is easy for children to learn foreign languages. ② This structure makes it possible for outside air to move throughout a building. ③ It was boring for her to ride a bike. ⑤ They don't have enough food to eat.

12 첫 번째 문장에서는 'the reason'이 선행사이므로 why가 적절하다. 두 번째 문장에서는 to부정사의 의미상의 주어를 to부정사 바로 앞에 'for+목적격'으로 나타낸다.

13 ⓐ which → where ⓑ where → when ⓓ of → for ⓕ getting → to get

14 (1) 선행사 'a city'를 수식하는 관계부사 where를 이용한다.
(2) 'It(가주어) ~ for ...(의미상의 주어) 진주어(to부정사)' 구문을 이용한다.

15 지구를 구하기 위한 창의적인 방법으로 칸쿤에서는 해저 박물관을 사용하였다.

16 Rosa Allison 교수가 칸쿤에 있는 수중 박물관에 대해 설명할 것이라고 하였으므로 ②번이 가장 적절하다.

17 ⓐ, ⓑ, ⓒ는 예술가들을, ⓓ는 조각상들을 가리키는 말이다.

18 현재 많은 관광객들로 인해 훼손된 칸쿤 근처의 바다가 회복할 시간을 갖도록 하기 위해 해저 박물관을 지었다.

19 앞 문장에 대한 예시를 제공하고 있으므로 ②번이 가장 적절하다.

20 ⑤ 녹지 공간이 그늘을 제공하고 직사광선으로부터 건물의 부분들을 지켜주어 건물을 더 시원하게 유지한다고 말하는 것이 자연스럽다. warmer → cooler

21 건축가들은 개방형 구조를 만드는 것 외에도 큰 정원을 더한다고 하였다.

서술형 실전문제
p.164~165

01 Many students just throw things away instead of recycling them.

02 He suggests reducing the number of trash cans at school.

03 He wants to place four different colored recycling bins on every floor.

04 (1) He was born in the year when the war ended.
(2) I know the reason why Jane didn't come here yet.
(3) This is the city where I lived 10 years ago.
(4) This is how he caught the big fish.

05 (1) for them to live　(2) for me to visit
(3) of her to kee

06 (1) for a baby to cry　(2) considerate of Jane to let
(3) of him to show

07 We can save paper or plastic.

08 It looks like a cup.

09 It's because Singapore is hot throughout the year.

10 It is providing people with a good quality of life as well as helping protect the environment.

11 (1) air conditioning (2) a lot of energy
   (3) climate change (4) an open structure
   (5) cool (6) gardens (7) from direct sunlight

01 소년에 따르면 많은 학생들이 쓰레기를 재활용하는 대신에 그냥 버리는 것이 문제이다.

02 소년은 학교에 쓰레기통의 수를 줄일 것을 제안한다.

03 소년은 모든 층에 각기 색이 다른 4개의 재활용 통을 두기를 원한다.

04 (1) 선행사 'the year'에 맞는 관계부사 when을 이용하여 연결한다. (2) 선행사 'the reason'에 맞는 관계부사 why를 이용하여 연결한다. (3) 선행사 'the city'에 맞는 관계부사 where를 이용하여 연결한다. (4) 선행사가 'the way'이므로 how를 이용하여 연결한다.

05 to부정사의 의미상의 주어는 to부정사 바로 앞에 'for+목적격'으로 나타낸다. 이때 보어로 쓰인 형용사가 사람의 성향, 성격을 나타내는 말일 때는 'of+목적격'으로 쓴다.

06 'It(가주어) ~ for[of] ...(의미상의 주어) 진주어(to부정사)' 구문을 이용한다. to부정사의 의미상의 주어를 'for+목적격'으로 나타내지만, 보어로 쓰인 형용사가 사람의 성향, 성격을 나타내는 말일 때는 'of+목적격'을 쓴다.

07 쿠키 컵을 사용함으로써 우리는 종이나 플라스틱을 절약할 수 있다.

08 쿠키 컵은 컵처럼 생겼다고 하였다.

09 싱가포르에 있는 대부분의 건물들이 에어컨 가동이 필요한 이유는 싱가포르가 연중 더운 곳이기 때문이다.

10 친환경적인 건물들의 목표는 환경을 보호하는 것을 도울 뿐만 아니라 사람들에게 양질의 삶을 제공하는 것이라고 했다.

11 싱가포르에서 대부분의 건물들은 에어컨을 필요로 하며, 이로 인해 많은 에너지가 사용되고 기후 변화의 원인이 되고 있다. 개방형 구조 덕분에 외부 공기가 건물을 관통하여 건물을 시원하게 유지할 수 있다. 또한 큰 정원을 더하여 직사광선으로부터 건물의 부분들을 지켜주어 건물을 더 시원하게 유지한다.

창의사고력 서술형 문제
p.166

|모범답안|

01 (A) the 3rd floor (B) taking the stairs
   (C) take all the way up there
   (D) that much energy
   (E) take care of the environment

02 (1) It is dangerous for her to ride a bike.
   (2) It's necessary for him to learn German.

(3) It is rude of him to talk loudly like that.
(4) It is difficult for her to take care of the children.

01 나는 오늘 반성을 했다. 나는 3층에 있는 과학실에 갈 때 엘리베이터를 타곤 했다. 내가 그곳에 가려고 했을 때, 지호는 계단으로 갈 것을 제안 했다. 사실 나는 그 모든 계단을 올라서 가고 싶진 않았다. 하지만 지호는 내가 계단으로 가야 한다고 설득했다. 나는 한 번 엘리베이터를 타는 것이 그렇게 많은 에너지를 사용하지 않는다고 생각했지만 지호는 내게 환경을 보호하기 위해 작은 것부터 시작해야 하는 것의 중요성을 상기 시켜주었다. 환경을 보호하기 위해 나는 작은 것들을 하며 에너지를 절약하기로 결심했다.

단원별 모의고사
p.167~171

01 ⑤   02 (1) shade (2) climate, temperatures
03 (1) a variety of (2) break down (3) contribute to
   (4) would like to (5) take the stairs
04 ④   05 ⑤   06 ④
07 (A) the number of trash cans (B) every floor
   (C) Separate
08 (C) → (D) → (A) → (E) → (B)
09 reduce our use of plastic bags, bring reusable bags
10 (1) We should protect the environment for future generations.
   (2) A creative person is good at coming up with new ideas.
   (3) China's underwater city attracts divers from all over the world.
11 ②   12 ②   13 ③
14 (1) the way how → the way 또는 how 또는 the way in which 또는 the way that
   (2) which → where, 또는 which → at which, 또는 문장의 끝에 at 삽입
   (3) of → for   (4) for → of
15 (1) for her to study English diligently every day
   (2) of her to explain the process of making a newspaper
16 ①
17 (1) She sometimes thinks about the time when she was healthy.
   (2) What was the name of the restaurant where we had pizza last week?
   (3) It seems impossible for some people to live without their smartphones.
   (4) It won't be easy for us to win the game tomorrow.

18 ④   19 how important it is to save the sea

20 They made an underwater museum away from
   the places where sea life was dying.

21 ②   22 (C) – (B) – (A)   23 ③

24 ⑤   25 people → air

01 '새롭거나 더 나은 생각, 방법, 또는 장치'를 가리키는 말은 innovation(혁신)이다.

02 shade: 그늘, climate: 기후, temperature: 온도

03 contribute to: ~에 기여하다, a variety of: 다양한, break down: 고장나다, take the stairs: 계단을 오르다, would like to: ~하고 싶다

04 플라스틱 쓰레기를 줄이는 데 도움을 주므로 reduce 또는 decrease가 알맞다.

05 대화를 통해 Brian이 기대하고 있는 것이 무엇인지는 알 수 없다.

06 주어진 문장은 (D)에 이어지는 문장에서 This가 가리키는 내용이 되므로 (D)가 적절하다.

08 (C) 희망 사항 언급 → (D) 의견 표현 → (A) 반박 → (E) 조언 및 의견 제시 → (B) 수용 및 기대 표현

09 환경을 보호하기 위해 우리는 비닐봉지 사용을 줄일 필요가 있다. 예를 들어 우리가 물건을 사러 갈 때, 재사용할 수 있는 가방을 들고 가는 것이 한 가지 방법이 될 수 있다.

10 environment: 환경, creative: 창의적인, underwater: 수중의, 물속의

11 to부정사의 의미상의 주어로 보어로 쓰인 형용사가 사람의 성향, 성격을 나타내는 말일 때는 'of+목적격'으로 쓴다.

12 'the way how'는 쓸 수 없으므로 'the way'나 how만 쓰는 것이 적절하다.

13 첫 번째 빈칸에는 의미상의 주어로 for가 적절하고, 두 번째 빈칸에는 관계부사 how가 적절하다.

14 (1) 'the way how'는 쓸 수 없으므로 'the way'나 how만 쓰거나 'the way in which' 또는 'the way that' 등으로 고치는 것이 적절하다. (2) 관계사절이 완전하므로 which를 where로 고치거나 which 앞이나 문장의 끝에 at을 넣어주는 것이 적절하다. (3) to부정사의 의미상 주어는 to부정사 바로 앞에 'for+목적격'의 형태로 쓴다. (4) to부정사의 의미상의 주어로 보어로 쓰인 형용사가 사람의 성향, 성격을 나타내는 말일 때는 'of+목적격'으로 쓴다.

15 'It(가주어) ~ of ...(의미상의 주어) 진주어(to부정사)' 구문을 이용하며, to부정사의 의미상의 주어를 'for+목적격'으로 나타낸다. 이때 보어로 쓰인 형용사가 사람의 성향, 성격을 나타내는 말일 때는 'of+목적격'으로 쓴다.

16 <보기>와 ①의 when은 관계부사이다. ② 대명사 ③ 접속사 ④ 의문부사 ⑤ 접속사

17 (1)~(2) 선행사에 맞는 관계부사를 이용한다. (3)~(4) 'It(가주

어) ~ for[of] ...(의미상의 주어) 진주어(to부정사)' 구문을 이용한다.

18 ④번에 이어지는 조각상들은 주어진 문장에 나오는 500개의 조각상들을 가리키는 것이다.

19 understand의 목적어로 간접의문문이 쓰인다. 따라서 '의문사+주어+동사' 어순임에 유의하자.

20 예술가들은 죽어가는 지역이 호전될 시간을 가질 수 있도록, 해양 생물이 죽어가는 지역으로부터 떨어진 해저에 수중 박물관을 만들었다.

21 위 글은 칸쿤의 환경을 보호하기 위한 창의적인 방법으로 해저 수중 박물관을 건설한 것에 관한 글이다. 따라서 ②번이 가장 적절하다.

22 싱가포르는 연중 더워서 대부분의 건물들은 기후 변화의 원인이 되는 에어컨 가동이 필요하고 (C) 그 결과 건축가들이 친환경적인 건물들을 디자인하기 시작함 (B) 친환경적인 건물들은 외부 공기가 건물을 관통하는 것을 가능케 함 (A) 이러한 자연적인 공기의 흐름이 건물을 시원하게 유지해 줌

23 관계대명사 that은 계속적 용법으로 쓰일 수 없다. that → which

24 각각 ① innovation ② eco-friendly ③ climate ④ architect를 풀이한 말이다. ⑤번은 tourist를 의미한다.

25 개방형 구조는 외부 공기가 건물을 관통하게 하는 것이다.

교과서 파헤치기

Lesson 3

1 exit, 나가다, 퇴장하다   2 curious, 호기심이 많은
3 properly, 제대로, 적절하게   4 common, 흔한
5 smash, 세게 부딪치다   6 collapse, 붕괴되다
7 wildfire, 산불, 들불   8 cause, 초래하다
9 flood, 홍수   10 include, 포함하다
11 earthquake, 지진   12 crawl, 기어가다
13 swing, 흔들리다   14 perform, 수행하다
15 destroy, 파괴하다   16 disaster, 재난

단어 TEST Step 1   p.02

01 최근에   02 인식하는   03 초래하다
04 극심한 공포, 공황   05 붕괴되다, 무너지다
06 세게 부딪치다   07 손상   08 나가다, 퇴장하다
09 피하다   10 심각한   11 들불, 산불
12 더 나쁜   13 제대로, 적절하게   14 흔한
15 영향을 주다   16 불안하게   17 실종된
18 지진   19 정확하게   20 파괴하다
21 폭우   22 전체의   23 기어가다
24 홍수   25 즉시   26 포함하다
27 자연 재해   28 언급하다   29 두들기다
30 혼란, 혼동   31 긴급하게
32 (일·사건 등이) 일어나다, 발생하다   33 반응
34 격렬하게, 심하게   35 ~에 바탕을 둔
36 역시 또한   37 할인을 받다   38 다양한
39 ~의 경우에   40 매우 많은
41 넘어지다, 기울어지다
42 길 한쪽으로 차를 대다   43 산산조각이 나다

단어 TEST Step 2   p.03

01 violently   02 cause   03 reaction
04 confusion   05 worse   06 properly
07 recently   08 destroy   09 common
10 damage   11 missing   12 chest
13 collapse   14 nervously   15 disaster
16 flood   17 earthquake   18 occur
19 crawl   20 smash   21 heat wave
22 panic   23 exactly   24 include
25 special effect   26 suddenly   27 exit
28 affect   29 tap   30 urgently
31 immediately   32 actually   33 heavy rain
34 serious   35 pull over   36 in the middle of
37 a variety of   38 tip over   39 in case of ~
40 based on ~   41 a large number of
42 put in   43 roll off

대화문 TEST Step 1   p.05~06

Listen & Talk 1 A

was, flood, hear about / floods, common, are, curious, how, happened / Let's, research

Listen & Talk 1 B

seem to be, natural disasters, these days / earthquake, south, storm / curious, which type of natural disaster, most damage / report, damage, each type, natural disaster, storms / guess, second / heavy, heavy snow / What / Based on, earthquakes, damage, been increasing, because, been happening / seems like, prepared, variety, natural disasters

Listen & Talk 1 C

hear about, fires / How serious / destroyed, number of houses, other buildings / Are, going on / actually, worse, living there / So do, curious about, leave / Actually more than, leave, homes, missing / terrible, somewhere safe

Listen & Talk 2 A

what else, need to put in, natural disaster survival kit / water, radio / Anything else / make sure, include batteries, radio

Listen & Talk 2 B

Performing, properly, save, Here, steps, proper, needs, Tap, Are, reaction, listen, feel for breathing, breathing, sure, place, hands in, chest, weight, harder, breaths, keep doing, until help arrives

Listen & Talk 2 D

In case of, what, do / Make sure, cover, wet cloth / else / Make sure that, exit, immediately

Do It Yourself A

hear, occurring, often, before / really, never felt / usually occur, southern, other places as well / curious, why, occurred, recently / Why don't, research / do / How about asking, help / Let's, find

Listen & Talk 1 A

B: There was a big flood in Europe. Did you hear about it?

G: No, I didn't. But floods aren't that common in winter, are they? I'm curious about how that happened.

B: Me too. Let's do some online research.

Listen & Talk 1 B

G: There seem to be many natural disasters in Korea these day.

B: I agree. There was an earthquake in the south last week. Also a storm is coming this week.

G: I'm curious about which type of natural disaster causes the most damage in Korea.

B: Actually I read a report yesterday about the damage from each type of natural disaster. Number on is storms.

G: I see. I guess earthquakes are second.

B: No, second is heavy rain, and third is heavy snow.

G: What about earthquakes?

B: Based on the report, earthquakes are fourth. But the damage from earthquakes has been increasing recently because they have been happening more often in Korea.

G: I see. It seems like we have to be prepared for a variety of natural disasters in Korea.

Listen & Talk 1 C

B: Hey, did you hear about the big fires in California?

G: No, I didn't. How serious are they?

B: They've destroyed a large number of houses and other buildings.

G: Are the fires still going on?

B: Yes, actually the wind has made the fires worse. I hope all the people living there are okay.

G: So do I. I'm curious about how many people had to leave their homes.

B: Actually more than 20,000 people had to leave their homes, and about 400 people are missing in that area.

G: That's terrible. I hope they're somewhere safe.

Listen & Talk 2 A

B: Mom, what else do we need to put in the natural disaster survival kit?

W: Well, we need water, some food, and radio.

B: Anything else, Mom?

W: Oh, make sure that you include batteries for the radio.

Listen & Talk 2 B

W: Performing CPR properly can save someone's life. Here are the steps for proper CPR. First, check that the person needs help. Tap the person and shout, "Are you okay?" If there's no reaction, call 119 for help. Second, listen, look, and feel for breathing. If the person's not breathing, begin CPR. Make sure you place your hands in the middle of the person's chest. Use your body weight to press harder on the chest. After 30 presses, give the person two breaths. Keep doing CPR until help arrives.

Listen & Talk 2 D

A: In case of a fire, what should I do?

B: Make sure that you cover your mouth with a wet cloth.

A: Anything else?

B: Make sure that you exit the building immediately.

Do It Yourself A

G: Did you hear that earthquakes are occurring more often in Korea than before?

B: Oh, really? I've never felt an earthquake in Korea.

G: They usually occur in the southern part of Korea, but now they are occurring in other places as well.

B: I didn't know that. I'm curious about why earthquakes have occurred so often in Korea recently.

G: Why don't we do some research to find out?

B: Sounds good, but where do we look first?

G: How about asking our science teacher first? I think she can help us.

B: Okay. Let's go and find her.

01 Waking Up, Earthquake

02 in, had gone, hit

03 woke up, because, shaking

04 thought, shaking, as, joke

05 heard, fall, break, pieces

06 what exactly was happening

07 whole, violently, turned, panic

08 shouted, earthquake, ran into

09 Since, experiencing, how, react

10 just kept saying

11 pulled, out of bed

12 ran, crawled under

13 swinging, falling, floor

33

14 dropped, covering, broke

15 tipped over, rolled off

16 Every second, something else

17 to worry, collapse

18 seemed to stop

19 crawling toward, door

20 At, moment, rang

21 coming home from work

22 shouted, stopped　　23 Get out of

24 Take, stairs　　25 Don't take

27 Where are

28 okay, asked urgently

29 answered, Don't worry　　30 I'm okay

31 driving home, shaking

32 pulled over immediately

33 right now, going on

34 made, way down, outside

35 looked around

36 Parts, fallen, had smashed

37 open, avoid, falling pieces

38 could, have happened, few

39 Although, drills, thought, real

40 get scared, remember

41 forget, panic, felt, falling

42 take, drills seriously

43 realized, prepared, occur, time

20 At that moment, rang

21 coming home from work

22 shouted, It stopped

23 Get out of

24 Take, stairs　　25 Don't take

26 Hurry　　27 Where

28 okay, asked urgently

29 answered, Don't worry　　30 okay

31 was driving home, shaking

32 pulled over immediately

33 right now, find out, going on

34 nervously made our way, outside

35 looked around

36 Parts of, had fallen, had smashed

37 to avoid, falling pieces

38 could, have happened, a few

39 Although, earthquake drills, experience a real earthquake

40 get scared, remember

41 can't forget the panic I felt, were falling to

42 After, take, drills seriously

43 realized, be prepared for, occur at any time

1 지진에 눈을 뜨는 것

2 2월 어느 날 밤, 내가 잠자리에 든 후에 지진이 일어났다.

3 침대가 흔들렸기 때문에 나는 갑자기 잠에서 깼다.

4 나는 남동생이 장난으로 침대를 흔들고 있다고 생각했다.

5 하지만 그때 나는 내 책상 위에 있던 거울이 바닥으로 떨어져 산산조각이 나는 소리를 들었다.

6 그때 나는 남동생이 그런 것이 아니라는 것을 알았지만, 정확히 무슨 일이 일어나고 있었는지를 여전히 알지 못했다.

7 머지않아 방 전체가 심하게 흔들리기 시작했고 혼란스러움은 공포로 변했다.

8 엄마가 지진이라고 소리를 지르며 내 방으로 뛰어 들어왔다.

9 지진을 경험한 것이 처음이었기 때문에, 나는 어떻게 반응해야 할지 몰랐다.

10 나는 그저 "어떻게 해야 하지?"라는 말을 반복했다.

11 엄마는 나와 남동생을 침대 밖으로 잡아끌었다.

12 우리는 주방으로 달려가서 식탁 아래로 기어들어 갔다.

13 나는 전등이 심하게 흔들리는 것과 책이 바닥으로 떨어지는 것을 볼 수 있었다.

14 우리 가족 사진이 벽에서 떨어졌고 사진을 덮고 있던 유리가 깨졌다.

15 컵이 넘어지고 식탁에서 굴러 떨어졌다.

16 매 순간, 나는 아파트에 있는 다른 어떤 것들이 부서지는 소리를 들을 수 있었다.

01 Waking Up, Earthquake

02 in, had gone to bed, hit

03 was shaking

04 was shaking, as a joke

05 heard, fall to the floor, break into pieces

06 then, still didn't, what exactly was happening

07 to shake violently, confusion turned to panic

08 shouted that, ran into

09 my first time experiencing, how to react

10 kept saying

11 pulled, out of bed

12 ran to, crawled under

13 see, swinging violently, falling to

14 dropped, covering it broke

15 tipped over, rolled off

16 Every second, hear, break

17 to worry, collapse

18 shaking seemed to stop

19 crawling toward

17 나는 건물이 무너지지는 않을까 하는 걱정이 들기 시작했다.

18 그때 흔들림이 멈추는 것 같았다.

19 우리는 문으로 기어가기 시작했다.

20 그 순간, 엄마의 휴대 전화가 울렸다.

21 전화를 한 사람은 바로 아빠였는데, 직장에서 퇴근하던 중이었다.

22 아빠는 소리쳤다, "지진이 멈췄어요!

23 건물 밖으로 나와요!

24 계단을 이용해요!

25 엘리베이터를 타면 안 돼요!

26 서둘러요!"

27 "어디예요?

28 괜찮아요?"라고 엄마가 다급하게 물었다.

29 아빠가 대답했다, "걱정 말아요.

30 나는 괜찮아요.

31 진동이 시작할 때 운전해서 집으로 가던 중이었어요.

32 하지만 즉시 차를 길 한쪽에 댔어요.

33 무슨 일이 일어나는지 알기 위해 지금 라디오를 듣고 있어요."

34 우리는 초조한 마음으로 계단을 내려가서 밖으로 나갔다.

35 나는 주변을 둘러보았다.

36 건물의 일부분이 떨어져 나갔고 몇몇 차들은 박살이 났다.

37 우리는 추가적인 낙하물을 피하기 위해 공터로 갔다.

38 어떻게 이런 일이 몇 분 만에 일어날 수 있단 말인가?

39 비록 학교에서 많은 지진 대피 훈련을 해 왔지만, 내가 실제 지진을 겪으리라고는 전혀 생각해 보지 않았었다.

40 그날 밤을 기억하면 나는 여전히 두려워진다.

41 가구가 흔들리고 물건들이 바닥으로 떨어졌을 때 내가 느꼈던 공포심을 나는 잊을 수가 없다.

42 그날 밤 이후, 나는 지진 대피 훈련에 진지하게 임하기 시작했다.

43 나는 언제든 발생할 수 있는 다음 지진을 대비해야 한다는 것을 깨달았다.

본문 TEST Step 4-Step 5   p.18~23

1 Waking Up to an Earthquake

2 One night in February, after I had gone to bed, an earthquake hit.

3 I woke up suddenly because my bed was shaking.

4 I thought my brother was shaking my bed as a joke.

5 But then I heard the mirror on my desk fall to the floor and break into pieces.

6 I knew it wasn't my brother then, but I still didn't know what exactly was happening.

7 Soon the whole room began to shake violently, and my confusion turned to panic.

8 My mom shouted that it was an earthquake and ran into my room.

9 Since it was my first time experiencing an earthquake, I didn't know how to react.

10 I just kept saying, "What should I do?"

11 My mom pulled me and my brother out of bed.

12 We ran to the kitchen and crawled under the table.

13 I could see the light swinging violently and books falling to the floor.

14 Our family picture dropped from the wall and the glass covering it broke.

15 A cup tipped over and rolled off the kitchen table.

16 Every second, I could hear something else in the apartment break.

17 I started to worry that the building would collapse.

18 Then the shaking seemed to stop.

19 We started crawling toward the door.

20 At that moment, my mom's cell phone rang.

21 It was my dad, who was coming home from work.

22 He shouted, "It stopped!

23 Get out of the building!

24 Take the stairs!

25 Don't take the elevator!

26 Hurry!"

27 "Where are you?

28 Are you okay?" my mom asked urgently.

29 My dad answered, "Don't worry.

30 I'm okay.

31 I was driving home when the shaking started.

32 But I pulled over immediately.

33 I'm listening to the radio right now to find out what's going on."

34 We nervously made our way down the stairs and outside.

35 I looked around.

36 Parts of buildings had fallen and had smashed several cars.

37 We went to an open space to avoid more falling pieces.

38 How could all this have happened in a few minutes?

39 Although I had done many earthquake drills in school, I had never thought I'd experience a real earthquake.

40 I still get scared when I remember that night.

41 I can't forget the panic I felt when the furniture was shaking and things were falling to the floor.

42 After that night, I began to take earthquake drills seriously.

43 I realized that I should be prepared for the next earthquake, which can occur at any time.

After You Read B

1. when, earthquake occurred

2. began to, because, was shaking violently

3. How scary

4. all crawled, got us out of bed

5. happening at the moment

6. Lot's of, were falling, heard, break

7. did, realize

8. should be prepared for, can occur at any time

Think & Write Step 3

1. would like to tell

2. is set in, in

3. main character, pilot, missing, during

4. special effects used, disaster scenes

5. a little, at times

6. Go, watch it

After You Read B

1. R: How did you feel when the earthquake occurred?

2. W: I began to panic because the whole room was shaking violently.

3. R: How scary! What did you do next?

4. W: We all crawled under the table after my mom got us out of bed.

5. R: What was happening at the moment?

6. W: Lots of things were falling to the floor. I heard many things in the apartment break.

7. R: What did you realize after that night?

8. W: I realized that I should be prepared for the next earthquake. It can occur at any time!

Think & Write Step 3

1. I would like to tell you about the movie *San Andreas*.

2. This movie is set in Los Angeles and San Francisco in 2014.

3. The main character, a search-and rescue pilot, must search for his missing family during an earthquake.

4. The special effects used in the disaster scenes are very good.

5. The movie is a little sad at times, but the story is very interesting.

6. I give *San Andreas* four stars. Go and watch it!

Lesson 4

01 엄격한	02 성취하다, 이루다
03 반드시 ~하게 하다, 보장하다	04 지지자
05 추리, 추론	06 자신감 있는	07 분석하다
08 논리적인, 타당한, 사리에 맞는	09 오해
10 배달하다	11 긍정적인	12 나누다, 분리하다
13 편집하다	14 접촉	15 능력
16 장식하다	17 선거	18 해석하다
19 귀중한, 존중 받는	20 대표(자)	21 효과적인
22 통찰력, 비전, 시력	23 결정하다, 결심하다
24 접근하다	25 불간섭주의의, 자유방임의
26 분석가	27 동기를 부여하다
28 돌아오다, 반납하다	
29 외향적인, 사교적인	30 발표
31 깨닫다	32 안심이 되는	33 바꾸다, 전환하다
34 조사, 연구	35 ~에 갇히다
36 솔선수범하다, 모범을 보이다	
37 ~을 생각해 내다, 내놓다	
38 ~을 담당하다, 책임지다	39 해결하다
40 잘 지내다, 사이좋게 지내다	
41 ~을 필요로 하다, 요구하다	42 다루다, 처리하다
43 어울려 밖에서 시간을 보내다	

01 analyst	02 confident	03 positive
04 valued	05 deliver	06 approach
07 contact	08 misunderstanding	
09 research	10 motivate	11 outgoing
12 supporter	13 switch	14 translate
15 relieved	16 divide	17 reasoning
18 edit	19 effective	20 ability
21 representative	22 prepare	23 achieve
24 presentation	25 run	26 election
27 determine	28 analyze	29 logical
30 goal	31 instead	32 strict
33 properly	34 vision	35 take sides
36 come up with	37 get along	38 let down
39 belong to	40 work on	41 take care of
42 be in charge of		43 deal with

1 leadership, ㅋ   2 run, (선거에) 입후보하다

3 task, 일, 과업, 과제   4 ability, 능력

5 logical, 논리적인, 타당한   6 switch, 바꾸다, 전환하다

7 approach, 접근하다   8 edit, 편집하다

9 supporter, 지지자   10 motivate, 동기를 부여하다

11 analyze, 분석하다   12 confident, 자신감 있는

13 effective, 효과적인

14 hands-off, 불간섭주의의, 자유방임의

15 representative, 대표(자)   16 election, 선거

Listen & Talk 1 A

problem / matter / going to, right, just realized, on Saturday evening, What should I do / like, decision, Let's, with / miss, best friend's birthday

Listen & Talk 1 B

What's the matter / problem / happened / had a fight, stuck in, what to do / why, had a flight / big deal, some kind of misunderstanding / Why don't, listen to / friends of mine, can't take sides / works out

Listen & Talk 1 C

What's the matter / What to do, asked me to help him, things to do / have to / return some books, presentation, have to prepare for / do, a lot / seemed let down / how about meeting, instead, everything, help / help me out, understanding

Listen & Talk 2 A

Sports Day, help out / to take photos / good at taking photos, have no doubt that

Listen & Talk 2 B

divided, into, be responsible for, translate, into, edit, are printed, in charge of, I have no doubt that, who receive

Listen & Talk 2 C

excited, field trip / Let's check, in charge of / taking pictures / some research / write our field trip report / ready / have no doubt that, turn out

---

Listen & Talk 1 A

G: Mom, we've got a problem.

W: What's the matter?

G: We're going to have dinner with Grandma this Saturday, right? But I just realized that Sujin's birthday party is on Saturday evening. She's my best friend. What should I do?

W: That sounds like a difficult decision. Let's talk about it with your dad.

G: Okay, Mom. I'd love to see Grandma, but I don't want to miss my best friend's birthday party.

Listen & Talk 1 B

M: Junsu, are you okay? What's the matter?

B: Hello, Mr. Smith. I have a problem.

M: What happened?

B: You know Jaewoo, Yunho, and I are best friends, right? They had a fight, and now I'm stuck in the middle. I don't know what to do.

M: That sounds hard. Do you know why they had a fight?

B: Yes, but it doesn't sound like a big deal to me. I guess they had some kind of misunderstanding.

M: Why don't you all meet together and talk about it? I think they'll listen to you.

B: That's a good idea. They're both good friends of mine. I can't take sides.

M: I understand. I hope everything works out.

Listen & Talk 1 C

B: Hey, Mandy. What's the matter?

G: I don't know what to do, Nick. My brother asked me to help him with his homework this Wednesday, but I told him I can't. I have so many things to do that day.

B: What do you have to do this Wednesday?

G: I need to go to the library to return some books. Then I have to meet you to work on our presentation. After that, I have to prepare for an exam at night.

B: Oh, you do have a lot to do.

G: Yes. But my brother seemed let down, so I feel bad.

B: Well, then how about meeting on Thursday instead for our presentation? Then you can do everything and also help your brother on Wednesday.

G: That would help me out so much! Thanks for understanding, Nick!

Listen & Talk 2 A

G: Sports Day is coming. How do you want to help out?

B: I want to take photos for Sports Day.

37

G: That's great. You are really good at taking photos. I have no doubt that you will take some wonderful pictures.

Listen & Talk 2 B

B: In the Send Our Stories project, we are going to make a picture book for children in other countries. We've divided everyone into three groups. Each group will be responsible for a different task. Group A will translate a Korean story into English. Group B will make drawings for the book and edit it. After copies of the book are printed, Group C will be in charge of sending them to the children. It won't be easy, but I have no doubt that the children who receive these books will really enjoy them.

Listen & Talk 2 C

B: I'm so excited about our museum field trip.

G1: Me too. Let's check our tasks. Yen, what are you in charge of?

G2: I'm in charge of taking pictures.

G1: Okay. Sejin, are you going to do some research on the museum?

B: Yes, I am. Are you going to write our field trip report, Emma?

G1: That's right. I think we're ready.

G2: Good. I have no doubt that our project will turn out well.

26 Maybe, wrong
27 other leadership qualities
28 decided, do, research online
29 what, found   30 Team Builders
31 Ensure, feels valued
32 Create, positive environment
33 friendly, talk to   34 Logical Analysts
35 Have, reasoning skills   36 Analyze, situations
37 effective, achieve, goals
38 Hands-Off Managers   39 Allow, on, own
40 try to control
41 advice, when, needed
42 Strict Directors   43 Make, role clear
44 Make sure, on time
45 Ensure, step, properly   46 Quiet Supporters
47 by example
48 Let, shine instead
49 Meet, members' needs   50 Creative Thinkers
51 Approach, in, ways   52 Come up with
53 Deal with, differently from
54 surprised, different, realized, reason
55 belong to, come up   56 call for, styles
57 Each, unique situation determines
58 part, different responsibilities, group
59 After reading, more confident
60 discovered, some of, qualities
61 make, better, pick, representative
62 let's try

본문 TEST Step 1   p.33~35

01 We, All Leaders
02 election, coming up
03 Why don't you run
04 No way
05 right person, position
06 never thought, running
07 Why not
08 Come on
09 special qualities
10 like, can be called
11 What, mean
12 good leadership qualities
13 really friendly, outgoing
14 also help, get along
15 no doubt, be elected
16 that, good leadership qualities
17 No, has ever told
18 Why, think so
19 just trying to be
20 When, however, think
21 Can, become, leader
22 don't know
23 vision, goals, ability, motivate
24 any of those things
25 suddenly, wonder if, qualities

본문 TEST Step 2   p.36~38

01 We Are All
02 election, coming up
03 Why don't you, representative
04 No way
05 right person, position
06 thought about running
07 Why not
08 Come on
09 special qualities
10 like, can be called
11 What, mean
12 good leadership qualities   13 friendly, outgoing
14 also help, get along
15 no doubt, will be elected
16 good leadership qualities   17 has ever told
18 Why, think so   19 trying to be
20 however, to think   21 become a leader
22 don't know
23 a vision, goals, to motivate others
24 any of those things   25 wonder if, qualities

26 wrong

27 other leadership qualities

28 do some research online

29 what, found   30 Builders

31 feels valued   32 positive environment

33 to talk to   34 Logical Analysts

35 reasoning skills   36 Analyze, situations

37 effective ways, achieve the team's goals

38 Hands-Off Managers   39 Allow, on their own

40 try to control   41 advice, it is needed

42 Strict Directors   43 everyone's role clear

44 Make sure, on time   45 each step, properly

46 Quiet Supporters   47 by example

48 shine instead   49 Meet, needs

50 Creative Thinkers

51 Approach, in new ways

52 Come up with

53 Deal with, differently from

54 realized the reason   55 belong to, come up

56 call for

57 unique situation determines

58 a part of, different responsibilities

59 more confident   60 some of the qualities

61 pick me, class representative

62 let's try

본문 TEST Step 3   p.39~41

1 우리는 모두 리더들이다

2 Brian: "선거가 다가오고 있어.유지해 준다는 것을 알고 있다.

3 유미야, 반 대표에 입후보하는 게 어때?"

4 유미: "아니.

5 나는 그 자리에 적절한 사람이 아니야.

6 나는 입후보하는 것에 대해 생각해 본 적이 없어."

7 Brian: "왜?"

8 유미: "이봐, Brian.

9 리더들은 특별한 자질을 갖추고 있어.

10 나 같은 사람이 리더로 불릴 수 있다고 생각하지 않아."

11 Brian: "무슨 말이야?

12 내 생각에 너는 매우 좋은 지도력 자질들을 갖추고 있어.

13 너는 정말 친절하고 외향적이잖아.

14 또 너는 사람들이 어울리도록 도와주기도 해.

15 만약 네가 입후보한다면 당선될 거라고 믿어 의심치 않아."

16 Brian은 오늘 오후에 내게 내가 좋은 지도력 자질들을 갖추고 있다고 말했다.

17 이전에는 아무도 내게 그런 말을 한 적이 없었다.

18 왜 그는 그렇게 생각했을까?

19 아마도 그는 그저 친절하려고 했을 것이다.

20 그러나 그가 내게 그렇게 말했을 때, 나는 생각하기 시작했다.

21 내가 정말 리더가 될 수 있을까?

22 나는 모르겠다.

23 나는 리더가 비전, 명확한 목표, 그리고 다른 사람들에게 동기를 부여할 능력을 가지고 있어야 한다고 생각한다.

24 나는 그러한 것들 중 어느 것도 가지고 있지 않다.

25 그때 나는 갑자기 이것들이 좋은 리더를 만드는 유일한 자질들인지 궁금해하기 시작했다.

26 아마도 내가 틀린지도 모른다.

27 어쩌면 다른 지도력 자질들이 있는지도 모른다.

28 그래서 나는 온라인으로 조사해 보기로 결심했다.

29 여기에 내가 찾은 것이 있다!

30 〈녹색 리더〉'팀 조직자'

31 팀이 반드시 가치 있다고 느끼게 한다

32 긍정적인 환경을 조성한다

33 친절하고 말을 걸기 쉽다

34 〈빨간색 리더〉'논리적 분석가'

35 좋은 추론 기술을 갖고 있다

36 문제와 상황들을 분석한다

37 팀의 목표를 성취하는 가장 효과적인 방법들을 생각한다

38 〈보라색 리더〉'방임적 관리자'

39 다른 사람들이 스스로 일하도록 해 준다

40 사람들을 통제하려고 하지 않는다

41 필요할 때만 조언한다

42 〈주황색 리더〉'엄격한 감독관'

43 모두의 역할을 분명하게 해 준다

44 모든 일을 제때 끝날 것을 확실히 한다

45 단계가 적절히 이행되도록 한다

46 〈노란색 리더〉'조용한 지지자'

47 솔선수범한다

48 팀원들이 대신 빛나도록 해 준다

49 팀원들의 요구 사항을 충족한다

50 〈파란색 리더〉'창조적 사상가'

51 새로운 방식으로 문제들에 접근한다

52 신선한 아이디어를 떠올린다

53 다른 사람들과 다르게 일을 처리한다

54 나는 실제로 서로 다른 많은 지도력 유형들이 있어서 놀랐지만, 곧 그 이유를 깨달았다.

55 우리는 서로 다른 여러 집단에 속하고, 우리 인생에서 서로 다른 많은 상황들이 발생할 수 있다.

56 그것들은 모두 서로 다른 지도력 유형들을 요구한다.

57 각 집단의 독특한 상황이 최고의 지도력 유형을 결정한다.

58 "나는 서로 다른 많은 집단의 일부이고, 각 집단에서 각각 다른 책임을 갖고 있어."

59 모든 것을 읽고 나서, 나는 더 자신감이 생겼다.

60 나는 '녹색 리더'의 자질들 중 일부분을 가지고 있다는 것을 알게 되었다.

61 만약 나의 반 친구들이 녹색 리더가 우리 학급을 더 좋게 만들 거라고 생각한다면, 그들은 학급 대표로 나를 뽑을지도 모른다!

62 좋아, 시도해 보자!

1 We Are All Leaders

2 Brian: The election is coming up.

3 Why don't you run for class representative, Yumi?

4 Yumi: No way.

5 I'm not the right person for that position.

6 I've never thought about running.

7 Brian: Why not?

8 Yumi: Come on, Brian.

9 Leaders have special qualities.

10 I don't think a person like me can be called a leader.

11 Brian: What do you mean?

12 I think you have very good leadership qualities.

13 You're really friendly and outgoing.

14 You also help people get along.

15 I have no doubt that you will be elected if you run..

16 Brian told me this afternoon that I have good leadership qualities.

17 No one has ever told me that before.

18 Why does he think so?

19 Maybe he was just trying to be nice.

20 When he said that to me, however, I started to think.

21 Can I really become a leader?

22 I don't know.

23 I think leaders should have a vision, clear goals, and the ability to motivate others.

24 I don't have any of those things.

25 Then I suddenly started to wonder if these are the only qualities that make a good leader.

26 Maybe I'm wrong.

27 Maybe there are other leadership qualities.

28 So I decided to do some research online.

29 Here's what I found!

30 GREEN LEADERS: "Team Builders"

31 Ensure that the team feels valued

32 Create a positive environment

33 Are friendly and easy to talk to

34 RED LEADERS: "Logical Analysts"

35 Have good reasoning skills

36 Analyze problems and situations

37 Think of the most effective ways to achieve the team's goals

38 PURPLE LEADERS: "Hands-Off Managers"

39 Allow others to work on their own

40 Do not try to control people

41 Give advice only when it is needed

42 ORANGE LEADERS: "Strict Directors"

43 Make everyone's role clear

44 Make sure everything is finished on time

45 Ensure each step is done properly

46 YELLOW LEADERS: "Quiet Supporters"

47 Lead by example

48 Let the team members shine instead

49 Meet the team members' needs

50 BLUE LEADERS: "Creative Thinkers"

51 Approach problems in new ways

52 Come up with fresh ideas

53 Deal with tasks differently from others

54 I was surprised that there are actually many different leadership styles, but soon I realized the reason.

55 We belong to many different groups, and many different situations can come up in our lives.

56 They all call for different leadership styles.

57 Each group's unique situation determines the best leadership style.

58 "I am a part of many different groups, and I have different responsibilities in each group."

59 After reading everything, I became more confident.

60 I discovered that I have some of the qualities of a "green leader."

61 If my classmates think a green leader would make our class better, they might pick me to be class representative!

62 Okay, let's try it!

Presentation Time Step 3

1. chose tasks to prepare for

2. will buy

3. will decorate the classroom

4. will play, party songs

5. no doubt that, will be a lot of

After You Read B

1. to lead my example, take care of others' needs

2. important thing, that, shine

3. enjoy approaching, in new ways

4. try my best, come up with

5. analyze, situations, look for, effective ways to achieve our goals

Do It Yourself B

1. Why don't you run

2. never thought about running

3. Why not

4. have special qualities

5. a person like, can be called

6. What do, mean

7. really friendly, outgoing

8. help people get along

9. no doubt, will be elected, run

구석구석지문 TEST Step 2   p.49

Presentation Time Step 3

1. Our group chose tasks to prepare for our class birthday party.

2. I will buy a cake.

3. Woojin and Taeho will decorate the classroom.

4. Yeji will play birthday party songs.

5. I have no doubt that our birthday party will be a lot of fun!

After You Read B

1. Hi, I'm Jennifer. I try to lead my example and take care of others' needs.

2. The important thing is that the members of my team shine.

3. Hello, I'm Heejin. I enjoy approaching problems in new ways.

4. I try my best to come up with new ideas.

5. Hi, I'm Chris. I analyze my team's problems and situations, and then I look for the most effective ways to achieve our goals.

Do It Yourself B

1. Brian: Why don't you run for class representative, Yumi?

2. Yumi: No way. I've never thought about running.

3. Brian: Why not?

4. Yumi: Leaders have special qualities.

5. I don't think a person like me can be called a leader.

6. Brian: What do you mean?

7. You're really friendly and outgoing.

8. You also help people get along.

9. I have no doubt that you will be elected if you run.

단어 TEST Step 1   p.50

01 (예술적) 작품	02 영리한, 똑똑한	03 건축가
04 포함하다	05 건축(술)	06 설명
07 조각, 조각상	08 끌다, 매혹시키다	09 곡물, 알곡
10 푸른 잎, 푸른 나무	11 바라건대	12 기후
13 혁신	14 추가적인	15 자료, 소재, 재료
16 손상시키다	17 오염	18 인식, 의식
19 원치 않는, 불필요한		
20 예방하다, 막다, 방지하다		21 믿기 힘든, 굉장한
22 보호하다, 지키다	23 친환경적인	
24 제공하다	25 표면	26 주제
27 줄이다	28 재사용할 수 있는	29 구조(물)
30 분리하다	31 사라지다	
32 격려하다, 장려하다		33 상기시키다
34 자원	35 ~ 이외에도	
36 무너지다, 고장 나다, (썩어서) ~이 되다	37 ~을 버리다	
38 ~에 지루해하다	39 ~와 조화하여	
40 ~에 기여하다, (~의) 원인이 되다	41 다양한	
42 ~을 돌보다	43 ~을 생각해 내다	

단어 TEST Step 2   p.51

01 pollution	02 additional	03 awareness
04 innovation	05 architect	06 contain
07 theme	08 prevent	09 throughout
10 damage	11 protect	12 eco-friendly
13 resource	14 encourage	15 attract
16 reduce	17 disappear	18 grain
19 underwater	20 unique	21 unwanted
22 reusable	23 incredible	24 suggestion
25 artwork	26 natural	27 opinion
28 explanation	29 seriously	30 properly
31 realize	32 statue	33 structure
34 separate	35 break down	36 get better
37 take care of	38 come up with	39 a variety of
40 have a point	41 in harmony with	
42 be bored with	43 in addition to	

1 damage, 손상시키다   2 disappear, 사라지다

3 surface, 표면   4 underwater, 수중에, 해저에

5 architect, 건축가   6 goal, 목표, 목적

7 greenery, 푸른 잎, 푸른 나무   8 climate, 기후

9 statue, 조각상   10 innovation, 혁신

11 grain, 곡물, 알곡   12 artwork, (예술적) 작품

13 explanation, 설명   14 opinion, 의견

15 reusable, 재사용할 수 있는   16 shade, 그늘

Listen & Talk 1 A

plastic bags / not good for, environment, reduce, plastic bags / In my opinion, should bring reusable bags

Listen & Talk 1 B

up, going up / third floor, Why don't, take the stairs / all the way / lots of, save, protect the environment / one elevator ride, much energy / adds up, In my opinion, taking care of, little things / have a point, Let's take

Listen & Speak 1 C

like to make a suggestion, throw, away, of recycling, As, because, resources, protect, in my opinion, trash cans, to encourage recycling, place, colored recycling bins, remind, separate, properly

Listen & Talk 2 A

holding / What kinds of / theme, are holding, raise students' awareness / wait to see it

Listen & Talk 2 B

article / What, about / looks like, plastic bag, made, of / amazing / breaks down, soil, disappears, three minutes / reduce plastic waste / company, selling, this year, wait to use

Listen & Talk 2 C

are, going to / sheep park / interesting / protect the environment / How can / chemicals, unwanted plants, chemicals, not needed / bright, can't wait to

Do It Yourself

to buy / In my opinion, any more / bored with / about using / find out how to do it / interesting, to make

Listen & Talk 1 A

B: I think we're using too many plastic bags.

G: I agree. It's not good for the environment. How can we reduce our use of plastic bags?

B: In my opinion, we should bring reusable bags when we go shopping.

Listen & Talk 1 B

G: Jiho, hurry up! The elevator is going up soon.

B: The science room is just on the third floor. Why don't we take the stairs?

G: I don't want to walk all the way up there.

B: Come on. Elevators use lots of energy. We need to save energy to protect the environment.

G: But one elevator ride doesn't use that much energy.

B: That's true, but the energy from all the elevator rides adds up over time. In my opinion, taking care of the environment starts with the little things.

G: You have a point. Let's take the stairs.

Listen & Speak 1 C

B: Today, I'd like to make a suggestion about the trash problem at our school. I've found that many students just throw things away instead of recycling them. As you know, however, recycling is very important because it saves resources and helps protect the environment. So, in my opinion, we need to reduce the number of trash cans at school to encourage recycling. Why don't we place four different colored recycling bins on every floor instead? This will remind students to separate the paper, glass, plastic, and cans properly.

Listen & Talk 2 A

B: Our club is holding a photo contest next week.

G: What kinds of photos will be in it?

B: The theme is pollution around the world. We are holding this contest to raise students' awareness of environmental problems.

G: That sounds nice. I can't wait to see it!

Listen & Talk 2 B

G: I read a cool article today.

B: What was it about?

G: It was about a new bag. It just looks like a plastic bag, but it's made mostly of corn.

B: That sounds really amazing.

G: Yes, but there's more. The bag breaks down in soil in only three months and disappears in about three minutes in warm water!

B: Wow! That will help us reduce plastic waste by a lot!

G: I know! The company will start selling the bag sometime this year. I can't wait to use it!

Listen & Talk 2 C

B: What are we going to do this weekend, Mihee?

G: Why don't we go to the sheep park near my house?

B: A sheep park? How interesting! Are there really sheep in the park?

G: Yes. They are there to protect the environment.

B: How can they help the environment?

G: You know, people usually use chemicals to kill unwanted plants. The sheep in the park eat those plants, so the chemicals are not needed.

B: What a bright idea! I can't wait to visit the park!

Do It Yourself

G: I want to buy a new bag.

B: You already have too many bags. In my opinion, you don't need any more.

G: But I'm bored with my old bags.

B: Then how about using old clothes to make a new bag? You can find out how to do it online.

G: Oh, that sounds interesting! I can't wait to make my own bag.

본문 TEST Step 1   p.57~58

01 for us to find

02 creative ways, save, earth

03 example, underwater museum

04 meet, professor, explanation, special

05 where, tourists travel

06 most popular, at, area's

07 However, damaging parts, near

08 To prevent, something interesting

09 attracted, part, dying, better

10 underwater, away, where, dying

11 about, below, contains, statues

12 made from materials, support

13 provide, for, live on

14 types, statues, artwork unique

15 people, variety, life, statues

16 realize, rich, important, save

17 using, protect, environment, land

18 what, architect, says, eco-friendly

19 hot throughout, year

20 need, which uses, contributes

21 why, begun, less, still

22 example, designed, open structure

23 outside air, move throughout

24 natural, how, stay cool

25 addition, making, structures, add

26 provides, protects, direct, keeps

27 only, also provide, with

28 goals, new style, architecture

29 keep coming up with

30 field, ways, protecting, environment

31 With, able, far into

본문 TEST Step 2   p.59~60

01 It, for us to find ways

02 creative ways to save

03 underwater museum

04 meet, professor, listen to, explanation

05 where, tourists travel every year

06 the most popular, to do, is looking at

07 However, are seriously damaging parts, near

08 To prevent this, something interesting

09 if, attracted, to, dying areas, to get better

10 made, underwater, away from, where, dying

11 about, meters below, surface, contains, statues

12 are made from, that support sea life

13 provide additional places for, to live on

14 will grow on, which will make, unique

15 want people to see a variety of, on

16 how rich sea life is, how important it is

17 using architecture to protect, on land

18 what, says about eco-friendly

19 throughout the year

20 need, which uses, contributes to climate change

21 That's why, have begun to design, that use less, are still

22 For example, are designed to have, open structure

23 it, for outside air to move throughout

24 natural, how these buildings stay cool

25 In addition to making, large gardens

26 provides, protects, from direct sunlight, keeps

27 not only help, but also provide, with, quality of life

28 goals, new style, architecture

43

29 will keep coming up with, eco-friendly ideas

30 Every field has, protecting

31 With, innovation, will be able to live together, far into

1 우리가 환경을 보호할 수 있는 방법을 찾는 것은 중요하다.

2 몇몇 사람들은 지구를 구하기 위한 창의적인 방법을 찾았다.

3 한 예로 멕시코 칸쿤에 있는 수중 박물관이 있다.

4 미술학 교수인 Rosa Allison 박사를 만나서 이 특별한 박물관에 대한 설명을 들어보자.

5 Rosa: 칸쿤은 매년 480만 명의 관광객이 여행하는 도시이다.

6 그곳에서 할 수 있는 가장 인기 있는 활동 중 하나는 그 지역의 바닷속의 아름다운 해양 생물을 관찰하는 것이다.

7 하지만, 관광 활동들이 칸쿤 근처의 바다 일부를 심각하게 훼손시키고 있다.

8 이러한 일을 방지하기 위해서, 예술가들이 흥미로운 생각을 해냈다.

9 그들은 만약 관광객들을 바다의 다른 쪽으로 유인한다면, 그 죽어가는 지역이 호전될 시간을 가질 수 있을 것이라 생각했다.

10 그들은 해양 생물이 죽어가는 지역으로부터 떨어진 해저에 수중 박물관을 만들었다.

11 그 박물관은 해수면에서 14미터 아래에 있으며 500개의 조각상이 있다.

12 그 조각상들은 해양 생물에게 도움이 되는 재료들로 만들어졌다.

13 그것들은 식물과 동물들이 살 수 있는 추가적인 장소를 제공한다.

14 시간이 흐르면, 많은 형태의 바다 생명체들이 그 조각상에서 자라게 될 것이며, 이것이 그 예술 작품을 독특하게 만들 것이다.

15 예술가들은 사람들이 그 조각상들에서 (살고 있는) 다양한 해양 생명체들을 보길 원한다.

16 만약 사람들이 해양 생물이 얼마나 풍부한지 깨닫는다면, 그들은 바다를 지키는 것이 얼마나 중요한지 이해할 것이다.

17 싱가포르에서는 사람들이 육지의 환경을 보호하기 위해 건축을 이용하고 있다.

18 건축가인 Rajesh Khan이 친환경 건물에 대해 말하는 것을 들어보자.

19 Rajesh: 싱가포르는 연중 더운 곳이다.

20 대부분의 건물들은 에어컨 가동이 필요한데, 이로 인해 많은 에너지가 사용되고 있으며 기후 변화의 원인이 되고 있다.

21 그것이 싱가포르의 건축가들이 에어컨을 덜 쓰면서도 실내에서 여전히 시원한 느낌이 들 수 있는 친환경적인 건물들을 디자인하기 시작한 이유이다.

22 가령, 싱가포르의 많은 건물들은 개방형 구조를 포함하게 디자인되었다.

23 이러한 구조는 외부 공기가 건물을 관통하는 것을 가능케 한다.

24 이러한 자연적인 공기의 흐름이 이 건물을 시원하게 유지해 주는 방법이다.

25 건축가들은 개방형 구조를 만드는 것 외에도 큰 정원을 더한다.

26 이러한 녹지 공간은 그늘을 제공하고 직사광선으로부터 건물의 부분들을 지켜주어 건물을 시원 하게 유지한다.

27 이와 같은 친환경적인 건물들은 환경을 보호하는 것을 도울 뿐만 아니라 사람들에게 양질의 삶을 제공한다.

28 그것들이 바로 이러한 새로운 건축 방식의 목표이다.

29 바라건대, 건축가들은 새로운 친환경 아이디어를 계속해서 생각해 낼 것이다.

30 모든 분야에서 환경을 보호하는 다른 방식이 있다.

31 더 나은 혁신으로 인해 먼 미래에 인간과 자연은 함께 조화를 이루며 살아갈 수 있을 것이다.

1 It is important for us to find ways to protect the environment.

2 Some people have found creative ways to save the earth.

3 One example is an underwater museum in Cancun, Mexico.

4 Let's meet Dr. Rosa Allison, an art professor, and listen to her explanation about the special museum.

5 Rosa: Cancun is a city where 4.8 million tourists travel every year.

6 One of the most popular activities to do there is looking at the area's beautiful sea life underwater.

7 However, tourist activities are seriously damaging parts of the sea near Cancun.

8 To prevent this, artists did something interesting.

9 They thought if they attracted tourists to a different part of the sea, the dying areas could have time to get better.

10 They made an underwater museum away from the places where sea life was dying.

11 It's about 14 meters below the surface and contains 500 statues.

12 The statues are made from materials that support sea life.

13 They provide additional places for plants and animals to live on.

14 Over time, many types of sea life will grow on the statues, which will make the artwork unique.

15 The artists want people to see a variety of sea life on the statues.

16 If people realize how rich sea life is, they will understand how important it is to save the sea.

17 In Singapore, people are using architecture to protect the environment on land.

18 Let's hear what Rajesh Khan, an architect, says about eco-friendly buildings.

19 Rajesh: Singapore is hot throughout the year.

20 Most buildings need air conditioning, which uses a lot of energy and contributes to climate change.

21 That's why architects in Singapore have begun to design eco-friendly buildings that use less air conditioning but are still cool inside.

22 For example, many buildings in Singapore are designed to have an open structure.

23 This structure makes it possible for outside air to move throughout a building.

24 This natural air flow is how these buildings stay cool.

25 In addition to making open structures, architects add large gardens.

26 This greenery provides shade and protects parts of the building from direct sunlight, which keeps the building cooler.

27 Eco-friendly buildings like these not only help protect the environment, but also provide people with a good quality of life.

28 Those are the goals of this new style of architecture.

29 Hopefully, architects will keep coming up with new eco-friendly ideas.

30 Every field has different ways of protecting the environment.

31 With more innovation, humans and nature will be able to live together in harmony far into the future.

Listen & Talk 2 D Talk Together

1. Have, heard, edible spoons, amazing
2. No, haven't, Tell me, them
3. are made of grain, save resources
4. sounds awesome, can't wait to use

Presentation Time

1. How, make our school eco-friendly
2. In my opinion
3. The front wall, a great place
4. helps to keep, cool by blocking sunlight

5. reduce the amount of energy used

Think & Write Step 3

1. Save the Earth
2. innovative, environmentally friendly item
3. a cookie cup
4. is made in the shape of
5. After, can just eat it
6. By doing this, can save paper
7. can chage the world
8. Be a part of

Listen & Talk 2 D Talk Together

1. A: Have you heard of edible spoons? They're amazing!
2. B: No, I haven't. Tell me about them.
3. A: They are made of grain. They will save resources.
4. B: That sounds awesome. I can't wait to use them.

Presentation Time

1. How can we make our school eco-friendly?
2. In my opinion, we need a green wall.
3. The front wall of our school is a great place for it.
4. A green wall helps to keep the building cool by blocking sunlight.
5. This could reduce the amount of energy used for air conditioning.

Think & Write Step 3

1. Eat Your Cup and Save the Earth!
2. Here' an innovative, environmentally friendly item!
3. It is a cookie cup.
4. It's a cookie that is made in the shape of a cup.
5. After you use the cup, you can just eat it.
6. By doing this, you can save paper or plastic.
7. The cookie cup can chage the world.
8. Be a part of the change!

MEMO

MEMO

MEMO

적중 100

영어 기출 문제집

정답 및 해설

능률 | 김성곤